NICE LEGS!

A Pairing of Wine and Words

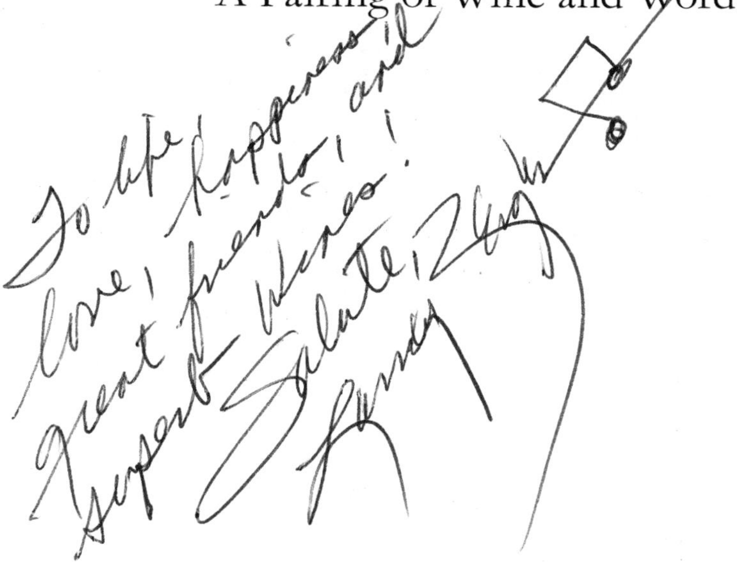

JACK BEDDOWS & LARRY ZEIGER

Copyright © 2013 Jack Beddows & Larry Zeiger

All rights reserved.

ISBN: 1493764632
ISBN-13: 9781493764631

ACKNOWLEDGEMENTS

Jack and Larry would like to dedicate NICE LEGS – A PAIRING OF WINE AND WORDS to their amazing families and friends for their support and inspiration.

Special thanks to all the owners, managers, bartenders, servers at the following restaurants and wine bars for their fantastic food and expertise in wine selections: *Barons Market, Zia's Bistro, Third Corner Wine Shop and Bistro, Busalacchi's A Modo Mio, El Camino, Brigantine, C-Level Restaurant at Island Prime, Trattoria Fantastica, Wine Steals, The Venetian, El Camino, Old Venice, Zia's Bistro, Monello, Caffe Calabria, Farouz Café and Gallery, Isola Pizza Bar, 98 Bottles,* and the *Courtyard Marriott Bar at Liberty Station.*

Larry wishes to also acknowledge his many creative students who inspired him throughout his teaching career with their wit, wisdom, and creativity.

Many thanks to Joy Woodward and Nöel Norcross for their editing expertise, Carlos DeLeon for his assistance with formatting, Adrian Ramirez for his inspired cover art, and Mary McDonald and Maurizio Cassone for their assistance with language translations.

You are all part of our lives and our stories whether you like it or not. A toast to your friendship is in order!

Almost all the stories in *NICE LEGS – A PAIRING OF WINE AND WORDS* are based on the authors' real or slightly embellished life experiences with heavy doses of magical realism and/or fantasy integrated in their writings. Names, characters, business organizations, places, events and incidents have been altered and/or are the product of the authors' quirky imaginations.

Advanced Praise for
NICE LEGS!
-A Pairing of Wine and Words

"A truly superlative read! Fine nuances balanced with charming wit! Be sure to keep this one on your shelf for years to come!"
–Art Acosta
Wine connoisseur of Barons Market in San Diego

"*Nice Legs – A Pairing of Wine and Words* is hilarious, insightful, and extremely creative, especially the stories of Larry Zeiger!"
–Larry Zeiger

"Jack Beddows has a flair for the unexpected that leaves one craving for more. His turn of phrase can only be compared to the finest of the Latin Poets."
–J.L. Beddows (no relation to the author)

"Larry Zeiger, whose outrageous short story, "Fade In-Fade Out" was selected as the *Short Story of the Year* by the San Diego Book Awards Association, is deeply honored by the expertise and superb talent of the judging committee."
–L.E. Zeiger (no relation to the author either)

"Jack Beddows didn't know about the San Diego Book Awards Association competition until after the deadline had passed, because SOME people are

afraid of healthy competition and do not inform others of these contests. If Beddows would have known about the Book Awards that year, doubtlessly, he would have won the Grand Prize!"
–Jacques Beddows

"Zeiger's stories have the wit and charm of David Sedaris, Woody Allen, Christopher Guest, Jon Stewart, John Oliver, and Stephen Colbert combined! I laughed until I cried."
–Lorenzo Zeiger

"Jack's musings, his insight and wit are equal to - and often surpass - those of Moliere, Aristophanes, Mark Twain, and George Bernard Shaw. Do yourself a favor and pick up a copy today. And he uses *bigger* words than Zeiger."
–Professor Beddows

"So entertaining! The perfect gift for Christmas, Chanukah, Kwanza, Valentine's Day, Passover, Easter, Cinco de Mayo, Labor Day, Presidents' Day, Rosh Hashanah, Flag Day, Thanksgiving, and the birthdays of all your friends, family members, pets, business partners, accountants, and bartenders. An exceptional and unique reading experience and every story is paired with your favorite wines! Buy it today!"
–Larry Zeiger and Jack Beddows

Contents

One — CULTURE SHOCK · · · 1

Fade In – Fade Out · · · 2

The California Nut Festival · · · 14

Two — MUSIC MAKES THE MAN · · · 25

Rites of Passaggio · · · 26

Going to Graceland · · · 35

Three — BIENVENIDOS TURISTAS · · · 46

El Americano Feo · · · 47

Un Navidad a Recordar · · · 55

Four — MONKEY BUSINESS · · · 62

Flight of the Primate · · · 63

The Evil Monkey · · · 72

Five — TWISTS AND TURNS · · · 77

An Accidental Career · · · 79

Storm Warnings – Category Five · · · 91

Six — LIFE AS A MUSICAL · · · 99

Gypsy Rose – The Musical · · · 100

OUCH! – The Transmogrification Musical · · · 110

Seven — ANIMAL HOUSES · · · 124

A Vegan's Nightmare · · · 125

The Death of the Easter Bunny · · · 137

Eight — THE ROAD TO VEGAS · · · 142

Viva Las Vegas · · · 143

You Forgot One Item · · · 152

Nine — EMBARRASSING MOMENTS · · · · · · · · · · · · · · · · · · · 162
Big Mouth Strikes Again · 163
Caught in the Act · 169
Ten — STOLEN DREAMS · 176
A Brief Encounter · 178
Thievery Corporation · 188
Eleven — LIFE AS AN OUTLAW · 195
Breaking the Law · 196
The Big Cheese · 212
Twelve — GAMES PEOPLE PLAY · 225
How I Beat the Champ · 227
Go for the Gold · 230
Thirteen – STORMY WEATHER · 240
The International Thanksgiving Thriller · · · · · · · · · · · · · 242
Children of the Night · 251
Fourteen — THE JOURNEY WITHIN · · · · · · · · · · · · · · · · · · · 260
The Poseidon Syndrome vs. The Big Wheel Effect · · · · · · 261
Microscopic Me · 266
Fifteen — SWAN SONGS · 279
How Gwyneth Paltrow Ruined My Teaching Career · · · · · 280
I Want My $55.00 Back · 290
The Celebration Begins! · 305

THE APERITIF

After the seventh grueling high school staff meeting of the year, Larry Zeiger and Jack Beddows, arts and humanities educators in a high school in San Diego, make the bold decision to escape into a more stimulating and creative universe.

The lifeless seminars on such mundane topics as tardy policies, mandated testing, discipline issues, accountability, truancy programs, parent conferencing, contract negotiations, and disaster drills inspire Jack and Larry to seek out the nearest wine bar to the school to indulge in antioxidant-rich liquid refreshments that would most certainly lower their blood pressure, clear their arteries, and provide an escape mechanism from the tedious bureaucracy of the institution of public education.

While drinking a superb *Pinot Noir*, Larry and Jack exchange tales about their outrageous college days and the bizarre characters they encountered shortly after they moved to California from the East Coast. This experience proves to be vastly superior to the sleep-inducing high school staff meeting they had attended just a few hours prior to this wine tasting indulgence.

As a result, Larry and Jack make the momentous decision to meet on a weekly basis and swap stories about their lives, trying to outdo one another with tales of unexpected deception, childhood ambitions, embarrassing moments, shocking nightmares, exciting adventures, medical dilemmas, musical moments, and first loves.

To make this experience even more unique, they decide to pair each story with an exquisite wine as they reveal their unpredictable lives and their encounters with such memorable characters as an evil monkey, a neighborly witch, a surfer on shock therapy, an inebriated landlord, an Italian thief, an alcoholic masseuse, an ice-skating penguin, a talking appendix, and a pet duck named George – to name a few.

We sincerely hope you enjoy *NICE LEGS! – A PAIRING OF WINE AND WORDS,* a delectable read as well as an epicurean delight.

Salute!
–Larry Zeiger & Jack Beddows

One

Culture Shock

After a sleep-inducing ninety-minute staff meeting about the new tardy policies for high school students, Larry and Jack agree that a fine glass of wine is in order. They make the decision that their first exchange of stories will focus on their experiences of settling in California as college students.

About a mile from the school is the conveniently located 3rd Corner Wine Shop and Bistro where the most knowledgeable wine servers, Nate, Todd, Daniel, Drew, Diana, Peter, Thomas, and Chris overhear Larry and Jack's conversation about the trials and tribulations of assimilating to California culture. After much intellectual discourse, the wine experts select a bottle of the *Migration Anderson Valley Pinot Noir* to compliment the storytellers' tales. The silky aftertaste, the canvas of flavors, and the brilliant finish of the wine are also the elements of storytelling the two authors aspire to achieve.

And so while indulging in this unique *Pinot,* Jack and Larry exchange stories about their introduction to California culture where they encounter witches, warlocks, Tarot card readers, neurotic prisoners, roller derby addicts, alcoholic message therapists, Yoga instructors with anger control problems, surfers on shock therapy, and a manic depressive nurse.

Fade In – Fade Out

by Larry Zeiger

Fade In

"Observe the world around you and become a voyeur. Jot down unique characteristics of people you encounter - their body language, the way they talk, the things they say, and the things they do. You just never know when you will meet that unique individual or witness an incredible event that will be the inspiration for your Pulitzer Prize-winning novel or your Oscar-winning screenplay." These words spoken by Dr. Wykoff, one of my favorite professors at the University of Miami, instantly became the mantra of my creative existence.

In order to achieve success as a writer, I decided to further my education by attending graduate school and ultimately pursuing a literary career to become the next Billy Wilder or David Mamet. And so, in the fall of 1970, I, along with three of my college buddies, John, Frank, and Rich, moved from Florida to California to embark on an adventure of a lifetime.

We arrived in San Diego and rented an oceanfront, two bedroom, completely furnished apartment with weekly maid service for a mere $185.00 a month. It was not the most lavish or modern apartment building, but in those days, I felt like I was living like a king. Through the swaying palm trees, I could see the sparkling blue waters of the Pacific, and at night I could hear the soft wafting sounds of the waves crashing against the shore. I was in a perpetual state of nirvana until that night in late September when I came home from my screenwriting class at San Diego State University. My peaceful life at Heavenly Shores Apartments was about to unravel into a dazzling three-act scenario to rival Hitchcock's *Rear Window!*

Act I

I entered the courtyard of our apartment building around 10 p.m. when suddenly, from under the staircase, a young woman in her early 20's appeared. Making weird, unworldly sounds, she looked up at the moon and then at me as her eyes widened with a look of ecstasy and yearning. "You are special!" she exclaimed.

The seductive, crazed look in her eyes made me feel tense. I didn't know how to respond. After all, I was born and raised in Cleveland Heights, Ohio, and this was Southern California!

"You are *soooooo special*," she repeated as she took my hands and pulled me towards her.

The strangeness of this girl overwhelmed me and left me momentarily speechless. I muttered a soft, "Well, thank you, but . . . but . . . do I know you? Have we met before?"

"I know who you are."

"Really?" I replied.

"You have extraordinary talents, gifts you may or may not know about."

I was ready to pull out my legal pad and start taking notes but decided to be more polite.

The bizarre young woman immediately changed the subject. "Do you know what tonight is?" she asked excitedly.

"Thursday," I replied.

Acting as if she didn't hear me, she responded, "It is the night of the *Autumnal Equinox*, a time when witches are attracted to one another. Look at the moon! The fullness of it appeals to you, doesn't it? Don't you just want to reach up and feel the moon, touch it, caress it, and just . . . *make love to it?*"

"Uh-huh, it's a nice moon," I replied, beads of sweat forming on my brow.

"Do you understand who I am? I . . . am . . . a witch! And, you know what that means? I am seductive, enigmatic, and lascivious. I'm everything you want me to be."

Just as I was about to politely excuse myself, her *surfed-out* boyfriend, Troy, appeared at the door of his studio. "Hey dude, you met my girl, Stephie? Believe what she says, or she'll cast a spell on you!"

"Dude, I'm very confused," I replied. "I'm not sure what Stephie is telling me."

And then with great dramatic intensity, Stephie threw her arms in the air and exclaimed, "What I am telling you is . . . during the night of the Autumnal Equinox, I am attracted to people like you who have the power to do things you never imagined. You may not even know that you possess extraordinary powers . . . biblical powers, to bring about change, to cure diseases, and perhaps . . . *to even move mountains.*"

"Me? I don't think so! I think you've got the wrong person. I'm a college student who was born in Cleveland Heights. It's in Ohio."

"What I'm trying to tell you is that you . . . *you* are a warlock! And I . . . I am a witch! And it takes a witch to identify a warlock. Do you understand what I'm saying?"

Troy slapped me on the back, *really* hard. "You have to believe in Stephie. That girl knows what she's talkin' about! Trust me, I live with her! She's a witch, and if she says you're a warlock, just go with it, or you may never know what could happen. "

At that moment, Stephie went into a trancelike state, tossing her head from side to side while babbling in tongues. It was like a scene from *Rosemary's Baby.*

"What's she saying?" I asked Troy.

"Beats the shit out of me, man. She gets this way now and then . . . it's fuckin' weird, but I still love her! She excites me when she's like this."

At that moment, she broke from her *mumble-jumble* trance and threw her arms around me. In a sensuous, slightly crazed voice, she pleaded, "Let me read your cards!"

"My cards?" I asked.

"*Tarot! Tarot!*" Troy responded. "She's an expert. She can determine your future and everything you need to know about survival. She's very talented! Why don't you come in our pad? Join us, and I'll make some exotic cocktails. Party up man! Let's go!"

How could anyone have refused this invitation? And besides, if I were to be an accomplished writer, it was important for me to experience alien worlds and meet exotic people, and these two certainly fit the bill!

I entered their studio apartment and within seconds, Troy mixed a $1.49 bottle of Sangria with Coca Cola and added a slice of mango for good measure. I sipped the drink slowly. It tasted like Geritol with a fizz.

"Mmmm, very nice. How did you ever come up with this concoction?"

"By experiment, man! Everything Stephie and I do is by experiment."

I didn't want to question the other experiments they did together, so I just nodded in agreement and took another swig of the sickeningly sweet drink. Meanwhile, Stephie brought out her deck of Tarot cards. I never had my fortune told and had no idea what Tarot readings were all about. In a matter of seconds, she began to describe Karmic situations, the Mamelukes of Egypt, Polo Sticks, Swords, and Slaves. Then came a discussion of the Hermit, the Hanged Man, and the Devil. Her eyes widened with enthusiasm. Troy stared lovingly at Stephie as he drank his second glass of the drink he called *Sangriola.*

In a full voice, Stephie proclaimed, "Tarot can predict your future, Larry. It can tell you about philosophy, social interaction, and . . ."

Troy piped in. "Gastronomical activity."

"Astronomical activity, you idiot!" Stephie shouted.

"*Gastronomical! Astronomical!* It's all the same!" Other than surfing eight hours a day, Troy's other main interest, I was later to discover, was analyzing flight patterns of moths.

Stephie placed the cards one by one on the floor. "I'm so happy to know that you are one of us, Larry. And now, I will provide you with the knowledge of the extraordinary powers you possess." Instantly, she started moaning, singing out words in different tongues as she placed the cards on the carpet. "Ahhhhhhh yaaa yaaa yaaa! Ahhhhhhhh yeeeee yeeeee yeeee!" She flipped each card as if it held the secret to the universe, and then all of a sudden, she looked at me with horror in her eyes. The card she held was that of the Devil!

"OH NO!" she screamed. "This can't be! I must have made a mistake!" She picked up all the cards and then furiously shuffled them. "Mistake! Mistake! This can't be true! No! No! I did something wrong! Let me try again!"

Suddenly, I felt nervous. My stomach was making horrible sounds. Was it the chemical reaction of the Sangria and Coca-Cola mix, or something so terrible that I might ultimately need an exorcist?

"Holy Shit! Dude, my girl saw somethin' that totally *creeped* her out! Some awesomely really scary, scary stuff!" Troy shouted and then casually added, "Want to smoke some weed?"

Before I had a chance to respond, Stephie had reshuffled the cards and began moaning something about "darkness" and the "messenger." And then suddenly, she shrieked, "The cards are cursed! The cards are cursed!" She then threw the cards one by one at all four walls of the apartment.

Even Troy looked terrified. To calm himself, he took another hit and passed the joint to me. "You need this, man! It's the good stuff from Colombia."

"The Sangriola is all I can handle right now," I responded.

"I think you better leave!" Stephie screamed. There's something terribly wrong, something *evil* . . . you must be careful! Look around every corner! Watch when you cross the street! Avoid dark alleys! And most important, be cautious of the wind . . . the wind . . . be cautious of the wind!" And then as if in a trance, she slowly walked to her bedroom and slammed the door shut.

Troy and I looked at each other with bewilderment. "Oh man, she really knows her stuff. You know what I think, Larry?"

"I have no idea," I answered.

There was a long pause, then a longer pause. I couldn't tell if Troy was searching for words or simply blanked out. After five minutes of silence, I exited their apartment, leaving the couple in their trancelike states. I approached the staircase to my apartment with caution. I surveyed the darkened courtyard, just in case there were other witches and warlocks lurking behind the trees and shrubs, and when I knew the coast was clear, I ascended the staircase.

The full moon continued to shine its bright light on my insecure soul.

Act 2

A week later after the rather *faux mystical* encounter with Stephie and Troy, a peculiar note was attached to the front door of every apartment at Heavenly Shores. It was from Gretchen, the tenant who lived two doors down from us. The note read as follows:

To All My Neighbors Who I Once Trusted –

I have been nice to everyone here at Heavenly Shores so there is no excuse for what some Evil Fucking Creep has done to me. This morning I discovered that someone stole my panties from the clothesline. Not just any panties - but the ones I wore on my wedding night! Obviously, they have sentimental value to me, and you were just trying to hurt me anyway you possibly could. This is not a Christian thing to do. I will, however, forgive you if my red silk panties are returned to me by 4 p.m. today. In the mean time, if you are the thief, I just want you to know that Jesus hates you. HE HATES YOU BAD!!!

Your neighbor in 4B,
Gretchen

Just as Frank, John, Rich, and I were jokingly accusing one another of taking Gretchen's undergarments, we had an unexpected visit from our neighbor in 4B. She stood at our door with a copy of the *New Testament* in her hand.

"Hello. My name is Gretchen."

"Uh-oh! I didn't do it. Honestly, I didn't!" my roommate, Richard, responded.

"I'm here to apologize for the note I wrote. I found my panties! They fell off the clothesline and must have blown into the Bougainvillea. And you know, the Bougainvillea was bright red so it must have . . . kind of . . . you know . . . camouflaged them. But just now when I looked one more time, and it was really windy out, I saw the wind pick up my red panties from the Bougainvillea and blow them into the Morning Glories . . . the contrasting colors, you know. And that's how I found my panties, the ones that hold sentimental value for me. Isn't it crazy how nature truly affects our lives so dramatically?

"Oh, I'm so happy you found them. We were really worried for you," Frank replied with an air of sarcasm that went unnoticed by our neighbor.

"That's so nice of you. I'm so sorry for writing all those letters and sticking them on everyone's door and jumping to conclusions the way I did. You see, I've been very tense lately. I feel like I might have an anxiety attack at any time."

"I'm so sorry," I interjected, trying to end the conversation as quickly as possible.

"You see, I haven't seen my husband, Derek, for nearly a year now, but he's coming home tomorrow . . . from prison."

The four of us responded in perfect unison, "PRISON?"

"Uh-huh. I think he was framed, but it was a huge mistake. All he did was smuggle some switchblades across the border and sell them to gang members in L.A. He really didn't make that much money. I mean like, it's not as bad as selling crack cocaine or cheating on your income tax."

None of us understood the connection, but I once again felt the urge to procure my notepad to write that Oscar-winning screenplay.

"If you'd like, I could read to you from the Bible," Gretchen continued. "It's so relaxing to read passages to new people I've just met . . . like you guys. Oh come on, you must have a favorite psalm. Or I can pick one for you about the Holy Spirit and read it out loud to you. I just love reading psalms."

"Uh . . . I really have to study for my exam tomorrow," replied John.

"Me too," Frank, Rich, and I responded in unison.

"Oh, I'm sorry for bothering you. I really am. It's been a difficult day for me."

She turned to leave and feeling sorry for her, I said, "I'm happy that everything worked out for you, Gretchen."

"Thank you so much. You're all so sweet! I can't wait for you to meet Derek, and I hope all of you will be his best friends. I really do! Prison life has been so hard on him, and I want him to see a new world, a moral universe that reveals itself in new surroundings with new friends like . . . *all of you!*"

She suddenly changed the subject and looked directly at me. "Are you sure you don't want me to read to you from *Revelations*? There are so many interesting predictions! Derek loves *Revelations*, and you will too! He reads it nonstop in jail. And he's now a better, calmer, and more righteous man than ever. You could be just like him, but you must believe in yourself and find the Lord, Jesus Christ. Amen."

It seemed everyone at Heavenly Shores wanted to make predictions about me. First Stephie . . . and now Gretchen. Both of these girls were weird, although I thought they would make interesting characters in a television pilot about a lonely Jewish grad student whose soul is being tormented by a crazy witch who allegedly can predict the future and an unstable pseudo-evangelist who is trying to "save" her neighbors. Gretchen correctly sensed that I was getting bored with her and finally left our apartment to dream about biblical allegories and the love of her life returning from his stay behind bars.

The next day I woke up early and after a morning swim in the Pacific, I jumped in the shower, thinking about the relaxing day ahead of me. I planned to go see the double feature at the Roxy Theatre of *Play Misty for Me* and *Sunday Bloody Sunday,* and then after the movie, my roommates and I would go to Tug's Tavern to hear one of our favorite local Pacific Beach bands and drink several bottles of Bud. I loved Saturdays, a perfect time to relax and forget about the pressures of the academic world.

Suddenly, someone pounded on the front door and interrupted my blissful contemplation and screamed, "I know she's in there! *I know she's in there!*"

My roommate, John, answered the door and tried to calm the irate stranger down.

"Hey, man, what do you want?"

"I want my wife back! I know she's in there with one of you!"

John then put two and two together and realized the man standing before him with his eyes on fire was Gretchen's husband, not looking at all rehabilitated from prison. "You must be Derek."

"How did you know my name? What has Gretchen told you about me? That I'm insane? That I'm overly possessive? That I'm . . . *capable of murder?*"

"No, she only had really nice things to say about you. She couldn't wait to see you and she . . . "

Derek pushed his way into the living room. From the shower, I could hear the commotion, and then suddenly, Derek began banging on the bathroom door. "Let me in! Let me in!" he shouted. "I know Gretchen is in there with you . . . in the shower . . . naked . . . and . . . and . . . and I'm going to kill both of you!"

Thinking Derek would break the door down. I immediately exited the shower, wrapped a towel around me, and thought about jumping out the window. I yelled through the door. "Gretchen is not here! I have no idea where she is!"

"I know what you're doing in there! You can't fool me! For two years I've been in fucking jail, and now I come home to my Gretchen, and she's fuckin' some loser in his fuckin' shower! How could you do this to your fuckin' husband?"

At that moment, I wished I had a pen or pencil to write down every word, every profound sentence, and every complex thought in Derek's depraved little mind, which would ultimately be the cornerstone of my Oscar-winning screenplay:

*Crazy woman marries crazy man who imports switchblades from Mexico!

*Crazy man sells switchblades to gangs in Los Angeles, and gets arrested!

*When released from jail, he breaks into bathroom of his wife's neighbor!

*And murders the poor son of a bitch!

No, wait a minute! That's not the ending I want!

"Let me in you mother fucker!"

At least, ask politely, I thought. This guy must be an absolute lunatic to think I would open the bathroom door and let him in!

John tried to pull Derek away from the bathroom door, but Derek elbowed him in the groin. Hearing the commotion from the laundry room, Frank and Rich ran upstairs just in time to witness the ensuing *Cirque du Insanity.* Derek successfully kicked the bathroom door open, and there I was, looking like a slightly pudgy junior Tarzan! With fists clenched, I was ready to punch him out when suddenly, Gretchen appeared at the front door. If this were a movie, there would have been a sudden change in the musical score from the screeching violins of the Bernard Herrmann *Psycho* variety to the lush sounds of a Michel Legrand love song.

"Derek! Derek!" she screamed. "I didn't realize you'd be home so soon. I'm so happy to see you and hear your sweet and loving voice. My kind, sweet Derek, *I love you so much!*"

As she pulled him away from the bathroom door, he instantly collapsed in her arms. They kissed passionately in front of us, acting as if the world had disappeared.

"Jesus loves you Derek, and he's forgiven you. You have been forgiven, and Jesus loves me too, because I've been loyal to you. I am so grateful that He has brought us together on this happy hallelujah day."

And then, true to classic romantic narrative, the two lovebirds walked out of our apartment, descended the staircase and did not emerge from their apartment for three days. At the end of the week, the police came for Derek and arrested him, this time for assaulting a dog. He wound up in prison for another three months.

That night, John, Frank, Rich and I had a meeting about terminating our lease and moving out of the neighborhood. We decided, however, to try one more month at Heavenly Shores in the hopes that life would be a bit calmer with our psychotic neighbors if we just simply avoided them. We paid the rent for the next month to the managers, Harry and Carla Littlefield, recent transplants to San Diego from Peachtree, Georgia.

I continued to write at a furious pace, keeping notes on all the colorful characters I had encountered during my first month in California. Things quieted down for the next few weeks, but unbeknownst to all of us, those days of peaceful contentment were about to unravel at breakneck speed.

Act 3

Harry and Carla Littlefield loved *Roller Derby.* Every Saturday afternoon like clockwork, the roar of their approval could be heard every time a derby competitor smashed her body into another.

"Fuckin' A! She's blockin' illegally! She gonna kill herself!"

"Harry, wanna another beer?"

"I do sweetie . . . with a little Johnny Walker . . . no, not Johnny. Give me the other guy . . . you know what I'm talkin' 'bout? That Daniels' guy! Uh . . . uh, *Jack!* That's the guy . . . yeah . . . a cold Bud and a shot of Jack, sweety cakes."

Seconds later, Harry's raspy voice rattled the windows of our apartment when he screamed out, "Shit Mama! She's using her head to block! Ain't that illegal? I know it is! I just know it!"

Carla echoed the sentiment and yelled, "Send that big fat fucker to the Penalty Box!"

My roommates and I were always entertained every Saturday afternoon by the amusing, earthy repartee of our landlords. Then one Saturday night, Harry and Carla got into a major brawl regarding Harry's constant drinking and smoking of cheap cigars, which aggravated Carla's asthma. Harry stormed out of the apartment to go to one of the many local bars he frequented, and his wife sobbed for well over an hour.

All was peaceful until about 2:30 in the morning when Harry returned home from a night of excessive drinking. He evidently had forgotten his key or didn't think to reach in his pocket to locate it. He began to scream at the top of his lungs. "Open the door, Carla baby. I lost my key. Sweet cheeks, answer me! I'm locked out. Harry loves you and wants to make wild love to you. Baby! Baby! You know you want me, and I want you so bad! Now open the door, so we can get it on *pronto gusto*!"

Bert Kapinski, our next-door neighbor, screamed from his living room window, "Harry, shut the fuck up! Quit carryin' on! We pay you rent and want to sleep!"

Losing his balance, Harry stumbled on the steps leading to the front door of his apartment. The noise of him accidentally knocking over a potted geranium caused several tenants to turn on their lights and come outside to see what all the commotion was about. The melodrama suddenly became more intense.

Carla shouted through the door, "You're drunk as a skunk, Harry!"

"I just had a few Jack and Cokes, Carla! Now open the damn door!" he demanded.

"Shit-faced is what you are!" she screamed.

Suddenly, the neighbors grew more vociferous, shouting for Harry to quit screaming at his wife, at which point, Carla opened the door, and Harry literally fell into his apartment. We all felt a sense of relief. A calm set in . . . but only for about two minutes. Suddenly, Carla burst out of the front door, shouting, "He's gonna kill me! He's gonna kill me! I know it! Somebody help me! Please! Please! *I don't wanna die*!"

Harry and Carla's neighbor, Jorge Ochoa, a construction worker from Cancun, opened his door. He was dressed in boxers and a t-shirt. Carla ran behind Jorge for protection, and in a matter of seconds, to everyone's horror, Harry came outside brandishing a shotgun.

Jorge shielded Carla and yelled, "Put that rifle away, Harry! Are you some sort of nutcase? *Un pinche idioto!* You don't know what you're doing!"

In a menacing voice, Harry responded, "Hey, *Pancho*, I know what I'm doin', and I know what's goin' on! You is havin' an affair with my sweet wife, Carla. I never done her wrong, and I been good to her, so now . . . I gotta kill her!" It was obvious to everyone watching this episode of *Life at Heavenly Shores* that Harry Littlefield had lost it . . . *completely!*

By this time, almost all the tenants were out on their balconies shouting to Harry to put down his rifle and stop acting like a lunatic. Moments later, to everyone's relief, he came to his senses and cried out, "I'm so embarrassed! I'm so sorry! I don't know what got into me . . . too much Jack, maybe. Oh, my honeybun, please forgive me! Come to Daddy!"

Just as Harry was about to make amends with Carla, he stumbled on the pavement and dropped the rifle, which accidentally went off. The bullet hit the sidewalk, ricocheted off the concrete and hit the neighbor, Jorge in his right leg. Carla, who honestly believed that the tenant was going to die, began to wail like a banshee, her scream piercing the night and harmonizing with the sirens of the police cars that had just arrived to take Harry away. Jorge was taken by ambulance to Mercy Hospital, and Carla was left on the sidewalk screaming to her audience of tenants, "I swear I will never, ever let that monster back in my life again! He's an evil, crazy monster from Hell! I hate him! I hate him! I HATE HIM!"

Three days later, forgetting about her definitive oath, Carla bailed Harry out of jail. Acting as if nothing had ever happened, she took a romantic walk along the beach with him at sunset. They kissed passionately and returned to their apartment to dine on sausage and grits. The neighbor, Jorge, who had actually been only grazed in the leg by the bullet, hobbled around more dramatically than necessary for two or three days in order to gain the attention of the single attractive young woman, Maria Garcia, who lived upstairs from him. Gretchen sat on her balcony longing for the day that Derek would return from his second prison sentence. Stephie continued to read Tarot cards to her neighbors and friends and eventually graduated to crystal balls. After attending bartending school for three years, Troy eventually became a fully certified bartender/mixologist at Harry's Hideaway Beach and Tennis Club where he referred to himself as a "social chemist" and was praised for his fruity Sangriola signature drinks. And in no time at all, my roommates and I made the unanimous decision to check out of Heavenly Shores Apartments forever.

With four legal pads filled with notes about the most bizarre characters I could ever hope to encounter, I began to contemplate my future as a playwright and an Oscar winner for Best Original Screenplay.

The dream begins . . .

Fade Out

THE CALIFORNIA NUT FESTIVAL

BY JACK BEDDOWS

For anyone who isn't already aware of this, I can tell you with confidence that moving to California from the East Coast is guaranteed to be an experience in culture shock. And this is especially true for Southern California. While San Francisco is strange with its cast of characters that often look like they wandered off the set of a *Star Wars* film, it does nevertheless have a certain cultural vibe that is far more understandable to an East Coaster than the heartland of weirdness that is Los Angeles. When I moved west as a teenager, I left the Boston area to attend the University of California at Santa Barbara, just about two hours north of Los Angeles, just a hop skip and a jump from the city that many of our finest contemporary thinkers have labeled, "The Arsehole of the Universe."

As a junior in high school, I had decent but not great grades, slightly better test scores, and not a lot of family money to fall back on. So I didn't shoot too high in my application process. But I was fortunate enough to be accepted to the few schools to which I applied: the University of Vermont, the University of Colorado at Boulder, and the University of California at Santa Barbara. Clearly, each school had its pros and cons, but being horrible at decision-making, I was influenced by my older brother, Lucas, who had transferred to Santa Barbara the previous year, and decided that it was the best option. And admittedly, all that he told me was, and still is, true. UCSB is very strong academically, the weather in Santa Barbara is great, the campus is right by the beach, and there are thousands and thousands of beautiful girls. None of this could be denied. On the other hand, while visiting him out there the previous spring, I had caught a glimpse of what life could be like living in a student ghetto/party zone, and I was definitely a bit apprehensive when I went ahead and made my final decision.

As the commuter airplane connecting me from LA touched down at Goleta Airport, I thought to myself, *At least I have a family connection to help make the transition a smooth one.* However, when Lucas met me at the baggage claim, I barely recognized him in his Oakley Blade sunglasses and the volleyball visor turned upside down on his head. Before I knew it, I was being whisked away from the airport in his new jeep, which was blasting music with the bass thumping so loud I could barely hear myself as I screamed to him, "So you're listening to rap now, huh?"

He had previously been a standard, classic rock kind of guy, and so I was slightly bemused and bewildered to hear the rapper Too Short's *I Wish I Was a Baller* issuing from the speakers.

"Oh yeah! Everybody's into that here!" he replied.

In fact, over the next several weeks, every comment I made on all of the emblems of the Californian lifestyle that my brother had apparently so eagerly embraced was explained away with that same pithy phrase.

Just a few minutes after Too Short had finished his eloquent lament, we arrived at our destination: a good-sized parking lot from which arose the two impersonal towers of the dormitory that I would be calling home.

Up to that point, I had been imagining that I would be invited to go to my brother's place first, to clean up and to get my bearings. But no, suddenly my bags were on the sidewalk along with a cheap bicycle that my brother took out of the back of the jeep and threw down on the ground with the information that this was how I would be getting around on campus. Then, Lucas was screeching off into the distance, the bass thump lingering even after the jeep was long out of sight, and I was left all alone. It didn't help that I had been reading Robert A. Heinlein's *A Stranger in a Strange Land* on the flight over. The protagonist doesn't fare so well in that particular tale, and I was starting to identify with him a bit too much for comfort.

For my living arrangements, Lucas had suggested the Francisco Torres dormitory to me, because it would be a good place to meet lots of people and make friends. Translated, this of course meant that it was the biggest party dorm on campus evidenced by the dubious sobriquet that the locals used to describe it, namely, *Fucked Towers*, which as I later learned, was a comment on one's chances of functioning academically in this crazy party-zone of drunken freshman and City College students.

I already knew dorm life were going to be bad, but it was not like I had any idea of what else to propose, so I assented to these arrangements without too much debate on the subject. However, hoping to mitigate the madness at least a little, I had requested and been assigned to the arts and drama floor. I didn't know if it would be any less crazy, but I thought at least I'd be around *artistic* and *introspective* drunks and druggies, which I considered to be a small step in the right direction.

It was certainly quiet enough that first afternoon as students straggled in, like me, confused and unsure of where to go. Finally, after a few false starts, I figured out where the front desk was located, got my room assignment and directions from the lone employee helping new residents, and off I went to get situated in room 2B on the second floor of the south tower.

As it turned out, to my academic if not social benefit, my new roommate was one of the few sophomores in the whole facility, excluding the Resident Assistants who stayed on for financial reasons. Although an engineering major, Brian chose to live on the arts and drama floor, because, like myself, he was hoping for a modicum more of sobriety and quiet. That's about where our similarities ended. When I first entered our small suite of two tiny bedrooms, Brian was already situated with his half of the room perfectly organized and a newly completed model airplane of a jet fighter prominently displayed on his desk. The first things I noticed were how small the room was and the permeating smell of model glue.

"Golly, it sure is nice to meet you!" Brian greeted me.

It was immediately apparent to me that Brian was a different sort of fellow. He came from the desert of the Inland Empire just east of Los Angeles, a locale that is primarily known for its crystal methamphetamine production, extreme heat, and the movie *The Hills Have Eyes.* I would like to add to that list the ability to produce social throwbacks previously thought unimaginable, because clearly, Brian had somehow been flash frozen in the 1950s and was only thawed out again to be my roommate as part of some bizarre social experiment. He dressed, talked, and acted exactly like a character from *Leave it to Beaver.*

Besides his tendencies to wear letterman sweaters in 80-degree weather and to sip on vanilla malteds, Brian was nice enough. But he was hell-bent on avoiding any distracting entanglements with his roommates and never having any conflict or conversation past what was absolutely necessary. To this aim, everything was separated into *Mine and Yours* categories. He even took his own toilet paper in and out of the bathroom with him. Part of the reason for his anti-social behavior was, very understandably, that he didn't want to be distracted from his schoolwork. But he also seemed desperate to avoid any cultural intrusions that wouldn't fit into his apple pie Americana lifestyle, a difficult trick to keep up, given his surroundings, but one which he managed admirably. In fact, the only sign of a world past the 1950s from Brian's half of the room came when, after having studied for two hours while listening to Johnny Mathis records and wanting to get fired up for his daily bike ride, Brian would put on some 'motivational music.' I was shocked to hear him sing, "*I wish I was a little bit taller. I wish I was a baller. I wish I had a girly on the phone, I would call her...*"

"Brian!" I exclaimed, "Are you listening to rap?"

"Oh sure!" he answered, "Everybody's into that out here! You don't like Too Short? What about Young M.C.? I love Young M.C. almost as much as the Everly Brothers!"

On my first day in the dorm, after Brian had left for his daily bike ride, I was just finishing unpacking and organizing my meager possessions, when in strolled Jonas, one of my suitemates from the other bedroom connected to ours by a small, shared bathroom. If Brian was an anachronistic anomaly, Jonas was the living embodiment of a certain segment of L.A. at the dawning of the nineties. He sported long ringlets of slightly oily brown hair, wore Vans sneakers, khaki shorts, and cotton T-shirts that bore the not-so-faint odor of marijuana. He had an endearing manner that said, "Hey bud! Let's party!"

"Dude!" he said, smiling, "What's happening? It's so nice to meet you! So like, my friend was thinking about switching rooms. You wouldn't mind if he took yours and you switched with him, right? So you just have to go talk to the dude in the office downstairs and everything will be cool! Thanks bro'! You're awesome!"

What could I say? I felt so welcomed. I managed to not start spouting obscenities, as I first felt obliged to do, and explained to Jonas in less colorful language, that this was not the greeting I had been hoping for and that I was not feeling particularly motivated to move again, if for no other reason than that I had just finally finished unpacking. He accepted my decision with a minimal amount of visible consternation and returned to his room, from whence in no time I began to hear a strange bubbling sound, followed by several quick coughs.

One of the best things about Jonas, I would later discover, was the fact that his father was Superman. Yes, Superman! Not the Christopher Reeve Superman or the George Reeves black and white Superman, but the *real* Superman, the one from the Hanna/Barbara Saturday morning cartoons, the cartoons that had meant so much to me in my developmental years. As soon as I found out about his amazing background as a voice-over actor, I used to beg to be put on the phone with him every time Jonas called home, just to hear him say, "Batman! I'll meet you at the Hall of Justice in fifteen minutes!"

But I'm getting ahead of myself, and at the time of this story, I had yet to experience any salve for the pain of adjustment that I was suffering.

"And he drives the new VRX H7!"

"NO WAY!" "YES WAY!" "Get out of here! That is *too* cool! He's such a *total hottie*!"

"*Totally*!"

No, this wasn't dialogue from a John Hughes film. This was part of the conversation I endured on my first morning in the dorm's cafeteria, standing in line behind two of my fellow students. What struck me even more than the Valley Girl talk was the fact that these two supposed friends never even looked at each other the whole time that they were speaking. Instead, they kept their gazes dead ahead, as if looking into each other's eyes would somehow be too real of a human connection.

"I *totally* want to have a piece of toast AND a bowl of cereal for breakfast! But I can't because I'm such a porker!"

"Get out! You're not even a heifer! *I'm* a heifer!"

"Oh my God! *No way!* I'm the total *roly poly*!"

Minutes later, after shoveling down a quick bowl of Captain Crunch, followed by a bitter glass of cafeteria OJ served in a vaguely smelly plastic cup and still feeling very, very groggy, I was off for my first ever college class, the 7 a.m. *Calculus for Engineers*. My family had pressured me into taking this course in order to keep open the possibility of my pursuing a science or engineering degree, thereby following in my father's footsteps. Who knows? Maybe if they had offered this class at a more reasonable hour, my whole life might have turned out differently, and I wouldn't have switched majors so quickly.

As I rode towards the unfamiliar campus on my beach cruiser, I looked down to see an unnerving inscription painted in White Out on the crossbar, *Bob's Bike! Don't Steal or I'll KILL YOU!* I later learned that bike stealing was more or less a sport at the university, and that the single most common reaction to finding out that your bike had been stolen was to quickly look for one of your own to nab.

A few minutes of groggy pedaling later, I realized I had completely misread my campus map. "Oh my God, I'm *like totally* lost." I found myself saying out loud before screaming "AHHH!" at hearing the infectious *Valley speak* coming from my own mouth. It was then that I panicked and made a quick decision to change directions and to cross the road, passing over a painted section of no-parking lines.

Suddenly, it seemed as if my bike were possessed as it started to violently jostle me around in a most distressing way. The crossbar was being jammed into my crotch repeatedly as I unaccountably bounced up and down like a jackhammer. *Had Bob died?* I wondered, *Is this his ghost taking revenge?* Then the thought that had been playing in my mind like a mantra was now being uncontrollably verbalized as I heard myself screaming, "God damn it! Where the hell am I?"

What I hadn't noticed in my groggy condition was that in Southern California, white lines on the street indicating No Parking weren't always just painted lines. Instead, they were often made of solid concrete bars that truly prevented parking, unlike my hometown of Boston, where this kind of device would play havoc with the snowplows. As I dragged myself off to the side of the road to lie down in agonizing pain, I felt my welcome to Southern California was complete. A few months later, my groin eventually healed. Eventually, I came to believe that I had not only become acclimated to Southern California but had more or less become immune to it.

After graduating from college, I had to face the fact that outside of going to school, I found little to do there. And so I had to make a choice: drive back to Massachusetts to my parents' home or to relocate to San Diego where my brother had moved two years earlier. After careful consideration, I chose San Diego.

At the time, my brother, Lucas, was living with his lovely girlfriend, Rebecca, in a small corner unit condo that he was renting on beautiful Mission Bay, in the picturesque town of Pacific Beach. They were kind enough to allow me to stay on their couch and to help me to get a job as a waiter at the same restaurant where Rebecca worked. However, when both money and space are tight, tensions can ride high, and we eventually had a meltdown. I owed my brother a very small sum for bills, and one day, he became furious about it.

"Jesus Christ, Jack! You could pay me back if you weren't always buying those crazy organic groceries!" he screamed, while running to the refrigerator for proof. When Lucas pulled out a box of soymilk that cost exactly $1.29 and started waving it in my face, certain that I would break down and confess to my vast extravagance, I knew it was time to go.

I again considered driving back to Boston, but a friend from the restaurant counseled me to instead check out places for rent in the local paper. I found one almost immediately in lovely Cardiff by the Sea in the northern part of San Diego County. The room was cheap, and surprisingly, no deposit or last month's rent was required. The house the room was in was advertised as a "Holistic Environment, complete with Organic Garden." It sounded like just the sort of restful retreat I needed. I should have suspected something was wrong, however, when the owner, William, eschewed a credit check and instead asked within ten minutes of meeting me when I would be ready to move in.

"Right away!" I answered eagerly, and the trap closed silently around me as I signed my name on the dotted line of the lease agreement. Instead of a restful retreat, this house turned out to be a rogue's gallery of demented weirdoes, each of whom represented a dark and twisted version of a pseudo New Age Californian lifestyle ideal.

Take Pete, for example. He was a decidedly nice man, a massage therapist with a gentle but masculine personality, who was also very knowledgeable about Chinese medicine and herbs. One day in the kitchen, not long after I had moved in, he noticed me looking down at his keychain with its shiny brass emblem from Alcoholics Anonymous.

"Ah! I see you've noticed my AA key chain there," he said, as he looked up at me with a thoughtful gaze, one that seemed to be full of the remembrance of battles hard fought and won. "Yup, I've been sober for nine years now."

Now I don't know if Pete later remembered telling me this or not, but within a week, he was inviting me to hang out with him and his friends after I got back from work, where his nightly ritual was to take massive hits of marijuana from his six-foot bong and to guzzle down a full twelve-pack of Sierra Nevada all by himself at an alarming rate. The one time I tried the six-foot bong, he and two friends were watching the *X-Files* on TV. At the sight of an alien creature devouring some poor man's liver, I lost it completely and had to quickly excuse myself. But generally, I was happy enough to have a beer or two with Pete, while surreptitiously enjoying his utter disregard for consistency. Yes, in the daytime he was Mr. Natural, just as healthy as he could be, but in the evening, he was a pot-addled, boozehound without the slightest sign of remorse.

As the days passed, I couldn't help but smile at the sound of the clanking empty bottles that Pete would sneak out of his room in his backpack every morning on his way to work, and in my mind, I would re-write the dialogue of our earlier conversation for him. "Yup," he would say, with his thoughtfully crinkled brow, "I've been sober for nine hours now...but I'm about to change all that."

Then there was Trey, a local yoga guru who was not only a devotee of the physical side of this ancient, peaceful tradition, but who was also a follower of the spiritual practices of yoga as well. When Trey, a tall and imposing figure, wasn't doing one-armed handstands while touching his head with his toes, he was dabbing his third eye with ashes and chanting.

Cool, I thought, *here's a together and mellow cat.* I even attended a few of his classes at a local gym and really enjoyed them. Then one morning, far earlier than I was accustomed to waking up, I heard a horrific pounding on my bedroom door. As soon as I opened it, both groggy and somewhat nervous about whatever could lead someone to disturb me like that, I was shocked to see Trey standing there, breathing hard with beads of sweat popping out of the sides of his red, anger-contorted face. As he shook with rage, he screamed at me.

"What the fuck, man? You crashed into my car!"

"Trey, what are you talking about?" I asked nervously. I instantly became concerned about his threatening body language. He started to lean towards me while clenching his fists in time to the beat of the pulsating veins at his temples.

"Trey, calm down, man," I said in my most placating voice, "I didn't crash into your car. Come on, let's go check it out." I was eager to have this problem resolved and to see Trey transform back from Shiva, the Destroyer into a more peaceful incarnation from among the gods of Hindu mythology.

So we walked outside to examine our two cars that were parked one in front of the other. I had parked in front of our house late the night before, and while I was often in a careless rush to get home from work, I was certain that I had made absolutely no contact with his car whatsoever. *Perhaps*, I thought, *someone slammed into me and forced my car into his*. But when we got outside and I crouched down to examine our two bumpers, there was clearly a good inch or two of space between them and no indication anywhere of contact.

I pointed this out to Trey, and he replied with a growing tone of hesitation, "Yeah, well, obviously after you slammed into my car there was a little recoil. You're just lucky there wasn't any real damage!"

"Okay, you're right." I said, my courage returning with the certainty of my innocence.

"Oh yeah, I'm lucky, and you're a lunatic. Now fuck off! I'm going back to bed!"

And so life continued during my stay at the House of Holistic Mania. Because William, the owner, was so greedy, he built a whole array of doubtlessly illegal studios in his backyard. The growing number of consistently crazy housemates never ceased to amaze me.

Another member of our fine family was Trevor, *the Prescription Kid*. Trevor was a sweet guy and once had been an excellent surfer. But, like many who had gone before him, Trevor had simply partied too hard. At one point, he had a meltdown from which recovery seemed unlikely. Who knows what nightmare visions he saw while tripping on a combination acid/mescaline cocktail? He soon garnered the nickname *Tremor* for his near constant shaking, and no matter what was said to him, he usually gave one standard response in a loud monotone voice, "OH! OKAY!"

"Hey Trevor! How's it going today, buddy?"

"OH! OKAY!" he would say, in a way that suggested that he had just reached a major breakthrough in his therapy.

"Hey Trevor, what's that you're having for breakfast?"

"OH! OKAY! HUH? WHAT'S THAT?"

To make matters worse, and perhaps this was the real cause of his near constant shaking, his family, who took almost complete control of his life in the aftermath of his breakdown, not only had him on a strict regimen of pacifying pills, but also placed him on a regimen of regular shock therapy. I had thought that this practice had been outlawed around the time of the making of the film *One Flew over the Cuckoo's Nest,* but apparently, I was mistaken.

The only other sane person in William's House of Fun was my friend Keith, a musician, writer, surfer, and social worker who showed up a few months after my own arrival. Together, we used to fantasize about kidnapping Trevor and taking him to Mexico where we hoped to convince him that Corona and lime was not a gateway drug. But surprisingly, Trevor did still manage to surf a little bit, and I could only pray that out there on the waves he managed to find true peace and a core of authentic experience that I felt was otherwise being denied to him.

Besides the alcoholic massage therapist, the yogi with anger control problems, and the surfer on shock therapy, William's home also boasted a manic-depressive nurse, a forty-year-old executive-success-life-coach who still drove his father's twenty-year-old Chevrolet, a swimming instructor who was convinced that she was one of the original members of the Spice Girls and a graduate of the Aleister Crowley School of Witchcraft.

Then of course, there was William, the ringleader. Besides running this lunatic asylum in the name of holistic health, William was also the published author of a book titled *Conscious Living for a New Millennium*, of which, several copies were always to be found lying conspicuously around the living room. The cover of this book showed a giant yellow chick hatching from a huge egg, both of which towered over a depiction of the planet Earth in the background. Keith and I used to joke that the oversized chick looked like it was about to crush, or at the very least, befoul the poor unsuspecting planet. We were certain that there was a metaphor for our feelings about William somewhere in that observation, but neither of us quite had the poetic gift to verbalize it. But in short, William was pretty much a lazy, greedy bastard, who couldn't seem to help but poke his nose in where it didn't belong. On the other hand, he did make a darn good organic salad.

I eventually scraped together enough cash to achieve escape velocity from William's Compound. Although I was only able to afford to move into a studio apartment replete with roaches, I positively wallowed in the joyous solitude. After settling in my new place, I swore to be on guard against California and to never be taken by surprise again. This was just a pipe dream as bogus rolling blackouts on order from Enron, bodybuilder governors, and the heart of the Internet and real estate economy booms and busts were all just lurking around the corner.

But I don't want to leave you with the wrong impression, because I have grown to love California. I love all the crazy trends that spring up here before they go anywhere else, and I also love California's unwritten state law that grants its citizens the freedom and the right to *just be yourself, no matter what anyone else thinks*, even if this liberating outlook can have disastrous results. This is very different from where I grew up, where everyone gets on the same track from birth to death, almost without exception. In California, we might be foolish, but at least we're free, and I think I prefer that in the long run.

Welcome to California Bro'!

Two

Music Makes The Man

Both Larry and Jack are musicians, and they often compose music hoping that one day, they will become famous songwriters and recording artists known throughout the world.

With musical themes as the topic of the week, they meet at the charming Italian restaurant, The Venetian, just across the street from the high school where they work. Overhearing Larry and Jack's exchange of stories, Joey and Frank, the owners, recommend a bottle of *Crescendo Cabernet Sauvignon* a superb blend of *Cabernet Sauvignon, Cabernet Franc, Malbec*, and a touch of *Petit Verdot.*

Jack and Larry instantly note the classical taste, the depth and balance, and the brilliant flavors of *Crescendo* that grow in intensity with each sip as memories, like music, begin to consume their conversation.

Rites of Passaggio

by Larry Zeiger

When I was five years old, my mother and father decided it was time for me to start training to be the next Van Cliburn, the renowned concert pianist who started his piano lessons at the age of three. According to my mother, I was already two years behind. Seeing no reason why I would be nothing short of a brilliant prodigy, she had recurring dreams of me performing a duet with Van Cliburn of Tchaikovsky's *Concerto for Four Hands* at Symphony Hall in our hometown of Cleveland, Ohio. My Aunt Betty, on the other hand, tried to convince my father that piano lessons would be a "huge waste of time and money" on me.

"Boys should *not* play the piano!" she barked. "They should play sports and prepare to fight the Nazis just in case they made a comeback!" Aunt Betty, however, had no problem with my sister studying the piano. "It's fine for a woman to play. She can use music to capture a young man's heart. Men like women who can play an instrument, but women like warriors - not piano players!"

With Aunt Betty's stamp of approval, my sister, Carole, at the age of eleven, was already playing Bach, Beethoven, and Dvorak, and secretly, when my parents weren't home, she'd pluck out a few Chuck Berry tunes.

I wanted desperately to play as well as my sister, and so with the support of my parents, I started taking classical piano lessons from Mrs. Von Rottenberg, an imperious, disciplinarian. My friend, Sammy Zelwin, would often refer to her as a *real ballbreaker!* I had no idea what Sammy meant by that, but I remained cautious when going to my lessons and left any kind of my balls at home.

When I sat at the piano, Mrs. Von Rottenberg would glare at me. In a demanding voice, she would scream, "Your timing is off! Listen to the Metronome! Listen! Listen! Can't you hear the beats? Your hands are too small! *Stretch them!* How do you expect to play the piano when your fingers are so tiny? You have matchstick fingers! Why are you wasting your parents' money on lessons?"

I would leave Mrs. Von Rottenberg's home feeling as deflated as a punctured beach ball, but I was determined to prove her wrong. I would follow in Van Cliburn's footsteps no matter what that Rottenberg lady said. I was ambitious, dedicated, and bound to succeed.

And then came the recital where I would have the opportunity to showcase my burgeoning talents. After one year, I had learned how to play piano *almost* with two hands. My spirit was soaring into the stratosphere. I was going to amaze everyone. All of Mrs. Von Rottenberg's pupils gathered at her home on that warm sunny day in September. I was the youngest kid to perform in the history of her teaching career, but I didn't feel nervous at all. I had mastered a short piece by a composer whose name I couldn't pronounce, and I played it like a master.

At the end of the recital, the students voted for their favorite performances. Mrs. Von Rottenberg explained that anyone who had four or more votes would win the coveted bust of Beethoven, a $1.59 (plus tax) dime store Plaster of Paris replica of the great master. Students were allowed to vote for up to six fellow performers, and there was no doubt in my mind, I would be victorious. My sister, Carole, voted for me, her twelve-year-old boyfriend, Tommy, voted for me, and of course, I voted for me. I only needed one more vote from the remaining twenty-two students to cement my name in the musical firmament. That's all - *just one measly vote.* All the parents and students waited in eager anticipation for our teacher to announce the winners.

Fifteen minutes passed, and Mrs. Von Rottenberg entered the living room with her list of the Outstanding Music Students of the Year. "And our first winner is . . . Joseph Allen!" she announced. "And our next winner is Barbara Brooks!" *Is she going in alphabetical order?* I wondered. *I'll just have to be patient. I'm sure I'll be the last winner just after my sister, Carole.* Having a last name beginning with "Z" always put great pressure on me. Twelve winners later, we had reached the "P's." "And our next winner is Leslie Perlis!" I was so thrilled to see so many of my friends being presented with the bust of Beethoven. I hooted and hollered for all the winners. But soon, we were in the "W's." "Our next winner is Mickey White!"

And then I started to do the math. There were only three busts left, but there were four of us waiting to hear our names called. And after awards were given to Jacob Youmans and Tony Xavier, suddenly, there was only one bust left. My eyes widened as I looked at my sister while Mrs. Von Rottenberg, her bosom swelling with pride, announced, "And now the moment we've all been waiting for! The last winner of the day is . . . Carole Ellen Zeiger!" My sister graciously accepted the award, and I, paralyzed with depression and doomed to a life of musical failure, stared at the empty awards' table. *Everyone a winner . . . but me!*

On the way home, my parents tried to console me by saying that I was one of "the best piano players at the recital," and I "should have won that bust of Beethoven." My mother tried to explain that this experience should motivate me even more to achieve greatness in my piano playing. Despite my family's support, I made the decision that day to quit piano lessons forever. I never wanted to touch a piano, take another lesson from that nasty Von Rottenberg, or hear the steady, dull, deadly beat of a metronome again! I decided Aunt Betty was right. *Piano was just not a boy's instrument.* Now the only thing left for me to do was to go fight the Nazis . . . if I could find any.

Seven years later, music reentered my life through my own natural instrument - my voice. Whenever I sang at parties, my friends assured me that I was destined to become a pop star bigger than Elvis, Jerry Lee Lewis, and Bobby Darin combined. Whenever I sang, girls would swoon, and guys wanted to be like me. I had it made!

At this momentous time in my life, I was attending religious school at the synagogue, getting ready for that pivotal moment of manhood, my *Bar Mitzvah.* My mother had been preparing for this event since the day I was born. Because she expected me to become the first Jewish President of the United States and because she insisted that I had "the most beautiful singing voice in the universe," she met with the Rabbi and insisted that my Bar Mitzvah be a solo affair. She did not want me to share the Torah reading with another fellow *Bar Mitvah-ite.*

No, my Bar Mitzvah was going to be my moment to shine with every relative, neighbor, and friend exclaiming to each other, "I've never heard anyone chant from the Torah with such passion, such clarity, such beauty in his voice!" "That thirteen-year-old is so articulate, so complex in thought, so mesmerizing." "What a magnificent vibrato!" "That boy is going places!"

For months I practiced chanting from the Torah and met with Cantor Rosen for instruction twice a week. "That voice! Simply Marvelous! You are a terrific contralto!" the Cantor exclaimed. "And there's an even greater voice building inside of you, waiting to come out that would make Abraham, Isaac, and Jacob so proud . . . proud . . . proud of you!"

"And Moses?" I asked. I always liked Moses especially after seeing Charlton Heston in *The Ten Commandments.*

"Ah yes, let's make Moses proud. Sing those scales I taught you, and sing them with perfect pitch, big rounded tones and full voice . . . from your heart, Larry. Sing from your heart!"

Despite his positive praise, I was always frightened by what could happen if I deviated even slightly from the standards he held to me. I dreaded his intimidating voice that often shook the rafters of the synagogue on those rare occasions when I sang slightly off-key, but I was determined to be *the best* Bar Mitzvah student in the history of the world!

Ironically, when the day of the big event, February 11, 1961, finally arrived, I was an absolute wreck. I wanted to run away, anything but go to the synagogue and face the hundreds of invited guests, and give anything less than a spectacular performance. My family and I drove to the temple while my heart pounded like a drum.

I immediately went to the Rabbi's office for my last minute instruction before I was to experience the biggest ceremony of my life, the moment where I would enter adulthood and all responsibility would rest on my shoulders. The Rabbi's words were encouraging, and I thought to myself. *I will do the best I can, and I will succeed. I am a Man!*

When the services began, I felt even more confident and poised. I convinced myself as I reached the microphone in the synagogue that I was instantly becoming a mature, responsible adult, ready to take on the world. My speech was powerful and eloquent, and when it was time to chant from the Torah, I sang with perfect pitch. The faces of my family, relatives, and friends beamed with joy. If applause had been appropriate, there would have been a standing ovation. I was on my way to becoming a scholar, an orator, and a professional singer. I was ready to meet up with Frankie Valli and become the *Fifth Season.* People even compared my smooth velvety voice to Johnny Mathis. I was floating on a huge cumulous cloud of adoration.

Immediately after the ceremony, Cantor Rosen approached me and insisted that I become the youngest member of the Temple Choir. I was flattered by the invitation, but I was not interested. I had finished one year of preparing for my *Bar Mitzvah,* and that was enough! With piercing eyes, the Cantor stared at me, waiting for my response. I feared that if I said "no" to him, I would be doomed to Hell . . . and then he dropped the bomb.

"I told your parents about inviting you into the choir, and your mother and father were ecstatic, Larry! They literally cried tears of joy . . . all for you! They're so thrilled and proud of your accomplishments!"

Jewish guilt consumed my soul. What could a person do when his mother and father had not only spent thousands of dollars on a party to which the entire world was invited, but they had also cried "tears of joy." I accepted the Cantor's invitation but immediately put all thoughts of singing in the choir out of my mind as I headed off to my party at the swanky Alcazar Hotel.

My Bar Mitzvah gala was the event of my lifetime! I danced with everyone to the live music of Gaylord Lipshitz and the Rhythmettes and amazed my friends and relatives with my ability to Jitterbug and Cha-Cha like no thirteen-year-old on the planet. For the Super 8 Bar Mitzvah movie, I staged the biggest Bunny Hop ever, followed by a huge *Horah* circle that filled the ballroom. Legions of fans complimented me on my vocal and dance skills. *I was a star!*

"You should train for Broadway. You have *the gift,*" said my Aunt Lil.

"What a voice! You should be a singer in a band. You could become rich and famous and support your parents and buy them a new house in Shaker Heights," my Uncle Isaac added. My father, who had overheard the conversation, was beaming with delight as he considered the possibilities.

Just before he left the party, Cantor Rosen notified me that choir practice would be every Tuesday night at 7pm. If I had been a bit more bold at that age, I would have told him that I much preferred to be the lead singer in a Motown band (if they would have me) than sing in the Temple choir but instead, I politely replied, "I'll be there . . . next Tuesday, Cantor. I promise."

The thought of singing with the twenty other members of the choir who were all accomplished operatic singers gave me a minor anxiety attack. A few days later, however, after my first practice, one of the choir members actually complimented me on my perfect pitch and my ability to enunciate in Hebrew.

I went home feeling a bit more confident, and thought to myself that maybe, just maybe, being part of this choir wasn't so bad after all.

About four weeks later, while attending Sabbath School learning all about the history of the Jews, the creation of the State of Israel, and the great philosophers, writers, and musicians like Shlomo Goren, Bernard Malamud, and Jascha Heifetz, Cantor Rosen frantically entered the classroom. He approached my teacher, Mr. Golden, and began whispering in his ear while looking directly at me. A wave of paranoia swept over me. *What did I do? Could it have been the cigarette I smoked behind the synagogue three weeks ago? Was it the smooching session I had during Rosh Hashanah services with Karen Lipstein?*

Mr. Golden announced that Cantor Rosen wanted to speak to me. Palms sweating, heart pounding, I followed Cantor Rosen into the hallway. He held my shoulder and looked pensively into my eyes and said, "Fern Greenblatt is out ill today and is not able to sing her solo in today's services."

Fern Greenblatt had the most beautiful soprano voice I had ever heard, and at Sabbath services, everyone looked forward to hearing her sing, *but what did this have to do with me?*

And then speaking with extraordinary force and perfect diction, the Cantor proclaimed, "I want you to sing Fern's solo in the Main Sanctuary today . . . in one hour!"

I could hardly speak. I thought my heart would pop out of my chest.

"Oh no, I can't . . . In front of everybody? I just don't know it well enough, Cantor Rosen, and to be honest, *I am no Fern Greenblatt!*"

He stared at me with his large piercing eyes and then as if he were announcing the eleventh commandment, he shouted, "You *will* do it!"

I was doomed and obviously had no choice in the decision-making process. *Is this what adulthood is all about?* I thought.

He ushered me into his study and left me alone to practice. I was so nervous. How could I compete with this fantastic singer that everyone loved? But I had to try and do my very best, so I sang the words slowly, making sure to enunciate each syllable and stay on key as the Cantor had instructed me in weekly choir practice.

May the words of my mouth
And the meditations of my heart
Be acceptable in your sight
Oh Lord, my Rock, and my Redeemer

Twenty-four words. It was certainly short enough, and truth be told, my singing had improved greatly in the last year. According to Cantor Rosen, I had even developed what he called a "natural vibrato." I had no idea what he was talking about, but at the same time I thought it was cool to be possessed of one. Maybe I had no reason to be nervous or tongue-tied after all. I continued to practice.

May the words of my mouth
And the meditations . . .

It was on the word, "meditations," that something strange happened to me. I tried to hit the notes, but my voice suddenly took a devastating plunge southward. My pitch was definitely off. *I must have a frog in my throat,* I thought. I sang again, but this time with an even lower voice on the phrase, "words of my mouth." *What was happening to me?* The more I tried to sing on key, the more horrible I sounded. *Calm down. Must be nerves. Sing the entire verse to the end, and just don't stop!* I tried once . . . twice . . . three times, but each time I sounded worse. I was all over the place. A tenor, a bass, then a baritone . . . and I was always horribly flat. I had no control over my voice. *Was it nerves? Was it a virus? Or was it some weird case of tonsillitis that I was feeling all over my body?* My brain was bombarded by waves of anxiety. *Why would God do this to me? And especially on a Holy Day!*

I looked at my watch. Not much time left. Soon I would be standing before the congregation - all eyes on me - just like at my *Bar Mitzvah.* Only then, I was good! What was I to do now? I tried singing in a much higher voice. *Not bad,* I thought, *and I was on key . . . well, sort of. Maybe I could get away with it . . . or maybe not.*

Suddenly, one of the members of the choir came to inform me that it was time to perform. Beads of perspiration ran down my forehead. Every step I took towards the entrance to the chapel echoed louder and louder in my head. The door to the *bema* opened. I was ushered to a seat between the Rabbi and the Cantor. In a matter of seconds, Cantor Rosen nodded to me indicating that it was time for me to sing Fern Greenblatt's solo prayer. I walked slowly to the pulpit and stared into the sea of unknown faces, and they in turn looked directly at me. I quietly cleared my throat. And then . . . I opened my mouth and in a shrill falsetto sang,

May the words of my mouth and the medi . . . medi . . . medi . . .

The voice which emanated from me was so high and squeaky that I sounded like a Jewish version of Mickey Mouse. I was horrified at the results and decided to drop the falsetto and sing in what I thought was my normal vocal range.

And the meditations of my heart . . .

Now my voice sounded like a Hoover Vacuum Cleaner. I decided to try the falsetto again.

Be acceptable in your sight . . .

But my singing was *not acceptable.*

It was downright dreadful! I had lost control of my voice. My body and soul had betrayed me, and my singing career was definitely over. I was doomed forever! I simply spoke the last words of the prayer.

Oh Lord, my Rock, and my Redeemer.

When I finished, I looked at the sea of stunned and silent faces. In another era the congregation would have pelted me with rocks as a form of retribution for my heinous performance. I turned around and saw Cantor Rosen looking at me with fireballs and brimstone spewing forth from his eyes. He looked as if he were going to go straight for my jugular!

After the service, he ushered me into the hallway and stared down at me. "Were you making a mockery of your religion?"

I was stunned and responded. "No! Do you actually think I wanted to make a fool out of myself in front of the entire congregation? I . . . I just couldn't help it!"

I didn't wait for a response and quickly walked away, emotionally drained, and humiliated. At that point, I decided to drown my sorrows at the *Oneg Shabbat* that was taking place in the social hall where honey cake and fruit were being served along with a sickeningly sweet punch for kids and small glasses of *schnapps* for the adults. My friend, Lenny, saw me looking distraught and asked what was wrong.

"I don't know what's happening to me, Lenny, but it sucks!"

"Yeah, I know, I've been having some issues too. I don't know what's goin' on. Getting' older or somethin' . . . it's so weird."

I walked over to the table and grabbed a piece of honey cake and when no one was looking, a shot of *schnapps.* I was thirteen and wanted to act like an adult. I drank it down quickly and felt a queasy burning sensation. It was the most horrible drink I had ever tasted. What a miserable day! Losing my voice, experiencing a *demonic possession*, and now my stomach was in utter chaos. It was then I realized the rest of my life was not going to be easy.

I came home and told my parents the sad, frustrating story of my singing experience at the synagogue and that I no longer wanted to participate in the Cantor's Choir. My voice had been ruined by something I didn't quite understand. I sensed my mother and father's disappointment, but I had an alternative plan.

"I made a big decision today. It's something I've been thinking about for the last few weeks. I'm *not* going to be a singer. That's obvious! But I *do* want to start piano lessons again. And . . . and . . . I want to do this, not necessarily to become the most famous pianist in the world, but because . . . I just . . . well . . . *I just want to learn to play the songs I love,* songs by the Beatles, the Temptations, Little Richard, Frankie Lymon and the Teenagers, the Four Seasons, and yeah, maybe even some Henri Mancini. That's what I want to do." At the ripe old age of thirteen, I was so proud of my newly discovered, mature decision-making skills.

I was an adult, ready to take on the world.

Going to Graceland

by Jack Beddows.

I was approaching a crossroads. I was almost finished with college and I needed to figure out what to do next with my life. For a long time, I had toyed with the notion of pursuing a career as a performer, and for the last several years I had studied guitar, piano, voice. I was constantly practicing my songwriting, and most importantly, I had watched several Rolling Stones videos in order to get Mick's patented rooster moves down pat.

Yet something held me back from committing to this kind of career, not least of all considerations of what the life of a performer would really entail. It was during this time of indecision that I started dating a young, professional musician named Sarah, who was getting ready to move back east, relocating for the new job she had recently started as a background singer for the *Godfather of Soul*, James Brown!

I'd met Sarah a few years before when she was pursuing her master's degree in opera performance while I was also in the music department working on my bachelor's degree in composition. Although her vivacious personality had always made her very attractive to me, I'd never had much of a chance to speak with her. And besides, at the time, she was dating a young man named Daniel. By the time, Daniel ended up being one of my roommates, they had long since broken up but remained friends. After Sarah gave up her apartment in preparation for her move, she stayed at our house as his guest. Thus began our *blitzkrieg* of an affair.

The only downside of our obvious attraction to each other was that Daniel clearly wasn't excited about the notion of Sarah and me spending time together. *Oh well,* I thought when I first realized his feelings on the matter, *perhaps, I don't need to pursue that particular avenue if it's going to cause friction.* That sentiment lasted exactly as long as it took for Sarah to beckon me over with a come-hither stare later that same evening. The next morning I consoled myself with the fact that Daniel had been dating another girl who lived with him for quite some time and, therefore, really had no right to be mad at me. *Ah, the complications of young love!*

This being the early stage of my new friend's blossoming music career, I was very excited for her. "Wow! You've really made it now, Sarah!" I said one night at a dinner with her and several of my friends at our semi-hippie college house in Isla Vista.

"And I bet you're doing alright with the money too, singing with a big star like that!" someone tactlessly commented while passing the shredded kale.

In response, Sarah's face puckered up like she had just licked a lemon. "My income's comparable to that of an entry-level Jack in the Box manager...the one who works the 4 a.m. shift." She then added, "I didn't find out how small my annual salary was until after I'd spent about a third of it on stage-worthy clothes!"

Now that she was all fired up on the topic, Sarah also told us how her eccentric, multi-millionaire boss enjoyed the comforts of flying his own private jet from venue to venue while the band had to take a chartered Greyhound bus on the never-ending James Brown's Greatest Hits Tour. "To save money on plane tickets, he'd have us driving that damned bus to Japan and Germany too. And there I'd be, underwater, waving at the fishes, while having to argue about making room for a place to sleep with some crack-head bass player from Alabama!"

On the other hand, Sarah admitted over dessert, it was great to be able to perform with such a big headliner. Every gig would be filmed and televised, and there would even be a performance in the upcoming Super Bowl half-time show. It all sounded very exciting to me, and as I pointed out, there were many musicians that would love to be in her shoes.

"Yeah, you're right!" she agreed. And I could tell, despite the none-too-ideal financial compensation, she was excited about her new job.

After spending a couple of days together, Sarah asked me if I'd like to join her on the trip back east to Augusta, Georgia. Augusta was, at the time, the headquarters of James Brown Enterprises, and it was also where Sarah happened to have grown up and where her family still resided.

Even though I was conscious of the fact that Sarah's request for me to join her on her trip was way too sudden to be wise, I was impulsive too, and readily accepted. After all, this was an exciting woman, and she did need to travel with someone. "Chivalry demands it!" I accidentally yelled out loud later that day, while musing on the subject outside of a grocery store, much to the disruption of people passing by.

The first order of business for the trip back to Georgia was to obtain a vehicle, and Sarah was hell-bent on getting a VW van right from the start. It just seemed to fit with her romantic notion of a cross-country journey. The one she called up about, after quickly scanning the *Auto Trader*, was a relic from the past: old, green, and rusted. And looking it over, along with the current owner who drove it over to my house for our inspection, I was sure it had seen more than its fair share of Grateful Dead shows

"You know, I really am a hippie at heart," Sarah drawled a half an hour later, in the most appealing version of her southern accent, as she put flowers behind her ear and on the dashboard of her new van. She had completed the purchase in record time, and now we were about to walk down to the beach together

"I'm going to call her Priscilla!" Sarah exclaimed with enthusiasm as we strolled along. I didn't quite know what to say in response. In a rare display of restraint, I had barely opened my mouth during the afternoon's transaction, but truth be told, I was harboring quiet doubts about this speedy purchase because while the van did offer a lot of space for Sarah's belongings, I wondered just how road worthy 'Priscilla' really was. But ultimately, I was too caught up in the excitement of my new romance to worry that much about it.

"Sure! Priscilla's a great name! *The Queen of the Desert*, right?" I finally answered her, smiling. "That's right! *Priscilla, Queen of the Desert!*" Sarah smiled back, and we continued on our way. My new friend was an intelligent, attractive, fun-loving, and multifaceted woman, but perhaps not surprisingly, she was also a little unpredictable. It was hard to tell what side of her personality I was going to be dealing with at any given moment: a serious minded opera singer, a pot-smoking hippie, a health-minded athlete, or the aggressive little Southern sparkplug that could go from sexy to argumentative in the blink of an eye.

Within just a few days of spending time together, Sarah confessed her love for me. This impulsive declaration made me more than a little nervous, and I told her that I would appreciate taking things a tad slower in the future. She agreed, but I'm not sure we were actually on the same page.

A few nights later, Sarah went out to meet a friend of hers for drinks, and I had long since headed to bed when she came bursting into the room, all fired up about a proposition that had developed earlier that evening, "Jack, what do you think about us having a threesome?"

Now, I'm always grumpy when someone wakes me up in the middle of night, but this time, I was rendered stupid too. True, my mind began reeling with thoughts of what could be the sexual adventure of a lifetime. However, coming on the heels of the weirdness of Sarah professing her love for me, it was simply too much. In response, I not only said, "No," I also yelled at her for having such a bizarre notion of what *taking it slow* meant. Big mistake!

For the next several weeks, I was haunted by a dream that I was on a game show, repeatedly up for the final question for the grand prize. "Aw! Isn't that a shame! I'm afraid that was the wrong answer. Five minus three in fact, equals two. Yes, two was the answer we were looking for. Thought you would have had that one...in fact, we were kind of just giving it to you."

A few days later, while both of us were still embroiled in hard feelings, but not so much so that we weren't still planning on going on our trip together, I felt compelled to ask, "So...Sarah, when you said 'threesome' you were talking about two girls and a guy, right? Not the other way around?"

"That's right," she answered curtly.

"Yeah, that's what I thought," I sighed.

"And my friend is very attractive," she added, while moving a box from the open door of her storage unit to the back of the VW. I stopped for a moment and wept a little tear onto the corrugated cardboard that I was holding.

It was the day before our departure, and by the time we finished getting all of Sarah's belongings out of storage and crammed into Priscilla, I was incredulous. "What the hell? You can't see a God-damned thing!" With all of Sarah's stuff, the VW's rear view visibility was pretty much non-existent. "Go ahead and hang all the flowers you want around the rearview mirror. We can't see out of it anyway!" I said sarcastically. "And just what's in all of these boxes anyway?"

"Clothes mostly. "Sarah said.

"All the clothes you bought to get ready for your new job?"

"No, I bought those back in Georgia, these are just old clothes."

"Jesus Christ! Can't you get rid of some of them?"

I should have known better than to ask such a question. And so, as road-blind as a drunken water buffalo, we were off the next day. It wasn't long before my suspicions about Priscilla proved justified. That very evening, after hours of driving through the desert on Highway 10, one of Priscilla's tires simply exploded.

"Oh great!" I moaned. "Well, time to put on the spare! I just love changing tires in the middle of the desert . . ."

It was then that we ran into a little snag. Instead of the larger jacks that I was used to, Priscilla came with her own small, multi-piece jack that was completely incomprehensible to me. To make matters worse, we weren't exactly in the most hospitable of locales. The desert to either side of us was filled with rattlesnakes and other deadly creatures according to numerous posted signs. I kept looking behind me obsessively while trying to work the jack. It wasn't long before I realized that all I was doing was scraping the hell out of my knuckles and damaging the metal frame of Priscilla's ancient underbelly. It was clear that we needed some outside assistance.

As I looked around, I couldn't help but think that this was the kind of place I wouldn't want to stop for anyone trying to flag me down. So it wasn't surprising that the occasional truckers and cars roaring past, breaking the otherwise uncanny stillness of the night, weren't stopping for me either. I could feel oppressive vibrations left by countless years of sordid human activity in the area, from biker gangs committing murder over crystal meth deals gone wrong stretching back to vicious tribes of Native Americans slicing off the ears of defeated warriors to adorn their necklaces.

At last, when I'd just about given up hope, an old white Camaro pulled over, kicking up waves of dirt and sand. "Thank you God!" I said in response with a quick nod up to the sky.

But now that someone had actually stopped for me, I realized that I was feeling more anxious than grateful. After all, this was the part of the country where the film, *The Hills Have Eyes,* was made, and I imagined that a crazed serial killer would find this road an ideal venue in which to pursue his predilections.

As I walked towards the car, I noticed its headlights illuminating a reflective warning sign on the side of the road. Inside the glowing halo was the white outline of a cartoon man falling backwards from a lighting bolt shooting towards his foot, the bolt being the sting of a scorpion by his side that, if the proportions of the drawing held true, would have been about three feet tall. Accompanying the scorpion was the squiggly image of a rattlesnake making its way to the already doomed victim. I probably would have found this sign amusing under normal circumstances, but clearly, danger was everywhere.

As I leaned over into the driver's side of the Camaro, I hugged a small lug wrench tightly to my lower back. While looking the driver over, I thought I saw a glint of something sharp held low in his lap, and my heart skipped a beat.

"Hey, thanks for stopping," I said, while wondering exactly how I had gotten myself into this.

Fortunately, the driver who had pulled over turned out to be a really decent guy. A little gruff perhaps, but certainly a big improvement over the murderous deviants I was imagining. After he explained the special groove on the side of the VW where the jack had to fit in order to make it functional, he said in an ominous tone, "You know, you're lucky I stopped. This is a bad road. Bad things happen out here sometimes."

I then confessed how when he first pulled over, I was holding onto the lug wrench behind my back, and he, in return, confessed that he had been holding onto a knife in his lap, just in case I turned out to be some sort of maniac. And then, thanks to this fine, knife-wielding Samaritan, Priscilla was back on the road.

After this rocky start, the trip started to become bearable. It was not exactly the leisurely romantic journey I had been hoping for, but still, we camped, we visited some tourist spots, such as a giant meteor crater and a petrified forest, and though I tried too hard to be sweet to make up for what had happened earlier, which of course had the opposite effect of what was intended, we alternately joked and bickered like a relatively normal couple might.

We passed through northern Texas, which soon turned into Arkansas, and by the time we hit Memphis …we were deep in the South. Life seemed to move a little slower down there...actually, a lot slower. At one point, we found ourselves lost on a heavily wooded road. We pulled over and asked for directions from a skinny, middle-aged man in overalls who was sitting around whittling sticks. After waiting a full eight seconds for him to say, "Mmmmmmmm whaaaaaaaaaaat?"

I quickly replied, "Never mind, sir, we'll find it ourselves."

Another challenge of our trip in the deep South was the fact that Sarah and I were both vegetarians, and apparently, nothing in that part of the country was prepared without heavy doses of lard.

"You want what? Some kind of lunch without any meat in it?" the waitress asked incomprehensibly. I may as well have requested that she serve my meal in a trucker's cap for all the sense it made to her.

"Well, there's the beans. They don't have much meat in 'em. Just a little ham hocks is all," she said helpfully.

But truth be told, we forgot all about our problems as we approached the last major attraction of the journey, the holy land of pop music, Graceland! Now I would finally have the chance to join the ranks of goofballs and souvenir hunters that have actually touched the very heart of kitschy Wonder Bread and Pickles America.

During the tour, it became clear that Elvis had redefined southern style for all eternity, as besides sporting pompadours and sideburns, which were just a given really, every visitor besides me was dressed in one of the several distinct stages of Elvis' career. There were the 50's Elvises in broad shouldered jackets and short-sleeved collared shirts, the late 60's Elvises, all in black leather, and finally, even a few fat and bloated 70's styled Elvises, sporting the requisite sequined jumpsuits. I began to think that maybe all anyone really did need to get through life was to emulate the King, who clearly represented all of the stages of existence as eloquently as any classic Greek tragedy.

I was about to ask the man next to me where he got his deep fried peanut butter and banana sandwich when the tour guide announced that we were ready to proceed to enter the King's home. While the home was palatial on the outside, the first thing I asked myself upon seeing the inside was if Elvis had perhaps turned to his pet chimpanzee for advice on interior design. "What's that Scamper? You think we should splash some more green and red over the foyer? Good idea boy! Jerry! Give him another banana! And the keys to your Cadillac, it's his now."

As we continued through the house, I was thrilled with this fantasyland of kitsch. Clashing colors, bizarre furniture and knick-knacks, and truly hideous paintings were all testament to a country boy run amok. But all good things must come to an end, and as the sun set, our time in Graceland was drawing to a close.

We returned to the parking lot, laden with indelible memories and souvenirs, only to discover that Priscilla, no doubt bitter at being left alone, refused to start, no matter how we coaxed her. To make matters worse, as we started to look around us in our distress, we realized that the area surrounding the now closed-off grounds of Graceland was really one of the worst neighborhoods either of us had ever seen.

As the last light of the fading sun gave way, it was like we were suddenly trapped in Michael Jackson's *Thriller* video. We saw strange figures babbling incomprehensibly, dragging themselves across the streets with blood-soaked bandages trailing behind them, pausing in the middle of traffic to scream at the moon. Several expensive, pimped out cars were parked down the road, bumping up and down, not on hydraulics, but merely the power of their bass amps, the booming thuds which were audible blocks away.

As nightfall deepened, we walked a long, frightening block, until we finally found a working payphone outside of a convenience store. Another bouncing and inscrutably tinted car was in the parking lot with fancy light strips racing along the trim in time with the music. Prison-like bars adorned the windows of the shop. Once inside, we couldn't help but notice a crazy white woman who came in from the parking lot screaming insanely to both everyone and no one in particular.

"You dears better come over here," counseled the poor soul behind the cash register, who doubtlessly saw this kind of craziness all the time. She gave us change for the pay phone and provided us with a phone book, as the one in the booth outside had long since been destroyed. Our mood became even more desperate when we were told by the dispatcher for the only mobile repair company that we could get a hold of that it would likely be well over an hour, probably closer to two, before anyone would be able to help us. When I asked her if there was any way to get someone out there faster, she informed me in a belligerent tone, "In all honesty, you're lucky to get anyone to come out that way after dark at all." But hope was not completely lost.

That very night was the anniversary of the death of Elvis, and so a crowd was gathering in an otherwise empty parking lot across the street from the entrance to Graceland for the beginning of an all night Vigil for the King. The lights started to come on one after another, until suddenly, there was a blazing oasis that filled the night sky. A few dozen devotees had set up a screen and were planning on showing Elvis films all night long, some containing rarely seen footage. I tried to brush my hair up into something resembling a pompadour in order to fit in. I had heard of crazy Elvis fans before, but I didn't realize the extent of their fanaticism until I experienced it first hand.

To this crowd, Elvis was like the second coming. In one of the films, Elvis was shown rehearsing with his band, and he was clearly out of his mind. He fell out of his seat a half a dozen times, and he kept giving commands to the band such as, "Okay boys, let's round 'er up, one more time, and we quit!" In response, the band would studiously ignore his instructions on the length of the ending. "Okay boys, two more times…" and so it went until he fell out of his seat, yet again.

"Wow!" I said, to one of the faithful next to me, "I had heard Elvis had problems with drugs, but man! He's really messed up here!"

"ELVIS NEVER DID DRUGS!" was the stern answer I received, along with a stony glare that indicated to me that I had better watch what I say, if I wanted to stay within the safety of the Elvis Oasis. In consequence, besides the occasional whisper to Sarah, I kept my mouth shut for the rest of the night, until finally, the cavalry arrived, in the form of Larry's Lickety-Split Towing and Tune Ups.

Soon Priscilla was up and running yet again. This time, we didn't intend to stop until the trip was done. Driving into the night, away from Memphis, the swampy woods around us grew deeper and darker. The moon hung low and the atmosphere thickened. The fog was so heavy that the sixteen-wheeler semis that passed us looked as if they came straight out of the swamp; long, low gators with bright yellow eyes ready to snap us up. Several hours later, as the sun was rising on a new day, we were relieved to finally make it to Sarah's home, where I stayed for the next week.

Truth be told, there wasn't much happening in Augusta. There was a golf course, a paper mill that permeated most of the town with its awful aromas, and, of course, a mall, and that seemed to be about it. Except of course, for James Brown's business offices and rehearsal studios. I saw the business park of the main offices where just a few years before James had burst into a staff meeting, threatening his business neighbors with a shotgun for using his private bathrooms, before taking the police on a high speed chase across state lines. Although I didn't get to meet the man himself, I did meet his hairdresser, Tiny, a man who looked like he could bench-press a small truck.

I spent my last couple of days in Augusta working for Sarah's father in order to get enough money for a one-way plane ticket back to California. Her dad was a very likeable and high-energy guy, and he was very good about having me work for him, cleaning up an unused rental property that he owned. However, we also picked up another woman to work with me on this task, and this was where things got strange. Everyone knows the phrase "the wrong side of the tracks," but I had never seen it realized so literally before.

Augusta had seemed to me an affluent town overall, but as soon as we drove over the unused railway, mostly hidden by miles of strategically planted bushes and trees, we were in an area that didn't really even deserve to be called a shanty town. The woman I worked with lived in a shack that was small, lopsided, and rotten with holes. But she did have a piece of corrugated tin slapped on the roof that no doubt made it the envy of the neighborhood. She ducked out of her hovel and into Sarah's father's expensive SUV.

As an outsider, I felt the disparity of these two very different worlds right next to each other. Soon after we were left alone to work together, I realized that this woman spoke an incomprehensible version of English that was an extreme combination of Southern accent and a complete lack of formal education. I doubt that the poor woman had ever set foot in a school. She was even harder to understand than my Scottish uncle after he's had a few too many, and that's saying something. Throughout the day's work, whenever she tried to communicate with me, I would pause for a second to see if there was anything in what I had just heard that I could decipher before nodding my head, saying, "Okay, sure," and continuing with whatever it was that I was doing. I was deeply saddened when I thought about our history of segregation and poverty and the shameful legacy of slavery. After a few days of this very sobering end to my trip, I finally had enough money to fly home. And so I said my goodbyes to Sarah and the South.

On the flight back to California, I thought a lot about Sarah's new position as a high-profile musician with all its benefits and drawbacks, and I thought about the legacy of Elvis Presley, perhaps the single most successful musician of all time. I also alternately meditated on the small slice of America I had witnessed and read through the copy of Herman Hesse's *Siddhartha* that Sarah had given me in an unexpectedly thoughtful parting gesture. The net result of all this being the strengthening of the idea that perhaps a low-key existence is better after all. And although I was only returning to delayed questions and instability, I nevertheless felt more than relieved as the plane touched down in Santa Barbara.

Sarah, and I met once or twice more in Santa Barbara, and besides occasionally seeing her perform on television, that was more or less it. Since then, other events and people have re-sparked my interest in performance including another former college acquaintance of mine, the famous folk-rock singer/songwriter, Jack Johnson. I remember driving in my car when I first heard his name on the radio. I also remember playing music with him one afternoon in his living room back in Isla Vista.

But I know Jack Johnson's story is a one in a million and fame seems to have landed in his lap without his even trying. I have also known musicians who've worked for peanuts selling instruments and equipment at small guitar stores despite the fact that they've made gold records, had videos on MTV, and had performance credits such as touring with idols like Iggy Pop and David Bowie.

Truly, all that glitters is not gold. In contrast, I was still performing occasionally, making my own records, even if no one knew about them, and sadly, I was making more money as a schoolteacher than in the world of music.

And yet I'm still tortured by the notion that I never went for the whole enchilada. After all, would it really be that bad to leave behind a more or less settled life as a teacher in exchange for the legacy of a poorly decorated mansion crawling with imitators that despite their occasionally shaky knowledge of personal hygiene would love you till their dying day? Perhaps, all things considered, it would be a small price to pay. And while it might be too late for me to start sporting the gold lamé of a 50's teen idol, I'm still young enough to fit quite nicely into my black leather jacket.

THREE

BIENVENIDOS TURISTAS

The atmosphere of El Camino Restaurant with its stunning paintings and Mexican themed murals created by owner, Mauricio Couturier, inspire Larry and Jack to exchange stories about their South of the Border experiences.

They sit at the colorful bar and cannot resist the flavors of the *2006 Rancho Zabaco Dancing Bull Cabernet Sauvignon.* The exotic floral taste with a hint of black pepper makes Jack reflect upon his first trip to Mexico and the huge mistake he made. Larry enjoys the *Dancing Bull,* but when he recalls his unexpected stay in a small home in Mazatlan, he is motivated to choose a second glass of the delicious *Hacienda Cabernet Sauvignon* to compliment his story.

To add to the theme of the day, the Latin Jazz ensemble featuring Gilbert Castellanos on trumpet performs some great music that ultimately enhances Jack and Larry's story swapping experience of the week.

El Americano Feo

by Jack Beddows

Early one April, a few years back, a close friend of mine suggested that I go with her on a weekend cruise to Mexico. I was at first hesitant to agree. Susan and I were good friends and always had a lot of fun together; it was just the cruise itself that I wasn't so sure about.

"Aren't cruises just for retired couples and senior citizens who want to have scenic views to enjoy while they get loaded by the pool?" I asked, thereby revealing my limited consideration of the subject.

"Sometimes, they are," Susan began in response, before continuing with a few simple points that convinced me that my pre-conceived notions could be getting in the way of a good time. It turns out she was right.

Cruises aren't just scenic boat rides for senior citizens to get drunk on. On the cruise that *we* took, for example, people of *all* ages were getting plastered poolside, ordering endless streams of frozen daiquiris, Bud Lights and piña coladas. Of course, this didn't apply to everyone. The children, for one, remained mostly sober. Only when we briefly slipped passed the international water lines did a few emboldened twelve-year-olds belly up to the bar with demands to "quench their thirst like any man."

Really though, while the ship's bars were doing a brisk trade, most of the passengers on this particular cruise seemed to be people in their thirties or forties, who, like Susan and me, just wanted a break that consisted of a little comfort, a little coddling, and a little entertainment. And with the one exception of being herded around a gigantic warehouse space on the San Diego wharf for the better part of the morning of our departure, that's exactly what we got.

At first, I felt the discomfort of the boarding process was a bad omen for the trip, and it wasn't long before I was whining like a ten-year-old. But that all fell away when we boarded. As our eyes adjusted from the bright outside light, we found ourselves in a massive open lobby, the ceiling of which stretched all the way up to the top decks.

It was shocking to see just how gigantic the boat really was. It had as many floors as a small skyscraper, and obviously would contain everything that anyone could possibly need to enjoy themselves, and more. After finding our room, which was adequate but nothing special, we decided to enjoy several of the daytime activities available onboard. We took in the fresh ocean air on the upper decks, did a quick work-out in the well-equipped gym, took a yoga class, and then of course, we visited the pool where we enjoyed one or two tropical beverages I'd ordinarily be ashamed to order in a bar. For those with money to burn there were also some incredibly expensive spas and shops, and for those without, there was a waterslide on the top deck!

Later that afternoon, as Susan was looking over some very pricey dresses and hats, I slipped away to go put on my bathing suit. After we met back up from the spa and waterslide, Susan and I still had time to lie in the sun for an hour or so. It was very relaxing, and the only thing that could pull me away was the fact that it was almost time for dinner. So we returned to our cabin, outfitted ourselves to meet the semi-casual dress code, and headed over to the dining area. The hall was spacious, and it had an elegant atmosphere that was created by a combination of good design, pleasant wooden furniture, and a sweeping view of the Pacific Ocean.

The food was delicious as well, the only downside being that there were no seconds on dessert, not even for ready money, which was a shame because the chilled fruit soup was fantastic. We enjoyed our meal in the company of a young couple of mixed international backgrounds. They had taken this cruise before, and over coffee they told us that if we were planning on going ashore the next morning after the ship came to port, then we should definitely visit the nearby beach about fifteen minutes outside of town. We thanked them, spent a few more minutes exchanging pleasantries and went back to our cabin to prepare for the rest of the evening, which consisted of a visit to a European style disco, going to see a very passable crooner in a jazz bar, and taking a class to learn the entire opening dance sequence from the second Austin Powers movie. When it's all just an elevator ride away, it's amazing how much you can squeeze into a single night.

The next morning, along with several hundred other passengers, Susan and I disembarked in the port where the ship had quietly docked overnight. We were both eager to check out the city. It didn't take long, however, before we started to feel disappointed with it. The center of town did have a few stately buildings from the 1800's to look at, but otherwise it had very little to offer in terms of activities or entertainment. After a quick walk around, including an accidental visit to a canal, the smell of which was enough to bring us to our knees, we decided to head to the beach that had been recommended to us the night before.

As we climbed out of the taxi soon after, I was surprised to see that the beach was bordered by a long adobe wall that looked as if it could have kept out an attack by the entire Sioux nation. The only way to get through it, to the beach and boardwalk beyond, was to pass through an artsy knick-knack shop built into its center. Suddenly I felt like George C. Scott in *Patton*.

"You Magnificent Bastards!" I muttered to myself, referring to the obvious genius of the Mexican tourism board. Inside the shop, all the men fidgeted like flies caught on a web, while the women gently strolled through the store picking up pricey items with their silky fingers. There were expensive dresses and hats, overpriced statuettes of Jesus, Don Quixote, Mickey Mouse, and *both* kinds of Madonnas, the mother of Christ as well as the eighties pop diva, and also a large display of turquoise jewelry. Although beautiful, I'd seen a lot of turquoise jewelry in my time, and I was bored silly after about two minutes of shopping, which was unfortunate because we were in the shop for about an hour.

Finally, I was able to drag Susan out through the other side of the store that I named in my own mind, *El Estado de Limbo*. "Welcome to *El Estado!*" I could imagine a store greeter saying to the poor suckers on the way in, as I was finally on the way out. "It's not hell, but it's not far off!"

And so, with exclamations of extreme relief from me, we at last started our stroll down the otherwise pleasant little boardwalk on the water. As we went along, the first thing we saw was a group of young people enjoying themselves by being dragged behind a power boat, on what looked to be a large, inflatable banana. Next to them were the bolder tourists among us, who opted for parasailing. If you don't already know, parasailing consists of being strapped into a parachute, sitting on the edge of a pier, and then being whipped fifty feet into the air by a motorboat driven by a nine-year-old boy. At least that's how it works in Mexico. We decided to leave the water sports for another day, and as it was then almost noon, Susan and I retired to a nearby restaurant.

The day was warm, but a pleasant breeze cooled us as we sat under the thatched umbrellas in the restaurant's courtyard, enjoying the play of the sun on the waves and the white puffs of clouds drifting sleepily overhead. It was all very quiet and peaceful. We were the only couple seated outside, and all we had to worry about was ordering from the Spanish language menu. Susan's Spanish was decent, and I probably could have managed with only marginal difficulties, but the waiters were more than proficient in English as well as particularly pleasant, and our orders were placed without any difficulty. It seemed that we were again going to enjoy a perfect dining experience. But then, a family of fellow-Americans, who seemed hell-bent on giving our country a bad name, joined us on the patio. This family consisted of a chunky little boy in an oversized *All I Got Was This* t-shirt, a plump, garish mother, and a blotchy, sunburned father, whose goal in life seemed to be to give every Mexican he met a hard time.

"Hey, Pedro! Over here! How come y'all don't serve hamburgers? You gotta just be servin' Americans here; no Mexicans could afford these prices!" Every time he opened his mouth Susan and I would roll our eyes.

"Can you believe this guy?" I said, in a voice loud enough to be heard, but which fell, nevertheless, on deaf ears.

"Well, at least there are people like us, who hopefully counteract the perception of American tourists all being total jackasses," Susan replied.

We finished our lunch, thanked our waiters and left a very generous tip out of pure sympathy for their tremendous patience. As we walked out of the restaurant to head back to the boulevard, we heard the man saying to his wife, "Now Margaret, fifty cents is a lot to leave for these people. That's probably close to a day's pay!"

I tried to forget about the 'ugly' Americans, and in order to take my mind off of them, I began to think about what we could do with the rest of our afternoon. I started by reconsidering the parasailing. "You know, I'd try it," I said to Susan, "I really would. But I shouldn't go into the water so soon after a big meal."

"Oh, I know it, Jack. I'm sure you'd be out there otherwise," she responded, but even better, I know what would be fun. Let's take a horse riding tour! I saw a poster for it back in the restaurant."

I thought this sounded like a much safer way for us to enjoy ourselves and replied, "Well okay. But are you sure you don't want to try the parasailing, Susan?"

"Okay, let's do the parasailing," she said."

"No, perhaps the horses would be best after all," I concluded with a conciliatory air.

"Thanks for being so understanding," she quipped back, and a few minutes of brisk walking later, we arrived at our destination. Unlike at the restaurant, there was no English spoken at the corral on the beach, so Susan was completely in charge of the negotiations. Thanks to her hardened business savvy, we were soon outfitted with the best horses the corral had to offer which turned out to be two ornery, flea-bitten geldings that sagged in the middle. We were also assigned to Pablo, our guide, who looked as if he could have been the younger brother of the boy we saw driving the powerboat earlier.

As we prepared to mount, I began to feel a little nervous. Susan's horse didn't look particularly happy about being taken out for a ride, but mine obviously had a real mean streak. As I looked him in the eye, he stared back as if to say, "You know, if I had a nickel for every A-hole like you that I've had to carry around on my back I'd be a millionaire!"

To make matters worse, I hadn't been on a horse since I was Pablo's age and knew pretty much zero regarding the equestrian arts. It soon became clear that I would be engaging in a struggle of wills with old Gunpowder, as I quickly dubbed him, just to get through this experience.

Susan and Pablo were off at a trot right out of the corral, but despite my best efforts, Gunpowder refused to follow suit. At this point I really wished I had kept up with my Spanish studies. *Maybe I could reason with the beast. If only I spoke his native tongue*, I thought, *I could let him know that I feel his pain.* "

Vámonos, Gunpowder! *Vámonos!*" I yelled in the beast's ear, but it was no use. He refused to move.

As my promptings utterly failed to get Gunpowder going, Pablo had to intervene. He doubled back and twirled overhead a thick rope with a large knot tied at the end, which whistled ominously in the air. Gunpowder was no doubt intimately familiar with that rope as just the sound of it quickly shuttled him into compliance. And so we were off!

Our route was to take us down a long stretch of beach, up a path to some nearby unpaved streets, and then back again. Although Pablo still had to reach for his rope occasionally in order to keep my horse in check, the first leg of the journey was relatively pleasant and uneventful. By the time we reached the dirt roads of the nearby neighborhood, Gunpowder seemed to have settled down almost completely. My confidence as a rider was growing as we passed through the little beachside residences, an odd assortment of ramshackle homes and nicer developments. The poor upkeep and almost complete absence of cars or people, suggested that this was mostly beach rental property still in the off-season.

After a while, on the otherwise deserted street, we saw another group of horse riders coming from the opposite direction. As we passed, I tried my best to look like I knew what I was doing, and fortunately, Gunpowder gave me minimal trouble as we all waved and smiled at each other. This lack of a shattering blow to the ego, which I had been half-expecting, did much to cement my feelings of comfort and confidence. After we turned around and started back down the path to the beach, I decided to experiment with my growing equestrian powers. I was going to assume command of our little party by taking the lead position for the last leg of our trip, despite my obvious lack of qualifications in ability and experience.

I was also determined to bring up the speed of our horses. The last part of this ill-conceived plan stemmed mostly from a simple desire for comfort. Keeping the horse at a slow walk was smooth but very tedious. On the other hand, the trot we had assumed was exceedingly jarring and the constant bouncing up and down was starting to wear on me. I thought I could both prove my manliness and enjoy a more exciting and comfortable ride if I could just get Gunpowder into a medium gallop for the last leg of the trip down the beach to the corral. So I gave the horse a little prompting "Hie!" and a shake of the reins. He shook it off. I repeated my actions a little more forcefully only to be ignored yet again.

The third time, I gave it my all as I prompted him, though I also decided to resign myself to the trot if this last effort proved fruitless. In response, Gunpowder stopped in his tracks, turned and looked back at me as if to say, *Oh! You want to go fast, huh? Ok. I'll show you fast, Jackass!* Then, much to my surprise, that old, broken-down horse set off immediately at a blazing pace. I nearly fell right out of the saddle as I found myself suddenly speeding down the beach on the back of this big, strong animal that clearly hated my guts.

My fears of falling off the back and being kicked in the head and permanently brain damaged caused me to hold on for dear life. But what I didn't realize was that squeezing your knees together means "go faster" in horse talk, and so instead of securing my safety, this only caused Gunpowder to increase the pace of his mad dash. Panic started to well up inside of me, especially as we were now entering the populated section of the beach. Up ahead, several small Mexican children looked up in horror as a mad gringo came bearing down on them at a furious pace.

They scrambled out of the way and were forced to watch their hastily abandoned plastic toys being smashed to bits under Gunpowder's hooves with a sickening crunch. There was screaming all around, and up and down the beach people were pointing at me and gasping as I plowed through the thankfully sparse groups of beach goers. Finally, I gained the presence of mind to pull back on the reins, though I was still squeezing with my legs for dear life. This confusion of signals led to Gunpowder slowing down, but in a manner that still was very much in contest with my desires. He jerked his head one way in a quick dignified trot, away from the corral where I was hoping to bring this nightmare to an end. So I pulled against him again, and he jerked his head the other way. Our heated struggle led to him dancing from side to side, back and forth repeatedly in a graceful, symmetrical manner that, ironically, to any outside observer must have looked like a fine example of horsemanship. This false appearance of control of the horse made it seem as if my dangerous ride through the crowd was nothing more than the reckless arrogance of a cruel and heartless man, a man completely devoid of concern for others, especially for the poor children of Mexico.

People from the boardwalk began to shake their fists and yell. Mothers hugged their children close to their breasts and spat at me as if I were some sort of monster. The owners of the corral ran out screaming incomprehensibly. A nearby federal officer came up to see what the hell was wrong with me. And to everyone except for Pablo and Susan, who were trotting up behind me, laughing their heads off, I was the worst example of an arrogant American tourist that anyone had ever seen.

Somehow, despite my best intentions, I had become the *ugliest* of the ugly Americans. The next day we had the opportunity to disembark yet again in another port in another Mexican town. But while Susan went off to sightsee, I could be found poolside, nestled in between several sunbathing seniors, muttering something about, "Damned Mexican horses!" over yet another frozen daiquiri.

Un Navidad a Recordar

By Larry Zeiger

After my third year of teaching high school, I decided I needed an R&R break from the world of standards, objectives, and accountability. After looking in the local San Diego paper for travel deals, I decided to fly down to Mazatlan during the winter vacation to swim in the warm Pacific, sip frosty Margaritas, and get a terrific tan, but this time I was going to travel by myself and create my own world of excitement. A month later, passport in hand, I arrived at my modestly priced oceanfront hotel far away from the world of teaching. It was by no means the most luxurious spot on earth, but I could hear the waves lapping against the shoreline from my room, and that was enough for me.

The hotel had a palapa-covered beach bar where I found myself in the late afternoons chatting with tourists and locals. I was proud of the fact that I had mastered some Spanish in high school and could almost communicate with the locals.

"*Hola mi amigo, Jose. Como esta usted*?" I also knew phrases like *Donde esta el bano? La pluma esta en la mesa. Cuanto cuesta?* And most important, *Cerveza, por favor.*

The bartender, Victor, spoke little English but understood every cocktail request I made. I did my best to speak Spanish (more like *Spanglish*) to him, and he was nice enough to recognize my deficiency and correct almost every word I said.

On the second day of my stay at the hotel, a big scruffy, overweight American man wearing an ill-fitting t-shirt approached the bartender with a demand rather than a request. "Give me a Boilermaker, and make me a good one like they do in Ohio where I'm from!"

Victor had a confused look on his face. I could tell he had no idea what this man was talking about.

"I said give me a Boilermaker! What's wrong with you, Boy?" Addressing Victor, who was my age, as "Boy" made me want to punch the guy in the kisser or at least inform him that he was a redneck-idiot-bigot loser who most likely did not have a single friend in the world.

The man rudely continued. "Don't tell me you don't know how to make a Boilermaker! What kind of a bartender are you? And for Christ's Sake, don't no one speak English in this place?"

Immediately, I wanted Victor and others at the bar to know that this man was not typical of other Americans, at least the ones in my circle of friends. Utilizing the conflict resolution techniques I had learned in Educational Psychology 101, I immediately tried to diffuse the situation. "You know, Boilermakers are my specialty."

This was a complete lie, but I remembered back in college, one night a group of guys decided to master the art of creating the "perfect" Boilermaker. My roommate, Mark had declared, "It's the easiest drink in the world to make. Simply fill a shot glass with cheap whiskey, and drop it into a mug of beer." At that time, I always found the drink disgusting, but it was the one drink recipe I always remembered.

"Victor, can I help you make a boilermaker for this *hombre?*" I asked.

Victor didn't quite understand what I was saying, so I decided to use a few more of the words I had mastered in high school Spanish class. *"Bebidos Boilermaker. Ayudo tu. Yo se hacer Boilermaker. Yo ayudo tu."*

Victor stared at me and smiled. "*Mi amigo*, you help. You be bartender *conmigo*. We make Boilermaker for *hombre de Ohio. Si?*"

All the patrons were appreciative that I had diffused what could have been an ugly situation. I went behind the bar and poured a shot of Jack Daniels into a glass of *Pacifico*. Chuck Kluckman, the man from Ohio, downed the drink, and everyone at the bar applauded including Victor and me. After his third

Boilermaker, Chuck even asked to take a photo with the two of us to show his friends back in Akron.

Towards the end of the afternoon, Sr. Bustamante, the manager of the hotel looked me in the eye, and said, " I see what you did at the bar." At that instant I thought for sure I had gotten Victor in trouble by making the Kluckman guy a drink, but that was not the case. "I want to tell you," he continued, "*esto fue algo muy bueno que hizo.* This is very nice thing you do. Anytime you like to assist Victor at the bar, please be my guest. I also want you to know that any drink you order will not be charged to you. *Sus bebidos son gratis por mi amigo. Muchas gracia senor por su ayuda!*"

I was completely amazed that Sr. Bustamante was not upset with my marginal bartending skills, and he was more than gracious with his reward. I had absolutely no professional experience making any drinks other than boilermakers but decided to try to learn as much as I could from Victor.

He taught me all about different Tequilas, how to make a *Margarita Perfecto*, how to create authentic *Sangria*, and why *Piña Coladas* are not drinks for real *hombres.* I had the time of my life, and to my surprise, the attendance at the bar increased greatly. Everyone wanted to see the *gringo simpatico* attempting to make a drink. Every now and then, Victor and I would put on a show, juggling limes and oranges. With this experience, I thought one day, I could be an ambassador to the United Nations. After all, this could be a new method of solving world crises. All it takes is a little courtesy, connecting to others and *exquisite* bartending skills.

That night after the bar closed, Victor invited me to meet his girlfriend, Lupe and her friend, Rosa. After a brief introduction we decided to go dancing at one of the neighborhood bars. Whenever I attempted to speak Spanish, Rosa and Lupe would laugh uproariously at me, and Victor would roll his eyes back and candidly tell me, "*Su español es terrible, Lorenzo!*"

Later in the evening after a few Margaritas, I stared at Rosa and looked deeply in her eyes and could tell she was coming on to me. I put my hand on my chest to show my beating heart and like a poet dramatically proclaimed, "*Mi cabron* is beating for you."

"You're *what* is beating for me?" asked Rosa with a painful expression on her face.

"*Mi cabron?*" I responded sheepishly, suddenly thinking I may have used an incorrect word.

"*Su corazon*, Lorenzo. *Un cabron es un . . . un* . . . it is an ass! Your ass is beating for me? I don't think so! *Eso es incorrecto!*"

"Oh! I mean . . . *Mi corazon*, not *mi carbon,* is beating for you, Rosa!" I knew my knowledge of the Spanish language was limited and decided to try one more time. "*Estoy embarazada.*"

I thought I had said that I was *embarrassed*, but Rosa looked at me as if I had just won the "Dimwit of the Year" Award.

"Speak English!" she exclaimed. "I *know* English. I studied at the university."

I thought I had only mispronounced the words so I repeated myself, *"Estoy embarazada, Rosa."* And then while looking in her eyes, I added with the burning intensity of a poet, "And Rosa, *Estoy intoxicado* by your . . . your looks and your . . . *bueno personalidad!"*

Rosa looked at me as if I were a genuine *idioto.* She turned and walked away and left me alone with Victor and Lupe. Later, I learned that *embarazada* is the word for *pregnant*, not *embarrassed,* and *intoxicado* was the word for *poisoned*, not *intoxicated.* I never saw Rosa again.

Even though I was a failure at speaking Spanish, I was still a hit at bartending at the hotel. My mixology skills were improving by the hour, and in less than a week, I felt confident that if I ever needed to change professions, I had the option of bartending. My knowledge of different types of Tequilas and Mexican beers was becoming quite impressive . . . at least it was to me.

After a few days at the resort, Victor was kind enough to invite me to have Christmas Eve dinner with his family. I told him I was planning a trip to tour the jungles of San Blas that day, but he convinced me that having a holiday meal at his parents' house would be a far more exciting adventure than touring hot steamy jungles. Late in the afternoon on Christmas Eve after Victor completed his shift at the bar, the two of us departed from the hotel for the holiday meal I will never forget.

After an hour-long bus ride, we walked several blocks, what seemed to be at least a mile, to a very poor part of town. When we reached his street, I realized I was in a world I knew little about. As soon as we entered the house, Victor's mother and father greeted me with a big hug as if I were part of their family. We sat down at the kitchen table for a huge holiday meal of *carne asada, frijoles*, *arroz* and *cerveza.*

All of Victor's relatives were extremely gracious with the exception of Uncle Raul, who felt all Americans were superficial and materialistic "aliens." Uncle Raul loved Tequila with such passion that there was no doubt in my mind that by evening's end he could easily consume the entire contents of a full bottle. He poured himself a glass of *Jose Cuervo Especial* and proceeded to down the contents at a very alarming rate. And then he poured himself another glass . . . and several more.

The more he drank, the more outspoken he became. "So, is Disneyland your great *monumento a cultura*?"

"I hardly ever go to Disneyland, but when I do, I always have a good time riding the rides and eating all the junk food. Have you ever been there?" I said naively.

"I never go to *los Estados Unidos* and have no desire to visit. Your *presidente* does not know his ass from hole in the ground! And our *presidente* is worse! Look at the way we live." He suddenly changed the subject. "How many cars do you drive?"

"One," I said, thinking about my old Volkswagen Rabbit that was on its last legs.

"Hay demaciados automobiles en los Estados Unidos. Too many cars! Too much everything! It's all about power. It's all about . . . *dinero!"*

Victor, who was sitting on my other side, whispered in my ear, "Don't listen to Uncle Raul. He never say nothing nice about nobody."

Moments later, Victor's mother announced that she and her husband were honored to have me as a guest in their home, that this was one of the best experiences they have ever had, and that I will always be *uno amigo del familia.* The inebriated Uncle Raul rolled his eyes back and downed another shot of *Jose Cuervo.*

After dessert, Veronica, Victor's younger sister, sang an off-key rendition of *Solamente Una Vez.* We all applauded, and I looked at my watch. It was 10:30 p.m. I thanked everyone for the wonderful meal and announced my departure at which point, Victor told me the buses had quit running at 9 p.m. in their neighborhood.

"Oh, that's okay. I can call a cab."

Victor immediately clarified to me that the family did not have a phone and even if they did, taxis never went into their part of town, even in daylight. In short, I was stranded.

"No problema!" Victor responded. You stay with us for the night and *mañana*, we go back to hotel together."

Uncle Raul, who was very drunk at this point, reached over to me and slurring his words in a lascivious manner, replied, "You will sleep with me, *mi amigo Americano,* and we will have good time together . . . good time . . . good time . . . you will see."

Suddenly, I had visions of the movie, *Deliverance*, with Spanish subtitles running through my head.

Before I could say a single word, Victor took me aside and said, "You no sleep with my Uncle. He's way too drunk. You sleep with me tonight." Victor's plan ordinarily would not have been met with great enthusiasm on my part, but under the circumstances with Uncle Raul breathing his Tequila-scented breath down my neck, Victor's solution to the sleeping arrangements provided me with a great sense of relief.

I poured myself a small glass of what was left of Uncle Raul's *Jose Cuervo Especial* and agreed to the sleeping arrangements. Victor showed me to his room. There were three mattresses pushed together upon which his older sister, Angelica, her husband, Oscar, Victor's younger brother, Enrique, the sister, Lorena, the Chihuahua, Julio, and Victor and I were to sleep. The loudest crickets and owls I have heard in my life combined with occasional snoring, burps, and other bodily sounds kept me awake for at least two hours at which point, I closed my eyes and began to count sheep until I finally fell asleep.

At the crack of dawn, the sound of crickets and owls disappeared and were replaced by the quacking of ducks and the crowing of roosters. I looked at my watch; it was 6:15 a.m. Victor was already getting dressed for work, so I quickly threw my clothes on and entered the kitchen.

Victor's mother had prepared a feast for breakfast, and as soon as we were done eating, the children ran into the living room to open their Christmas presents. I had never seen such a happy family gathering. Even Uncle Raul, who had obviously forgotten the previous night, was as cordial as he could be in spite of a heavy hangover.

Six-year-old Enrique opened a gift which turned out to be a little toy piano. In a matter of seconds, the boy began to bang on the keyboard to the delight of the family. "I'll bet he becomes a concert pianist," I predicted.

"What a dream that would be," the mother responded. *"Lorenzo, tocas el piano?"*

Everyone looked at me for a response, and I nodded my head in the affirmative. I put the piano in my lap and played *Moon River,* followed by an anemic rendition of *Malaguena.* No sooner had I stopped playing, the mother said she needed to talk with the neighbor who lived next door to them. At least that's what I thought she said. Within minutes, she returned with a dozen neighbors waiting to hear me perform on Enrique's toy piano. And so, on the two-octave keyboard, I played *I Want to Hold Your Hand, Yesterday, I Left My Heart in San Francisco,* and for my "concert" finale, *Solamente Una Vez.* To the delight of the family and neighbors, Veronica did vocals, this time a bit more on key than the previous night. When she finished, thunderous applause erupted throughout the house, and I must admit, it was the most appreciative, attentive audience I had ever experienced.

Before departing, Victor's mother gave me a bag of almonds and candy as a token of the family's friendship and told me the next time I was in Mazatlan, I should stay with them, that I would always be part of their *familia.* Everyone hugged me and repeatedly told me to come back and visit whenever I was in their city. Victor had to be at work by noon on Christmas Day, so we quickly walked the eight long blocks to catch the bus back to the hotel. Upon arriving, I took the elevator to my room, luxurious in comparison to Victor's house, but not as warm, nor as inviting.

I left Mazatlan a few days later and returned to San Diego. Victor and I corresponded for about three years and then one day, the Christmas card I had sent was returned to me, marked as an incorrect address. I never saw my good friend again, but I think of those days often and how meaningful friendships develop from such small things as knowing how to make a proper drink and playing a toy piano.

FOUR

MONKEY BUSINESS

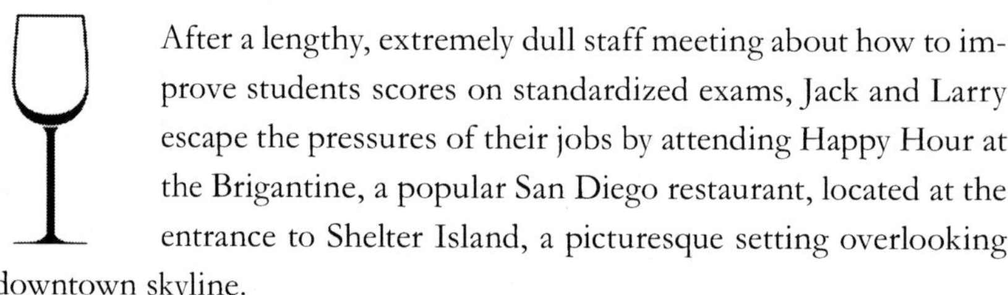

After a lengthy, extremely dull staff meeting about how to improve students scores on standardized exams, Jack and Larry escape the pressures of their jobs by attending Happy Hour at the Brigantine, a popular San Diego restaurant, located at the entrance to Shelter Island, a picturesque setting overlooking the downtown skyline.

Shortly after they sit down in the bar, they try to outdo one another with childhood tales of their mischievous brothers' adventures with monkeys - one, a furry toy creature and the other, a living breathing figure-skating primate. As a result, it is an easy choice for them to select a bottle of *Monkey Bay Sauvignon Blanc*, a delicious Australian wine, which perfectly compliments their stories.

The late afternoon meeting at the bar is a soothing reminder that the art of lively conversation combined with the correct choice of wines can create inspiring moments in a writer's life.

Flight of the Primate

by Larry Zeiger

When my mother discovered at the age of forty-three that she was going to have a third child, she was absolutely stunned. My father at the age of fifty-four looked lovingly at my mother over the breakfast table with a sense of pride in his eyes and responded, "We've still got it, honey!" at which point my mother came close to placing her head in the plate of scrambled eggs she had just prepared.

At the age of six, I was utterly perplexed and asked my father, "*What do you have?* I don't get it." In an abbreviated, highly edited response, he told me that fathers and mothers love each other so much that babies are born. *Wow*! I thought, *that's all it takes?* I wondered then why I didn't have a much larger family. He then concluded that a little brother or sister was currently growing in my mother's stomach and would "pop out" in a little more than half a year.

"*Pop out?*" I responded, "Why couldn't we just adopt? Sounds like it's a lot easier for Mom."

My father then explained to me about "the miracle" of having children, and how it was time for me to have a baby brother or sister that I would "learn to love."

"Why?" I asked. "*Why now?*"

The news hit me like a brick wall. I was in a total funk. It was one thing to have an older sister who was treating me as if I were a subservient robotic toy, but to be demoted to middle-child status was just far too much for me to comprehend.

My friend, Lenny, gave me some advice. "When the new kid comes, you're finished! You're no longer the favorite child. Your Mom and Dad will never pay attention to you. It's like you're *invisible*! You don't count. You get nothing. You are nothing. And you know how your dad always brings home model airplanes, model cars, and model trains for you almost everyday? Well, now you'll get *zilch!*" Lenny possessed a great deal of psychological insight for a six-year-old and knew exactly how to rattle my already jangled nerves.

Those nine months passed quickly, and in the winter of 1955 my brother, Richard, (we called him *Dickie* until he hit puberty) was born. Always begging for attention, he made annoying whimpering sounds from the first day of his life. Then the whimpers turned to cries, piercing screams that would drive any normal human being insane. Only lavish attention from my mother, father, and sister could stop those torrential tears that emanated from my little brother's eyes. Just like Lenny had predicted, I had been denigrated to the role of the "middle-child" or "the outsider."

When Dickie was one year old, my turtle, Igor, died and I cried and cried, hoping I would get equal amounts of attention from my family like my brother was receiving on a daily basis. Tears streamed down my face, soaking my shirt. I came inside after burying Igor under our rose bush next to the gold fish, Melvin. My sister was immersed in an episode of *The Donna Reed Show,* my father was smoking a cigar and reading his medical news magazines, and my mother was bouncing Dickie on her lap as he made cute little *goo-goo-mama-look-at-me* sounds. No one even looked at me. No one cared about my intense suffering, my great loss, or my broken heart. I approached my father and looked in his eyes. "Dad, I'm so sad."

"Not now," he replied. "I'm busy."

I turned to my mother, "Ma, Igor died. I buried him under the rose bush."

"Could you get me Dickie's bottle?" she asked. "I left it in the kitchen."

Out of desperation and with a forlorn look in my eyes, I approached my sister. "Carole, Igor, my turtle . . . my turtle is dead! I buried him under the rose bush. I'm so sad."

Just as she was about to speak, the phone rang. It was her new boyfriend, Bob, who she ultimately married seven years later. She looked down at me without an ounce of remorse and replied," Not now! It's Bob!" and that was it. It was if I had become invisible and no longer part of the family portrait.

I went out to the turtle-goldfish-guppy graveyard by the rose bush and sat by Igor's grave, contemplating my lonely future as the middle child, the forgotten one.

In the first four years of his life, my younger brother became the beneficiary of endless amounts of toys and stuffed animals – dogs, cats, penguins, giraffes, bears, kangaroos, and finally, a funky-looking monkey that caused a major uproar in our family.

"I don't want that monkey! I don't like that monkey! That monkey scares me! Why did you buy me a monkey? Monkeys are small. I want a gorilla, not a monkey! GET ME A GORILLA . . . NOW!" Dickie screamed in piercing tones creating a symphony of whimpers, moans, and shouts building to a heightened crescendo of such raw emotion and irritating sounds that our neighbor, Mrs. Jackson, was forced to close her doors and windows.

Finally, my mother, who was holding her ears, screamed out in desperation to my father, "Get rid of the monkey! It's too frightening for poor little Dickie. Get him what he wants. I can't stand the crying!"

"I think Dickie is going to have problems when he grows up," I said with great psychological insight. "Just because he doesn't get what he wants, he cries. And you and Dad always respond by buying him yet another toy. *This is wrong!* And imagine what he will be like when he grows up? " I was a mature eleven-year-old probably struck from the same genetic code as Sigmund Freud or Carl Jung. But in this current situation, my brilliant observations meant very little to my parents. It was obvious my brother had mastered the art of manipulation.

No sooner had I expressed my incredibly insightful and mature observations, my father picked up the monkey and tossed it in the garbage. He then hugged my little brother until he stopped crying. "I'll tell you what, tomorrow, we'll go to the toy shop by the Cedar and Lee Theater, and I'll let you pick out what ever toy animal you want. How does that sound, Dickie?"

"Tomorrow?" my brother said, "What's wrong with *today?* Why can't we go right now?"

Realizing that perhaps Dickie was becoming a bit too demanding and spoiled for a four year old, my father quietly responded, "Tomorrow is good enough. You have enough toys to play with right now, my son. Look, here's a giraffe. Play with your giraffe."

My brother looked disdainfully at the stuffed animal and then tossed it on the floor.

"There are many poor children in the world who have much less than you, Dickie. You need to be satisfied with what you have," my mother sensitively said.

"No!" Dickie responded. "That's not fair. I want a gorilla for my very own, and I want it *now*! Give me a gorilla!"

Being the obnoxious older brother that I was, I retrieved the discarded monkey and began to taunt my brother. "Ooooo, the monkey will get you! He knows you hate him! Tonight when you're sleeping, Monkey Terror (I gave the monkey a name) will come into your room and bring all of his monkey friends and jump into your bed and . . . and eat you alive!"

"Stop it!" my mother yelled. "That's enough! You're frightening poor little Dickie."

Immediately sensing another opportunity to play the role of the poor persecuted little child, my brother sweetly asked my mother, "So can we go to the store, Mommy, and get a toy gorilla for me? Please, Mommy, *please?* And I promise I will never cry again . . . ever! I will always be your best little boy. "

My mother, an astute woman of philosophy and logic, responded with a simple, "No."

My brother looked at my mother with a blank stare. My mother returned the stare with a logical explanation mothers are so good at. "You have enough toys, Dickie. It's a beautiful day. Why not go next door and play with Heidi Rosenblatt? She's such a sweet girl, and she likes you."

Dickie tried to conceal his frustration and decided his only option was to follow my mother's advice and meet up with his best friend and confidant. He wasn't happy, but in his mind, he had no other choice, at least for the moment.

Heidi Rosenblatt had just turned five and felt this was a major turning point in her life. She was two months older than my brother, but she acted as if she could conquer the world with her creative thinking skills and leadership abilities. Heidi was also a lover of great mischief. From our kitchen window, my mother watched as Heidi and Dickie climbed into a refrigerator box together and rolled down the hill in the backyard screaming and yelling. Alarmed by the potential danger of the two children hurting themselves, my mother went outside to prevent them from participating in the sport they affectionately referred to as *Boxing*.

"Dickie, it's time to come in for dinner."

"Why?" Dickie always questioned everything my parents said.

"I don't like you rolling around in that box. You could hurt yourself."

"No he can't, Mrs. Zeiger. It's just a box made out of cardboard. Dickie is perfectly safe with me," Heidi declared.

My mother did not buy Heidi's weak rationale about safety and insisted that my brother remove himself immediately from the refrigerator box and come into our house for dinner. A forlorn Heidi remained inside her cardboard home uttering profane statements about the "unfeeling adult world," finally settling down to read her Little Golden Book about the adventures of Davy Crockett. A frustrated Dickie stormed up to his room and refused to come down to dinner. He was a marvelous little "actor," and at such a young age, he unknowingly had become an expert of the Stanislavski School of Method Acting as well as demonstrating Machiavellian tendencies of obtaining power through manipulation.

That night, we had a late dinner around 7 p.m. Everyone was at the table except for my brother. "He's probably throwing a temper tantrum," I surmised. My mother called upstairs for him to come to the dinner table, but there was no answer. "Oh, I'll get him," Trying to be helpful, I went upstairs and looked everywhere, but . . . *no Dickie!*

I came down to inform my parents who became extremely alarmed. We immediately searched every room of the house. We even looked in the dark, damp basement and the spooky attic but he was nowhere to be found. We searched the backyard, front yard, driveway, and garage. *Nothing*. When reality set in that my brother had apparently disappeared, my parents' screams of agony echoed through our neighborhood.

For a moment, the possibility of again being the youngest child rushed through my mind. I began to think of the attention that would be lavished upon me . . . and the stream of gifts I would receive. *Perhaps we could begin with a new bicycle*? But those screams of anguish squashed the whole fantasy.

Panic set in. My father knocked on the neighbors' doors, my mother phoned everyone she knew. No one had seen Dickie for hours. The street we lived on had huge oak and evergreen trees that provided an arc of shade and creepy shadows, plenty of places to get lost or to hide.

It was now 7:30 p.m. and the sun was sinking behind the clouds into the horizon. And then the worst of all thoughts; *could my brother have wandered off to the end of the street and gone into the dark and dangerous ravine*? Suddenly, it became a battle between the last remaining minutes of light and the darkness that would make it even more difficult to locate him. Police cars and even a fire truck arrived. The neighbors grabbed flashlights, formed a search posse and entered the ravine shouting, "We will rescue you, son! We're here for you!" Suddenly, he was *everyone's son,* and all the neighbors wanted to save him, but Dickie did not respond. Every now and then, someone would hear the soft rustling of leaves, footsteps, and a cry in the night, but it was not my brother. My father instructed me to stay at home, just in case someone called with information.

I sat on our front porch and was terrified that something devastating had happened to little Dickie. My mother was in tears as she walked through the streets with several of the neighbors who offered optimistic views that everything would turn out all right.

In a matter of minutes, I was completely alone. It seemed as if my parents and all the neighbors on our street had disappeared in pursuit of my missing little brother. I could feel the soft breezes of the warm August night as I sat there, waiting and waiting, consumed by guilt. *Had I caused my brother's disappearance? Did I not pay enough attention to him?*

All I could hear was the sound of crickets and birds in the trees as the last seconds of fading sunlight brought an end to the day. Out of loneliness and fear, I walked up and down the sidewalk in front of our house. I tried to race ahead of my shadow under the streetlights, a game to pass the time and escape impending doom. Exhausted and frightened, I sat down on the curb of the street. The thought of losing my brother for whatever reason began to consume every thought . . . and then . . . and then . . . out of the darkness, came a small, frightened voice, almost a whisper.

"Larry, I'm so afraid."

Was it my imagination, or was it really my brother calling out? I decided that the night was playing tricks on my mind.

"Larry, I *need* you. I'm so scared."

At this point, my senses sharpened. I looked around to the right, to the left, behind me, in the trees . . . but nothing. *Was I hallucinating or was it the voice of . . . my brother?*

"Over here, Larry. I'm over here."

The voice, so soft and melancholy, was definitely coming from nearby.

"Dickie, *is that you?* Where are you?" I shouted.

"Over here."

I looked in the direction of the Rosenblatt house next door, but my brother was nowhere in sight.

"I'm next door at Heidi's house."

I searched all around the front yard of the Rosenblatt's house and still did not see my brother, but his voice grew louder and louder. "I'm under Heidi's father's car . . . in the driveway. *Oh Larry, I'm so scared.*"

I turned and looked down and there was my little brother, shaking from fear, hiding underneath Mr. Rosenblatt's '58 Edsel. I couldn't believe what I was seeing. Half the community was searching for my brother in the nearby ravine, and there he was, perfectly safe hiding underneath an Edsel, right in front of me.

"What are you doing under the car, Dickie? Do you know Mom and Dad called the police and the fire departments? You're in big trouble! I mean *really big!*"

And then he gave the response I will never forget. "No one loves me, Larry! No one cares about me! *I'm so alone in the world!*"

"Mom and Dad are going to kill you, Dickie! They are going to kill you in . . . in a very big way! I'm not kidding. You've scared them half to death with your stupid act!" I reached for his hand and pulled him out from underneath the car and held him in my arms to take him home.

He began kicking me, screaming, "Let me go, Larry! Let me go!"

At this point, my parents, along with about thirty neighbors, eight policemen, and six firemen emerged from the ravine and saw me walking towards them with Dickie in my arms. He was trying to break loose from me, but I held him tightly. I yelled to my parents, "I found him. He's okay!" He continued squirming in my arms, for fear that my parents would kill him, which I had thought might be perfectly justified in this situation. But to Dickie's and my surprise, my parents grabbed him from my arms, hugging him as if there were no tomorrow.

My mother cried out, "Oh Dickie, I love you so much more than my life!"

My father echoed the sentiment. "I love my little man! I am so happy you're okay! You are a brave little boy!"

'Brave little boy?' I couldn't believe he said that! I thought for sure my parents would kill him in front of all the neighbors. So much for my logical thinking skills.

My brother was thrilled with the outpouring of love and affection. The guilt disappeared from his face as he embraced my parents. The neighbors applauded. One man took a photograph of the scene, which no doubt could have been placed in the Cleveland Museum of Art and would have been titled *The Rapture Revisited.* The police and firemen finished their reports and patted my brother on the back. Even they were touched by this poignant scene. My brother looked at me and gave me a triumphant smile, a sort of - *Wow! This turned out better than I thought* expression.

Holding his little hand and placing it on his heart, my father took him from me and carried him into the house. My mother followed and showered him with kisses.

Just before they entered the living room, my brother triumphantly took center stage and declared, "Mom and Dad, I want my monkey back. I like that monkey you bought me. I really do!" My father then retrieved the discarded stuffed animal and handed it over to Dickie who hugged the creature as if it were his newfound best friend. "I love my monkey! I love my monkey!" he exclaimed.

Tears in his eyes, my father looked at him and responded, "And tomorrow I will buy you the gorilla you want. No! I will buy you two gorillas!"

"And a penguin too? Can I have penguin too? Oh Daddy, please . . . *please?*"

And then the words that plunged daggers in my heart: "*You can have whatever you want, Dickie! Anything in the world – it's yours!"* My father hugged my brother who had the most joyful expression a child could have.

It was that day that I realized that my younger brother would either wind up being a psychologist, a business entrepreneur, a lawyer, or an award-winning actor.

Years later I found out that my brother and Heidi Rosenblatt were in cahoots and the masterminds of the *Hiding Under the Car Method of Gaining Parental Attention and Whatever Object You Desire.* It only worked that one time, however. When Heidi was six she ran away from home and wound up under my father's '56 Buick. This time the scheme backfired badly. Heidi was grounded for a month and had to donate 25% of her toys to the Salvation Army. My brother kept silent about his prior involvement with Heidi Rosenblatt.

Meanwhile, his animal collection grew in size for at least another year until he became obsessed with collecting every model car he could get his hands on. Thanks to my parents' generosity and my brother's charm and innocence, his car and animal empire became the envy of every child in our neighborhood.

The Evil Monkey

by Jack Beddows

One weekend in upstate New York, when I was six and my brother, Lucas, was eleven, my mother took the two of us to the mall, for one of our biannual excursions to outfit us in the latest and greatest fashions from K-Mart and Sears. My dad stayed behind. As was usually the case, he escaped from shopping by complaining of his bad back. And after citing his sciatica, he wrapped up his argument with, "Besides, it will give me a chance to enjoy some peace and quiet!" No doubt "enjoying peace and quiet" meant watching a movie on TV while cracking open a beer or two. I desperately wanted to stay home with him.

My brother always loved to shop and took great pride in his choice of ensembles, but I hated it. I couldn't stand going to the different clothing stores, trying on shirts and pants at my mother's direction. More often than not, engaging in this drudgery under the soul-sucking fluorescent lights would put me into a swoon from which I could only recover under the nearest rack of clothes. I would first say a quick prayer that my mother wouldn't find me and then lie there, daydreaming about watching black and white monster movies with my dad. My prayers notwithstanding, sooner or later, I would always be aroused by a surprised patron's squeak, which would then alert my mother as to my whereabouts. "There you are!" she'd say while reaching down to haul me up off the floor. "I wondered where you'd been hiding!"

The only joy to be had in the mall was when my mother had either finished selecting our outfits or, as was more often the case, simply could no longer stand my whining. She would then send us off so that she could finish her shopping in peace, and my brother would proceed to take me on a tour of all the best that the mall had to offer.

On this particular weekend, our first stop was the record store. My lasting impression is of the rock posters that my brother was so fascinated with and which, to me, were just a mystery of silly looking, longhaired men standing on boulders. Since I was too young to have any interest in this sort of thing, I just had to wait until my brother had his fill. This was still *infinitely* superior to trying on yet another pair of OshKosh B'Goshes.

Our next stop was the hobby store whose window displays made it look like such a fun place on the outside, but which was such a miserable disappointment on the inside. Looking around, my brother and I realized that many of the things that were considered 'fun hobbies' were actually extremely boring. In fact, besides the train sets, there was nothing in the store to elicit anything except a terrible sense of malaise, and I pity the people who must have been on the receiving end of presents bought from that shop. *Oh Gee! Thanks for this 5,000-piece puzzle of President Carter's head. Merry Christmas to you too!*

But then there was the Orange Julius, the corner refreshment stand where we gorged ourselves on the most delicious drink in the world, a gastrointestinal disaster of orange juice and heavy cream that, despite swelling my belly to near bursting, always left me begging for more.

After ingesting our oversized liquid creamsicles, we still had one last store to visit. Unbeknownst to my mother, Lucas and I then snuck off into the officially off-limits Gags N Gifts, a store that was always full of the most reprehensible knick knacks, all thematically based on fart jokes and sexual innuendo. My mother most definitely would not have approved. We, of course, thought all the junk in there was hilarious. I still remember the sense of shame, shock, and titillation that came from looking at flatulence inducing jellybeans. But apparently, we weren't just there to window shop.

Whether because Gags N Gifts was preparing for Halloween, which was still about two months away, or because someone had been too lazy to put away the previous year's leftovers, the store was stocked with a number of quick and easy costumes and accessories, such as the fake blood and vampire teeth that my brother decided to purchase with the money that was left over from what Mom had given him for Orange Julius. So it was in a giggling, conspiratorial mood that Lucas and I met back up with our mother, and together, we headed off towards the center of the mall on our way to the parking lot and then, home. *Or so we thought.*

As the three of us were walking, we noticed an unusual gathering of shoppers. *What,* we wondered, *could all of these people be looking at?* And as my brother and I pushed through the crowd, we could hardly believe our eyes! *Why?* Because it was the greatest thing we had ever seen! Right there in the middle of the mall, a display had been set up, and performing in the open, behind only a hanging rope divider, was a chimpanzee dressed in a pair of green lederhosen, a small, feathered cap, and roller skates. Behind him was his trainer, who immediately reminded me of the old man, Professor Marvel, from *the Wizard of Oz*, and looming large behind both of them was the recently hoisted sign that bore the single ominous word, ZIPPY! in bold, dark print.

Those five letters said a mouthful. This chimp did it all: he skated, he skipped rope, he told jokes—or rather he delivered the non-verbal punch lines for the gags set up by his trainer—and he wowed the audience with his gracious, toothy smile. And that's not all! He did all of this while rocking side to side in his best approximation of dancing to the music of Gloria Gaynor's disco classic *I Will Survive.*

My brother and I just about lost our minds with the sheer wonder of it all. If only that could have been the last pleasant remembrance of the day! If only our mother would have pulled us away while we were still happy and begging for more. How different things might have been!

Perhaps it was envy at all the attention Zippy was getting, but for whatever reason, my brother simply could not leave well enough alone. It was then, at the apex of our happiness, that he slipped his fake vampire teeth from his pocket, put them in his mouth, and while one perceptive old lady in the audience looked our way and mouthed the questioning words, *what the hell,* my brother revealed his new amplified fangs at Zippy followed by a hideous growl. Time froze for a moment, and I had to wonder, *what was my brother actually thinking?* That the rope offered some sort of real protection? That Zippy's trainer would be able to stop any serious misbehavior on the chimp's part? That he could rely on our mother to save him or on Zippy to play fair and *not* rip an arm out of its socket? Whatever he thought, he was sadly mistaken in his assessments.

When Zippy was confronted with that most basic of primate communications, a direct challenge, the shallow mask of humanity that he was wearing along with his lederhosen was discarded with a wild animal howl. Zippy dove at Lucas with outstretched arms, and if his sudden anger hadn't caused him to forget that he still had on his roller skates, which caused him to slip, splay, and tangle himself in the rope, that would have been the end of my brother right then and there. As it was, it took Zippy a few seconds to regain his balance, and by that time, amidst the screams of horror from my mother and all of the other onlookers, my brother was off like a shot. The chase was on.

My brother was running faster than he ever had before. Behind him, was the oddest and most terrifying apparition of vengeance that had ever scourged the earth. Like some monster out of ancient Swiss mythology, the determined Zippy, now freed from the tangle, moved his legs with all the coolness and coordination of a champion figure skater while the upper half of his lederhosen-clad body was flailing in animal fury.

As we chased after them, despite my rising sense of horror at the thought that I might soon be an only child, I still considered for a moment whether or not I should bend down to scoop up Zippy's discarded hat as a souvenir. By this point, the whole mall was in an uproar. People were screaming and everyone we passed was being swept into the chaos as we chased after my brother and his primal pursuer.

When we finally caught up with them, my brother was making a last lap around a large, penny-filled fountain with the chimp gaining quickly behind. Sensing the end drawing near, Lucas, in total desperation, dove in. *Are monkeys afraid of water?* I asked myself. If not there would soon be more than pennies for maintenance to clean out of the shallow pool. As it turned out, my brother's gamble paid off, and whether it was a personal dislike for water or the limitations of the skates, Zippy screeched to a halt at the edge of the fountain, arms still flailing, with horrible screams of frustration issuing from deep within him. As he paused, his trainer finally caught up with him. Meanwhile, my mother jumped into the fountain to protect and console her firstborn child.

Zippy's trainer had a devil of a time pulling the creature away from the fountain's edge. While doing so he alternately made attempts to soothe the beast as well as pausing to curse the 'other rotten little monkey' out of the side of his mouth. Finally, he was able to restrain Zippy, and slowly, order began to reassert itself.

The mall's manager quickly arrived, but after the chaos subsided, he was unsure of whether he should shower us with gift certificates or ban us for life. Neither response could have mattered one bit to me. The strain of this whole scene had been too much for my limited faculties. I could barely utter a word for the next several days, and the next morning at the breakfast table, my mouth was a silent 'O' as I absently shoveled Kellogg's Cornflakes down my throat, my mind still reeling from the images I had been witness to.

For the next several years, I had to avoid my previously adored old horror movies, as whenever I watched them, I would have strange dreams about giant lumbering chimps with bolts in their necks or chimps in black cloaks and riding boots with fangs that didn't need to be augmented by Hollywood's special effects or by Gags N Gifts' cheap plastic Halloween accessories. And to this day, I still jump like a scared cat whenever I hear Zippy's disco theme song, *I Will Survive.*

FIVE

TWISTS AND TURNS

Jack and Larry spend a late afternoon at the beautiful C-Level Lounge at Island Prime Restaurant on Harbor Island. The bar with its beautiful views of boats sailing across the sun-drenched, glistening water instantly stimulate a nautical theme to Larry and Jack's storytelling.

Jack's tale is about a discovery of a giant halibut in Santa Barbara which changes his life forever, while the focus of Larry's story is his brilliant sister who experiences a major "plumbing problem" while visiting a lavish resort on the island of Kauai.

To enhance the storytelling sessions Jeff Pitroff, the general manager, and Maurice DiMarino, the wine sommelier, recommend a bottle of the 2004 *King Fish Cabernet*, a perfect compliment to Jack's tale. After his first taste, Jack raves about the spicy, toasty flavor amidst the aroma of blackberries and blackcurrants.

Larry's story calls for a bottle of *Plungerhead Zinfandel,* which contains a nice viscosity and depth. Larry loves the wine, because it compliments his story so well. He is also particularly impressed with the symbolic literary reference to the strange tale of his sister's Hawaiian disaster.

To add to the ambiance of the afternoon, Deborah Scott, the award-winning chef, serves a delicious appetizer featuring grilled halibut and other culinary delights. Both wines, along with the tantalizing food selections, stimulate Jack and Larry's imaginations and swapping of two unforgettable tales.

An Accidental Career

by Jack Beddows

There is a time and a place for everything . . . and it's called college! One day, while walking home from a very early class on a sleepy Friday morning, I saw a large, white delivery truck come careening around one of the main corners of the dirty little hamlet I called home. As it went past, with that catchy little horn line from War's *Low Rider* blasting from the radio, I noticed that sliding door at the back of the truck was not completely closed. Just then, a large, white plastic bin came bouncing out of the opening, landing on the ground not far in front of me. "Huh," I said to myself, "You don't see that everyday."

As a man, who also saw what had happened, leaned his head out from his bicycle repair shop door to give a half-hearted "Hey!" to the driver, I stood out in the street and tried to wave the truck down. But neither of the two gentlemen in the cab of the truck noticed our attempts, and they continued to speed along their merry way with the still audible horn line fading out around the next corner. That's where the shopkeeper's interest ended; he turned around with a shrug and went back inside. Suddenly, it was just the white plastic bin and me.

I looked around to see if anyone else was planning on doing anything about the rather large obstruction in the middle of the road, but on this morning, the usually busy little area was bereft of people. So with a grumble and a moan, I dragged myself over to the closed container and tried to pick it up by its handles. It didn't budge. In fact, it felt like it had been bolted to the ground.

So I tried again, this time with a better grip and a better position to lift with my legs. But that didn't work either, and I quickly realized that whatever was in that bin weighed more than I did. At this point, I was extremely curious about what was inside, but I also wanted to avoid getting run over in the middle of an intersection, so I grabbed one of the indented handles, and with some huffing and puffing, managed to drag the container to the sidewalk for a more leisurely inspection.

As I opened up the large plastic lid, I felt a little bit like Indiana Jones coming across an archeological find. Inside the container were several large, wrapped frozen packages, all scrawled over in black Sharpie with the words, *Fresh Halibut for Brophy Bros.* The intended recipients of these packages had a name with which I was very familiar, as Brophy Brothers was a very successful seafood restaurant on the waterfront in downtown Santa Barbara.

Although this excellent restaurant was quite expensive for me, my brother and I had gone there with our parents every time they had flown out from Boston to visit us. Now, I suddenly found myself facing a moral dilemma of what to do with the nearly two hundred pounds of high quality seafood right in front of me. As I stood on the sidewalk, next to this unique find, I spent several moments wrestling with my conscience over the obvious question of whether I should give the fish back or keep it. At first this may seem like an elementary problem, one that any child fresh from Sunday school could answer without hesitation. But in my case, there were many mitigating factors that had to be considered. For one, fate had obviously made me the steward of this fine halibut, and to buck fate was a dangerous proposition. And two…well, I guess there was just that one mitigating factor after all. Clearly, it was time to start considering logistics.

The facts at hand: I didn't have a phone with which to call Brophy Brothers, as this was just prior to the era of the cell phone, and the container of fish was too heavy to drag all the way home by myself. Additionally, just down the block, on the same side of the street I was standing, was the main office of the Isla Vista Foot Patrol, the local police department. *I could*, I supposed, *drag the bucket the fifty yards or so down to their front door and let them deal with returning this property to its rightful owners.* But then again, I was fairly certain that those yahoos would just keep the fish for themselves anyway. So then, with a great sense of moral ambiguity, I decided to try to get this treasure trove back to my house and just take things from there. But unfortunately, there was no way I could do that without some help. I would have to wait. And in the meantime, I would have to do something about this giant tub of fish.

So while images of officers marching down the street and angry truck drivers circling back around the block looking for stolen property played in my head, I nudged the oversized tub into the high growing plants along the sidewalk and the street. And as I stood whistling in front of the plastic bin in my best inconspicuous manner, it seemed like I was going to have to wait forever for someone I knew to float by in the thin stream of students still trickling out from campus. But it wasn't really more than a few minutes before an acquaintance came pedaling towards me.

"Dusty, my friend!" I exclaimed while flagging him down.

"Hey Jack, what are you up to?" he asked.

"Well, Dusty, I have a proposition for you." With great enthusiasm, I explained the situation to Dusty as he sat astride his bike looking antsy. But the shortsighted fool didn't appreciate the value of what I was offering. Either that or he'd once had a bad experience with some guy trying to sell him "overstocked" stereo equipment from out of the back of a van, which is kind of what I felt like while I was trying to convince him to lend me his assistance. In any event, he declined to participate and continued on his way. So there I was again, sweating in the increasingly warm sun as I stood next to my thawing treasure. Before long though, a young man I was even friendlier with sauntered by, and unlike Dusty, he was all smiles as I called him over.

There was a reason for this. Sam was a good looking and talented young man, and one of the few straight men I knew who was serious about ballet and modern dance. As a result, he was *always* dating some cute dancer girl. In fact, there was no doubt from the glowing look on his face that he had just come from a morning class in which he had once again been surrounded by a bevy of young beauties in leotards who all, it seemed, took a fancy to him. Not that I was jealous mind you. It was more of an all-consuming envy, technically speaking.

Not only did Sam agree to help me, but his enthusiastic, "Hell Yes! I'll help you carry this fish home!" also did wonders to placate my guilty conscience. We then hammered out the particulars; we'd split the fish in exchange for Sam's assistance in lugging it down the road. Fortunately, his house was on the way to mine, so our load would be lightened before too long, which was a good thing, because even with both of us working at the task at hand, it was still going to be a hell of a job!

We each got a hold of the container, distributing the weight equally between us, and started on our way. The first thing we had to do was get by the IV Foot Patrol without incident. As we struggled past, there was no doubt that we looked somewhat suspicious. But our obvious need for a little assistance seemed to provide ample protection from their prying into our situation too deeply. In any event, no officers emerged to investigate. And although I kept a cautious eye out for angry truck drivers, the rest of our walk to Sam's house was also uneventful.

While unloading Sam's share out of the bin and into his freezer, we started to discuss what to do with all of this fish. As it was, Sam couldn't get even a quarter of the load into his freezer before it reached capacity, and what the hell was I going to do with a hundred plus pounds of fish? Then it hit me. There was only one answer. *Fish Fry!* I would have the biggest Fish Fry the town had ever seen! There was a large backyard at the house I was sharing with about six other roommates, give or take a few come-and-go girlfriends, and we had a barbeque pit and a large ring of rocks used for bonfires, so we already had the perfect setting. *And now we had the fish.* So as soon as Sam and I got to my house and we put down our load in the kitchen, I told the first roommates I saw about my plans.

"Hey guys! Check this out!"

Eric and Tanya, a nice couple who did enjoy a chill Californian lifestyle, liked to smoke pot, go running, and play Ultimate Frisbee while still having a good work ethic, good grades, and part time jobs to help pay for school. We never got too close, but I liked them a lot. They greeted the notion much like Sam had, with an enthusiastic, "Hell Yeah! Let's have a fish fry!"

Before long, my other roommates including Matt, the "older" guy of the house at twenty-seven who worked as an EMT; Gina, his girlfriend; Daniel, the drummer and composer; his girlfriend Melody, and a few others were all mobilized. One of the girls immediately went to the store, and upon her return, she prepared vast amounts of garlic bread to go with the fish. Someone else volunteered to marinate the fish with a recipe he got from his mom, and we all put in a little money to procure a few kegs of beer. By the early afternoon, the house was packed with friends and neighbors who magically appeared to make guacamole, bruschetta, and dozens of other appetizers.

Being fairly introverted for the most part, I was very happy that I was able to be the impetus for getting this big affair going. In fact, as the preparations continued, I proudly looked around at the social machine that I had helped wind up and that now had taken on a life of its own.

Early in the evening, I looked outside to see a young man named Paul Moore sitting out in the yard. Paul was an influential person in my life, someone I looked up to as a slightly older and very accomplished musician. He was the main songwriter and singer for a high profile local band as well as a piano player and composer in the same music program that I was in. He was a very avant-garde artist, and walked through life with a faraway stare, but consistently produced interesting work at school while at the same time being the charismatic center of a little music scene of which I wished I had been a bigger part.

In the long green grass of the backyard, I asked him how everything was going with him and his girlfriend.

"Things between Alice and me are great," he said.

"I know I'm pretty out-there in most regards, but I'm very traditional when it comes to relationships. Keeping it simple, nothing too crazy."

I wasn't sure why he felt like telling me this, but like everything he said to me, it carried a sense of weight.

The weather was excellent that day, and the crowd became even larger just as the sun was going down. We had torches in the backyard, beer to drink, and a Jesus-miracle-sized portion of fish to feed everyone. Before long, there must have been a hundred people or more enjoying themselves, including the entire Black Tide Ultimate Frisbee Team and several musicians singing and playing guitars. Even some random guys from Jamaica were drawn to the party by the reggae music and pescatarian fare. It was a truly festive atmosphere, and as I mingled amongst the crowd, many of whom were strangers or at the most, casual acquaintances, I felt more than a bit like Robin Hood, who had stolen from the rich in order to throw a lavish banquet for all to enjoy.

At one point, I found myself sitting next to a sprightly, black gentleman, in his late forties with a slightly grey beard, Caribbean accent, and a dazzlingly white suit.

"Yes, I tell you, I love that Forrest Gump boy!" he exclaimed to me with a big grin on his face. "You saw that movie didn't you?"

The film had just come out, and though I had yet to see it, I lied and said I had to facilitate the conversation's flow, and also because I hated to be left out of anything.

"Yes sir!" he continued as I sat struggling with my little transgression, "That movie's on to something. No matter what happens, we gotta keep goin' boy! Gotta keep runnin' along, right there in the moment!"

He smiled at me one more time, and then one of my roommates tapped me on the shoulder to ask me a question. When I turned back, the unknown gentleman had disappeared in the throng. I'd see his jacket floating around from time to time, but I didn't have a chance to talk with him again.

The time went by pleasantly. Everyone was enjoying themselves, and the strong hippie, stoner/athlete contingent in the party kept us from the drunken excesses that often darken other college get-togethers. As the evening progressed, however, there was one problem: we were running out of wood for the bonfire that had been adding so much to the general mood of cheeriness. It had been hours since I had done anything constructive, and as I didn't want my 'founder of the feast, mega-host status' to wear off too quickly, I decided that I should be the one to take care of this situation. So I recruited a few friends of mine from the party, including Paul Moore, who had a pick-up truck, as well as my roommate Steve, to help carry the firewood, and off we went.

Conveniently enough, we knew of a place where the parks and recreation department had recently done some work and where we could find the remains of several freshly cut trees. Without a moment's hesitation, we drove to the location, loaded the back of the pick-up truck with enough wood to last for several bonfires and prepared to head back, but just as we were leaving, a woman in a nondescript VW rabbit pulled up next to us.

"Say, can one of you guys help me?"

Now right away, those are words that appeal to the chivalrous nature of any young man, at least when delivered by a reasonably attractive female. However, there was something in this young woman's face that also suggested caution might be appropriate. Perhaps it was the layers of makeup.

"What do you need?" my friend Paul asked. He was in the driver's seat and closest to her while I was in the middle of the truck's cab, between him and Steve.

"Um, my name's Summer, and I'm a dancer . . .and I'm uh . . . I'm about to go do a show and my driver couldn't make it, so I just need someone . . . um . . . to come with me as my driver."

"Uhhhh" was our collective response. This was something a bit more involved than asking for directions, and we were all somewhat taken aback.

"So, what do you guys think? It's no big deal, shouldn't take too long, and I'll give you forty bucks for your trouble."

Now I had never even been to a strip club, so this was completely out of my range of experiences, but I was always eager to try new things, I said, "Screw it, I'll do it!"

"Are you sure you want to do that, Jack?" Paul asked me.

"Sure, why not?" I instantly replied. If I had thought about it, I'm sure I could have come up with a good laundry list of reasons why not to go with a stripper I didn't know, to a party full of random drunks.

"Okay!" my friends both answered at the same time in a manner that suggested they saw nothing good coming of this, but that they weren't about to impinge on my freedom to be an idiot.

As I scrambled out of the pick-up and into her car, the woman repeated exactly what she said before, about just "needing a driver," and my nerves settled a little bit. After all, being a 'driver,' surely I would just be waiting in the car while she did whatever she did and still make it back in time for more of the festive party at my house forty bucks richer!

However, my sense of calm was somewhat disturbed as we pulled into the driveway of the house where she was going to perform. I noticed immediately that it was not what you would call a quiet residence. It was in fact, a raging party, with guys spilling out from everywhere. The front door, the steps, the upstairs balcony, they were all overflowing with drunken, horny guys. It was then that my new friend's story started to change.

"So yeah, you just need to come inside with me and act like you're my bodyguard. It's a big birthday party, and I'm sure things won't get out of hand, but you never know..."

"Huh? What's that?" I asked.

"Oh nothing," she replied, before continuing, "Besides, you don't have to worry. About half an hour into the show, my partner is going to show up, and she'll have her driver with her, and he'll take over for you by the time things start getting crazy."

"Huh?" I asked again, even more forcefully, but she was already walking up the stairs to the front door of the upstairs apartment. As I caught a glimpse of her long legs disappearing up her very short skirt, she turned around beckoning me to follow, and I found myself right behind her, though I wasn't completely happy about it.

The young gentleman in charge of the party met us at the door, and as he looked me over, I felt none-too comfortable, and I did not feel any better when I learned that he and his buddies were planning on tricking a number of guys by locking them out on the balcony for crowd control purposes.

Why I chose to forego my own party for this one was rather baffling. But clearly, a large part of the reason was that I had never seen a stripper before and was titillated by the notion. As the show got underway, as much as I would like to consider myself as having been more of a cultural anthropologist in the whole proceedings, part of me was doubtlessly on the same nasty tack as everyone else in the room.

Interrupting the ribald festivities taking place, the guys at the party who had been locked outside realized that they had been tricked, and they were clearly angry. They screamed and pounded on the sliding glass door while I stood against the wall trying to look inconspicuous. It was then that two rather large, but fortunately friendly looking guys came up to me.

"Hey bro', how ya doin'?" the larger one of the two asked while extending his giant mitt in greeting.

"I'm doing okay. How are you?" I returned, glad for the friendly encounter in this sea of testosterone-driven maniacs.

"Good. Good," he answered. "Hey man, I just want you to know that I've got your back."

I wrinkled my brow in reply, and my nonplussed facial expression made it clear that he needed to expound further on the topic.

"I got your back if something goes down," he said, now more directly. "You know how it is, a party like this, all these drunk guys, and a stripper getting them all worked up. You get fights all the time right? Well, since it's just you, I'll jump in there man, no worries. Just letting you know, I've got your back, dog!"

I suddenly found myself feeling heavily conflicted. On the one hand, I had a horrible sinking feeling in the pit of my stomach related to an image of me being dog-piled to death by a dozen or so drunken idiots, but I was also feeling exceptionally grateful to this rather large young man for his offer of assistance. I told him this was most greatly appreciated while simultaneously imagining sneaking out of the room while he fought off initial attacks in any potential fracas. I shook his hand again, a little too enthusiastically perhaps, and as he went away, he looked a little puzzled, as if I hadn't quite acted like he expected. After he and his friend departed, I tried again to look composed while keeping my eyes half on the gyrating form on the floor in front of me and half on the room of potential troublemakers around me.

"So, what do you have your black belt in?" another young gentleman about my size and age asked out of nowhere as he approached me.

"What's that?" I asked in return, a little jumpy, and again completely confused.

"You must be some kind of martial arts expert, huh? Cuz you're not very big."

"No, I guess not," I said in reference to his last comment, hoping to avoid answering his other questions.

"I mean, there's always a fight at these kinds of parties!" he continued, "so you've gotta be *some* kind of bad ass."

Oh my God, this just keeps getting worse! I thought to myself. But in response to his statements about my supposed fighting prowess, I merely nodded knowingly and folded my arms in an attempt to bulk up my biceps, a trick I had first learned while watching a *Little Rascals* episode in which Spanky was impersonating a circus strongman. Meanwhile, sweat was starting to pop out on the sides of my head, and as I brushed away a bead of it, I was reminded of my current hairstyle as well. *Oh goddamn it!* I thought. *Why do I have this stupid haircut?*

You see, while I had forgotten all about it till then, a week or so before, I had opted for a short Mohawk, a la Robert De Niro in *Taxi Driver.* And while my choice of cut stemmed from more a fashionable and artsy place, I realized that this particular hair-do also had a tough guy connotation that I couldn't at all back up. Now as I stood there, stiff as a statue, against the wall, probably making faces like Don Knotts all the while, I realized that I was ensconced in a theater of the absurd that I had maybe not quite scripted for myself, but at least co-authored.

So why was I there? I suppose guys in general are fascinated each to their own extent by a darker world of sex, machismo, and violence. A quick peek at our entertainment choices in movies, television, and video games makes that abundantly clear. This fascination was also no doubt why some of the guys at the party kept coming up to talk to me. They were doubtlessly thinking, because of my position at the party as the stripper's supposed 'driver/bodyguard,' that I was further advanced down that dark road of depravity than they were, and could therefore illuminate it for them a bit, either to lead them further along the way or to comfort them in the notion that they were fine right where they were.

But in reality, they were the ones who were more experienced and who were illuminating things for me. And nothing they shed any light on did anything but make me feel increasingly nervous. Besides simple curiosity, I had another, more laughable reason for sticking it out at the party. I was, and don't judge me too harshly here, actually concerned for the wellbeing of the stripper. As I looked around at the leering faces and increasingly regressive body language of the crowd, I imagined that it would be a heck of a spot to be in, to be a naked chick acting like a sex-crazed nymphomaniac in front of a bunch of horny guys who were all consuming copious amounts of alcohol, without having some sort of lifeline to the outside world. Of course, on some level, this less-than-upstanding young lady must have enjoyed stirring these guys up, walking that fine line of frenzy and fury, all whipped up by her bumps and grinds.

Forget this crazy woman! Get the hell out of here! I thought to myself, as a large drunken football player stumbled into me.

No! You have to stay and make sure she's okay! I countered nobly, while simultaneously trying to get a better view of the increasing gyrations of her posterior.

But things didn't get any better when my lovely young lady's dance partner arrived, and she also inexplicably arrived without her driver as well. *What? What the hell's going on here?* I asked myself, as I didn't really have much of a chance to ask the girls who were obviously busy at work. Suddenly, I was there alone in a sea of potential problems, next to *two* naked, crazy girls, attacking each other with whip cream.

The already borderline maniacs in the room were further driven to frenzy by the ensuing partner calisthenics happening on the floor in front of them. Guys started to approach me hinting at back room deals to be made with the ladies, to take the entertainment that one step further.

I referred them to the dancers for all further inquiries, and hoped that the promise of those sorts of shenanigans would help to keep guys in line for the remainder of the performance.

Finally, the nightmare drew to a close, and the girls were punctual if nothing else. The hour-long performance was over, and amazingly, it all wound down without incident. And although I felt the need to go home and watch old Disney movies for the next three days as part of a much needed purification ritual, at least I had escaped physically unscathed.

Back in the car, as I was getting dropped off by the crazy woman I had spent the weirdest ninety minutes of my life with, I was informed that, "Um, yeah. Because you got a free show that usually costs a lot more than forty bucks, I'm just going to go ahead and keep that money I promised you. But at least you got a free show!"

Wow! I thought. *Gee thanks! I could have gotten killed! Amazing!* But I didn't bother to argue with her. *What would have been the point, really?*

So I went back to my own party, which I never should have left, and which had wound down considerably. I told the story of my adventures to my friends, while listening in return to all the cool things I had apparently missed, including Paul and a bunch of other musician friends getting together and jamming, which I would have loved to have been a part of.

Damn! I thought, I gave up a chance to play music with these guys that I idolize, and for what? I really am an idiot. I went to bed soon after, trying unsuccessfully to digest all that had happened to me on this one unexpectedly eventful day.

A month or so later, while driving down the road a few miles outside of town, who should pull up right next to me but my favorite adult entertainer? At first I felt like screaming obscenities at her, as not getting my promised forty bucks still stung a little, but as I looked across at her through my open window, I noticed that in the daytime her face was much harsher, the lines down the sides of her mouth more pronounced, clearly earned more by experience than age. Her skin seemed pale and lifeless. She felt my prolonged gaze and just before the light changed, she turned to look back at me with a blank face that didn't signal recognition of any kind.

As she drove off and I turned in another direction, I suddenly wasn't angry at all. In fact, I felt even more grateful than when a few hundred pounds of fresh fish fell right into my lap. I had places to go and things to do, and it was time for me to keep running along, right there in the moment.

STORM WARNINGS – CATEGORY FIVE

BY LARRY ZEIGER

In May of 1995, my sister, Carole, and her husband, Bob, called me from Boston with an invitation I simply couldn't refuse. Bob, a prominent professor of radiology and bioinformatics, had been invited to speak at a medical conference in Hawaii, and he had reserved a large oceanfront suite with room enough for me. His much anticipated talk on *How Biomedical Informatics Will Affect the Future of the Medical World* was to take place at the luxurious Kauai Lagoons Hotel. I checked my Mileage Plus card and, fortunately, had accumulated just enough miles for a free round trip ticket. Imagine - free airfare and free lodging at one of the most lavish resorts on the planet! I booked the trip immediately.

What an honor it was for my brother-in-law to be part of this international group of great minds that would intermingle and exchange brilliant and innovative theories about diagnosis, prediction models, and treatment - all for the purpose of improving the health of humanity. I, on the other hand, was looking forward to a more direct means of achieving health and happiness through a daily dose of ultimate Mai Tais and frenzied luaus.

The day before the trip, all I could do was dream about my five-day sojourn to paradise, and before I knew it, I was on the plane to the breathtaking island of Kauai where I met up with my sister and brother-in-law.

Upon entering the Kauai Lagoons Hotel, I stared in awe at the massive Japanese sculptures, colorful fountains, priceless paintings, and elegant marble staircases, which filled this majestic palace. After we checked into our oceanfront suite, we dressed for dinner, and then took a gondola ride in the lagoons surrounding the resort. As we watched the brilliant sunset, we were certain we saw the green flash for the first time in our lives. My sister, a mathematics professor at Boston University, was impeccably dressed for the warm balmy summer's evening. In fact, I always thought that in another life, Carole could have been a fashion model for Nordstom or Saks Fifth Avenue. She spoke about Ellen Tracy, Tracy Reese, and Liz Claiborne as if they were her best friends.

As soft breezes enveloped the night, we dined at the outdoor terrace restaurant - Bob and I dressed in our discounted Macy's Hawaiian shirts, and my sister looking as if she were waiting for a photographer to snap her picture and place it on the cover of *Vogue*. The food was strictly gourmet. I ordered the macadamia nut-encrusted mahi-mahi, my brother-in-law chose the succulent Hawaiian steak kabobs, and not being much for gourmet cuisine, my calorie-conscious sister selected a Portobello mushroom burger minus the bun, the cheese, the tomatoes, and the onions.

Just after the food arrived, a beautiful white dove made its way under our table and began to tickle my sister's toes. Carole looked down by her feet and saw what most people would perceive as a harmless bird and suddenly let out a piercing scream that shattered the night. She knocked the table with her knee, and our Mai Tais went flying in all directions.

"It's only a bird, Carole," I said wiping the pineapple off my shirt.

"A dove - the bird of peace," Bob added.

"*Bird of peace*? Are you kidding? What's a bird doing on my foot at a $400.00 per night luxury hotel?"

"We're outside, Carole. Birds fly outside!" I was always the more logical sibling in our family.

"We're kind of invading *their* territory," Bob noted, attempting to give a more cerebral interpretation.

"I don't care. I just don't like birds!" And that was the end of the conversation.

I always knew that Carole suffered from Ornithophobia ever since she was sixteen and saw Alfred Hitchcock's film, *The Birds*. Anything with feathers sent her into a frenzy. Aliens from outer space also terrified her. At the age of eight, she had a traumatic experience watching a Saturday matinee of *The Thing*. Fortunately, there were no aliens in Hawaii, but the island was a sanctuary for birds, thus causing my sister's constant state of ornithological anxiety.

For the rest of the meal, I steadied the table with my hand, just in case a snowy egret or a large black-footed albatross should make a sudden appearance.

Three days later, while my brother-in-law attended his medical conference, Carole and I took advantage of the lavish pools with their many fountains and swim-up bars. From poolside, we could see the shimmering white sand beach and the crystal clear blue-green water of the sea. In the late afternoon, a light rain began to fall. A magnificent rainbow appeared, and the hotel guests filled the upper terrace to view nature's glorious special effects.

"I hope this isn't a sign of bad weather. It would be horrible if it rained tomorrow, especially during the evening outdoor reception in Bob's honor," Carole said.

"Only a 20% chance of showers," I reported, acting so knowledgeable about meteorology. "The most we'll get is a light sprinkle, and maybe even another rainbow."

"But this is Hawaii, Larry! The weather is unpredictable. It can be beautiful and sunny one minute, and then suddenly, out of nowhere, a major thunderstorm could erupt."

"Oh suddenly, you're an expert meteorologist. Hey, I'll make a bet with you. For the rest of the trip we will have nothing but beautiful weather. Mark my words!"

The next morning as we walked to the convention center, there was not a cloud in the sky. Bob gave his talk, using medical and scientific terminology and concepts that were beyond anything my arts and humanities brain could handle. I pretended to understand what *graphical user interfaces* and *interoperable electronic health records* were, and I nodded my head in the affirmative just like the rest of the audience at the sounds of acronyms like GPASS, LOING, and MUMPS. After Bob's brilliant presentation, he would certainly be the center of attention at the closing night reception, and my sister wanted to be "picture perfect" when being introduced to this international group of celebrated physicians and scientists. Still, it was one of our last days in paradise, and we all decided to make the most of a beautiful afternoon.

After sitting around the pool for an hour, I announced that I was going to take my daily swim in the ocean. "It's smooth as glass today, " I scientifically noted, trying to get my sister and brother-in-law interested.

"I hate the ocean," replied Carole, completely immersed in Mary Higgins Clark's latest murder mystery, *Pretend You Don't See Her.* "You go. I'll watch."

Free from the constraints of preparing for his medical address, Bob decided to join me for a swim, at which point, my sister, feeling somewhat alienated, muttered, "So you're both going to leave me alone? By the pool? Thanks a lot!"

"We don't have to leave you alone, Carole. You could join us for a swim," Bob suggested.

"But I *hate* the ocean. I mean, I like looking at it, but I don't like swimming in it! But if you insist," she said reluctantly, "I'll go with you."

My sister's response took me by surprise. She was actually going to be daring and try something unique in her life. No pools for Carole today - she was going to walk on the gleaming white sands of the beach and plunge into the warm, calm waters of the Pacific. Just before we reached the shoreline, Carole sat herself down comfortably in a lounge chair about fifteen feet from the shoreline.

"You've got to be kidding," I said. "You're not going in the water?"

"I said I'd join you *at* the beach. Not *in* the water."

"Your sister is so stubborn . . . and very *high maintenance,*" Bob said jokingly. "When she makes a decision - that's it!"

Once my sister heard that remark, she suddenly felt challenged. She hated the words, *high maintenance* and *stubborn*, especially when they applied to her.

"I would *love* to go into the water. It's something I've wanted to do all week!" she replied sarcastically. And then to our surprise, she proudly marched to the sea. We followed behind, and I noticed that Carole was clutching her Mary Higgins Clark paperback in her hand.

"Hey, Carole, didn't you forget something?"

"No, what?"

"Your book! You forgot to leave it on the chair."

She looked at me just like she might have done when we were kids, as if I were her unworldly younger brother who just didn't know what I was talking about.

"I know what I'm doing," was her only reply - and *she did.* Carole's idea of going for a swim in the ocean was to stand in ankle deep water, work on a glorious tan, and read a good murder mystery. Later at the reception, she would most likely tell everyone about her *vigorous* afternoon swim.

"You go out and enjoy the barracuda-infested waters. Have fun! And say "hello" to the jellyfish," she said sarcastically, followed by a wink of her eye.

Bob and I left Carole at the seashore submerged in no more than a foot of water, reading a novel, safe and secure, at least for the moment, as we swam in the peaceful, azure waters. Occasionally, a school of tropical fish would scurry by, and once in a while a small wave would envelop us and lift us off the ocean floor. But then I noticed about forty feet from us, a much larger wave that was growing in intensity. A few surfers, who had been waiting patiently, got ready for best wave of the day. The rest of us delighted in the huge lift we got, but as the wave passed us by, it grew larger and larger and larger, and it was heading right towards . . . my sister!

Completely immersed in *Pretend You Don't See Her*, Carole had her back turned towards the ocean as the huge wave approached the shore. We raced towards her, screaming, "Get out of the water! Huge waving coming right at you! Put the book down and run!"

Hearing our pleading voices, she turned towards us, just as the wave enveloped her entire body. As we got closer to where she had been standing, we suddenly saw an arm, a leg, and then . . . the rest of her mangled body. She tried to stand, but another wave hit her, and once again, she was nowhere in sight. We finally reached her submerged body, grabbed her arm and got her to stand. She had wet sand in her hair, mouth, eyes, ears, nose, and every other orifice of her body. And she had almost lost the top of her bathing suit. My sister was an extraordinary sight to behold. An absolute mess of catastrophic disorder!

"I told you I hate the ocean! Why don't you ever listen to me! The ocean is for fish – not for humans!" She began to cough up water mixed with sand and seaweed.

"Well yeah," I said, " especially when you're not paying attention."

"That's not funny. What kind of brother are you? Making fun of me like that! I nearly drowned."

"In twelve inches of water? That would have made an interesting obituary!"

Eventually, she saw some humor in the situation, as Bob and I fell into a frenzy of laughter imitating my sister's twists and turns.

We went back to the room for my sister's dramatic recovery. She had water in both ears and trouble hearing.

"Do you think I have surfer's ear syndrome?" she asked.

"That's impossible. You don't surf!" I told her to get rid of the water in her ear, jump up and down on one leg. She did this for several minutes until the people in the room underneath us began to bang on the ceiling.

"It's not coming out," Carole sadly replied. "I'm going to be deaf for life!"

"No you're not. Try hanging your head over the bed," Bob suggested.

I thought this was an odd remedy coming from a Harvard doctor, but maybe he knew something that I did not. Once she had her head dangling over the bed. Bob grabbed his camera and took a picture of her in a most unflattering pose. She jumped out of the bed, realizing Bob's prescriptive advice was nothing more than a ruse. She ran up to him, and he acted like he was trying to escape from her clutches. During all the insanity, Carole's ears popped - first the right, then the left.

"Oh my God! I can hear! It's *amazing*!"

"Did you think otherwise? My advice never fails. That's why I'm a doctor!" Bob proudly proclaimed.

That evening at the reception, everyone was elegantly attired against a spectacular backdrop of a starry night and a sparkling sea. There was still talk of a light evening shower, but no one seemed particularly concerned. I was amazed at how my sister's serenity and sophistication at this event were in complete contrast to what had now become known as the "catastrophe with mother nature" earlier in the day.

Dr. Slali from India, Dr. Andrey from Australia, Dr. Allen from California, and their spouses were immersed in a conversation with my brother-in-law, complimenting him on his "exemplary" presentation and "remarkable work" at Harvard's Brigham and Women's Hospital. My sister spoke about Bob's dedication and how their son, David, who was currently at Harvard, was planning to pursue a career in pediatrics. It was like the party scene from F. Scott Fitzgerald's *The Great Gatsby*, only in Kauai. I stepped back from the crowd and sipped on my Mai Tai and listened to the musicians. I was particularly amazed at how well my sister was holding up. She looked incredible, and everyone was fascinated with her intelligence and dynamic personality. She gradually became the center of attention. As Dr. William Burrows and Dr. Ana Marquez from New York City joined the conversation, Carole spoke about how she loved New York, especially the theater.

"You know at our wedding, Bob and I selected the song, "One Hand, One Heart," from *West Side Story,* and it was so symbolic and meaningful to have that song performed when we exchanged our wedding vows. And then on our honeymoon, we went to New York City and saw the Broadway production. The year after that, we went to London and saw it again. I just love those beautiful lyrics, 'Make of our hands - one hand; make of our hearts - one heart.' It's all so poetic and romantic, and it means so much to both of us," she said while patting Bob on his hand. Bob looked lovingly into Carole's eyes and Carole returned the stare. It was a very personal moment. He was so proud of her accomplishments and her ability to connect with these medical dignitaries from all over the world.

Suddenly, amidst the spectacular setting of Japanese marble statues, swaying palm trees, and breathtaking pools and fountains of glistening water, the scene abruptly changed. Carole lifted her glass of Chardonnay to her lips, gave two tiny coughing sounds, and then in a most dainty way, cleared her throat. "Excuse me," she uttered sweetly at which point, two doves flew overhead and circled around her.

And then . . . the storm hit with such strength, such velocity, and such indignity, that all the guests at the reception stepped back aghast at the sight of my sister's sinuses draining like power hoses at full blast. Two jet streams shooting forth from her nostrils caused partial flooding on the marble floors beneath her. People had to step away to keep their shoes out of the briny mess. No one had ever seen anything like this before. My sister's dress was drenched. The look on her face was one of sheer terror. With the last moments of the sunset behind her and with so much water spewing forth from her nose, for a second, I swore I saw a rainbow, a dazzling, somewhat surrealistic effect that I shall never forget.

For the first time in her life, Carole could not speak, and neither could anyone else. She must have broken the *Guinness Book of World Records* and may have even created a new category. After recovering from nature's nasty surprise, she began to laugh. Carole's nervous laughter, so unexpected, made everyone feel somewhat less tense. She then politely excused herself, and we returned to our hotel room where I got absolute hell for suggesting my sister take a swim in the calm waters of the Pacific Ocean that afternoon.

"Don't you ever tell me what to do, Larry! If I tell you, I don't like swimming in the ocean, that means I DO NOT LIKE SWIMMING IN THE OCEAN! I know what I'm talking about! Do you *hear* me? Do you *understand* me?"

I never asked my sister to go for a swim again, but the memory of the hurricane force of her sinuses sending out cascading waterfalls as two white doves circled above her . . . *will last forever.*

SIX

LIFE AS A MUSICAL

Feeling in a musical mood after a hard week of preparing students for yet another federally mandated standardized exam, Jack and Larry decide to develop stories based on real life incidents and adapt them into show stopping, toe-tapping Tony Award-winning musicals.

While dining at *Busalacchi's A Modo Mio* in the Hillcrest area of San Diego, Joey, the owner of this charming restaurant, assists Jack and Larry in the selection of a bottle of *The Show,* a 2005 *Cabernet Sauvignon* from The Three Thieves Winery in St. Helena, California. The succulent bouquet and high profile of blueberries and plums dance across Jack's taste buds while the aroma of dark fruit flavors inspires Larry to conjure up intoxicating images, exotic choreography, and scintillating melodies to rival any Stephen Sondheim musical.

After a few sips of this superb wine, Jack and Larry immerse themselves in musical worlds in which they *compose* real life stories - stimulating to the senses, the palate, and their creative spirits.

GYPSY ROSE
-THE MUSICAL

BY JACK BEDDOWS

If I were to write a musical based on any episode from my life, it would have to be about the shocking events that transpired soon after my family moved from upstate New York to the small town of Cohasset, Massachusetts, located just outside of Boston on Massachusetts's South Shore. The lyrics of the opening song performed by the child protagonist would probably go something like this:

It's a brand new place, a brand new start,
We're living by the water now! And everyone's dressed so smart!
The TV has a hundred channels, and preppy life is heaven,
The South Shore is the greatest place,
When you've just turned seven!'

I know, I know. It's lyrics like these that are the reason why I don't like most contemporary musicals very much. But let me tell you the *whole* story.

In the summer of 1978, my father had been offered a new job with General Dynamics, overseeing the safety of their east coast ship building plant. Since this new position came with a significantly larger salary than his job at General Electric in upstate New York, he took it without hesitation.

When my parents went looking for a new house that summer, they took me along with them despite the seven-hour drive we'd all have to endure together. I'd never been on a trip that long before, and after the first hour, when the initial excitement of the journey had worn off, I started in with the eternal question, "Are we there yet?" I kept making my annoying query at more and more frequent intervals, until finally, my father threatened to put me in the trunk if I didn't cut it out. Of course, since the car was a station wagon, it didn't really have a trunk per se, just that un-cushioned back area for groceries and such. But given his tone of anger and frustration, I thought it best not to point this out to him.

Several hours later, we finally made it to our destination. It was dark as we pulled off the road and into the parking lot. Though I was quite groggy by then, I remember seeing a bright light shining up from the ground onto a carved wooden sea captain, who had a wooden lamp in one hand, a pipe in his mouth, and one leg up resting on the sign that bore the legend, *Kimball's by the Sea*. Though I didn't know it at the time, this was the main hotel and the centerpiece of the quaint town that my parents had decided to settle in. It late Friday night when we arrived, and after checking in and washing up, we all went straight to bed without seeing much of anything. The next morning, however, it was as if I had awoken in some sort of fantasyland.

While my parents were still asleep, I got up and peered out of the window of our second floor room, gazing down on the light shining off of dancing waves that were populated with fishing trawlers and sailboats, some moving in and out of the small harbor, others bobbing gently up and down on their moorings, which pleasantly littered a rough and curving bay. About a third of a mile past all that, lit by the morning sun, the ocean stretched on forever to the horizon. It was then, looking out over the magnificent vista in front of me, that I instantly knew that I never wanted to be far away from the sea again, and I decided it was time my parents knew that too, so I quickly woke them up with my excited yelling.

"Look! Look! It's the ocean! It's the ocean! What ocean is that again?"

A few minutes later, after I had changed out of my pajamas and beaten my hair down with a brush, I looked over to the television set. It was Saturday, and for me that usually meant watching the hour or so of cartoons that were available on one of the two main stations we had back in upstate New York in those dark, pre-cable days. So out of habit, I idly flipped the hotel set on, before setting to work on my shoelaces. But as I started to turn the station dial, I was shocked to discover that, even without cable, the television had ten times as many stations as we had back in New York. What's more, almost all of them, VHF and UHF, were showing cartoons. As I began to flip faster and faster, I caught glimpses of Hong Kong Fooey, Space Ghost, The Herculoids, All Star Blazers, Tom and Jerry, Underdog, The Superfriends, Bugs Bunny, Scooby Doo, and even Rocky and Bullwinkle, all playing at the same time and vying for my attention. It was mind-boggling. I felt like I had won some sort of pre-pubescent lottery. As I sat in stunned silence, the music began to play in my heard.

Stop where you're going
Don't worry about what you need to do
We've got something better, well not better
But what's it to you?
You don't have a choice now, do you?
No, you've never really had a choice,
So sit down until it's through . . .

Hours later, my senses and mental capacities were completely overloaded as I staggered out of the hotel to wince in the sunlight, as my parent's loaded me in the car for a scenic drive along Cohasset's beautiful coastline. I was instantly won over by the powerful combination of the area's natural beauty and the astounding amount of Saturday morning cartoons that I could watch. When we got back to New York, I couldn't wait until we were packed and ready to move for good.

It was true that I did have a few friends that I had to leave behind, like the Enrights, who lived down the road. They were a ragged troop of rowdy boys whose favorite pastimes were giving each other the finger, swimming in their backyard pool, and hanging out of upstairs windows trying to moon each other and any other passersby. But I was a quiet child, one who could do without the dirt bike riding and the smoking of marijuana in the woods by the age of ten. Besides, what helped make the transition even easier for me was the fact that some of my friends gave me parting gifts, far and away the best of which came from my quiet and respectable neighbor, Jeffrey Covey.

"What do you have to say to Jack?" Mrs. Covey prompted her son on the eve of our departure.

"As a going away present, Jack," Jeffrey said in response, "you can pick any one of my records to take with you to Massachusetts."

My young friend and neighbor recited this practiced offer of generosity with a measured tone that signaled an awareness that, while this was a measure of sacrifice, it was one that was doubtlessly going to make him a better person. But as I looked through his collection, his lips tightened in consternation as I flipped past the typical late seventies fare of Captain and Tennille and Disco Duck records to handle the one item whose removal would leave a gaping tear in his heart. No doubt hoping that I would continue to flip on past, Jeffrey inhaled sharply as I pulled out his *Dracula and the Wolf-Man* double album with the accompanying, high-gloss comic book built into the well-designed packaging. It was clearly the jewel of his collection, and I meant to take it. I hunched over like Richard III as I turned to ask in faux innocence, "Would it be okay for me to take this one Jeffrey?" as if I weren't aware of either the record's place in his collection or the pain its removal would cause him.

I was fully prepared for chastisement by Jeffrey, for daring to ask for his best record, but to his credit, he said nothing in reply other than a rehearsed, "You're welcome Jack. Best of luck in Massachusetts," just one turn too early in the conversation.

In the months ahead, every time I read that comic book while listening to its wonderful record singing out a permanent memory of voice-over actors, low budget sound effects, and theme music, I couldn't help but think of poor Jeffrey. But every time I did so, I pitied my old neighbor a little less until finally, all that was left was my unalloyed love for the album. It was a truly great story: a sympathetic portrayal of the emotionally complicated gypsy/wolf-man and his struggles against the machinations of the evil Prince of Darkness, a blond-haired and goateed Dracula who wore an earring no less. It was a fashionable twist on the typical portrayal, and one that made me realize that I would have to keep an eye out for vampires of a more contemporary variety from there on in. It also made me consider what my life would be like if it came with a musical soundtrack, an idea that as a composer and songwriter I've never quite been able to shake.

Finally, after having waited for several nearly cartoon-free weeks, we started on our long, and this time, final car ride back to Cohasset: my parents; my brother; our Siamese cat Simon, moaning all the while in his traveling crate; our puppy, Golda who alternately ran all over the backseat and slept by the rear window of the family station wagon; and me. It was still summer, and we were heading to a beautiful and affluent new town that would be the perfect setting for the decade soon to come. Yes, I was now poised to enter the nineteen-eighties as a spoiled suburbanite in the preppy northeast, and though I didn't always think of it in those terms, I couldn't have been happier.

Preppy Boy!
You think you're a Prince of the Universe!
You think that the way things are now is a promise for a lifetime to come
Your parents did better than theirs ever could
So surely the same holds for you
The fame and wealth are all waiting for you
Preppy Boy!
How little, how very little you know

Once we settled into our new home, I took to exploring the woods and beaches close at hand. I was glad to find that the water that August, while not as warm as Lake George, was still plenty warm enough to swim, and unlike our old neighborhood, there were plenty of pizza shops and video arcades. In the next town over, there was even a moderate-sized amusement park where I would soon be biking regularly to squander all of my pocket money.

For the rest of that first summer in Cohasset, I spent the majority of time running around familiarizing myself with the neighborhood. There were trees everywhere. Hundreds of years before, Cohasset had been carved out of a forest, the remains of which still connected various neighborhoods, allowing kids to navigate much of the town through wooded paths, away from cars and roads and the prying eyes of adults. As dusk approached while walking on those paths, I couldn't help but imagine the possibility of turning the corner only to be face to face with the blonde haired Dracula that I had spent so much time focusing my imagination on.

Our house was across the road from quaint cottages that used to be servants' quarters. Down another branch of the street was the main building of the former estate, a mansion now converted into condominiums, which was set on a cliff and replete with glass atriums, towers, and very high and dangerous rooftops that in the near future would prove excellent for climbing. Throughout the surrounding woods on Howe Road were granite cliffs and abandoned fountains, dilapidated wooden bridges, broken statues and footpaths, all of which made a perfect background for an imaginative child's games. And in the places of the Enrights and Jeffrey Covey were two gigantic Catholic families, one Italian and one Irish, which offered more kids to play with than I could count on all of my fingers and toes combined. Their lives were so different than mine - no privacy, no peace or quiet, but also no lack of companionship or potential allies in ever-shifting allegiances that populated the ever-shifting family dramas.

All the Catholic girls and boys
What's it like to share your toys?
Share your rooms, Catholic girls and boys?
You're never alone for good or bad
You're never, ever, ever alone . . .

The rest of that summer came and went rather quickly, but before I had time to lament its passing, I was surrounded by the fiery beauty of a northeast autumn. That fall, I had the best Halloween of my life. *More people means more candy!* I reasoned to myself the next morning, in a very self-satisfied manner, while trying to dislodge the remains of yet another bite-sized Bit-O-Honey from my back molars. Then came a wonderful winter with a snowy Christmas for which I received lots of presents. Then spring came with the breath of new life and the hints of weather once again warm enough to ride my bike with just a t-shirt on.

But then, just when everything seemed to be going perfectly, I began to notice something troubling during my walks in the woods. *Why do so many trees have all of that white webbing on them.* And as the weeks passed, I noticed it was no longer just in the deeper sections of the woods that I would come across these wintry-looking trees. The webbing was spreading, and getting closer and closer to our homes. I told my father about it and asked him what was going on.

"Not to worry, just some caterpillars," he said, "No big deal!"

To be on the safe side though, he decided to put some protective rings of chemicals around the trees on our property. As it turned out, that was like trying to gird against a forest fire by sprinkling your house with holy water. But since I was the only one in the family who had walked in the woods lately and had seen how bad it was getting, I was the only one that knew that my dad was acting on borrowed faith as he painted the rings of chemical paste and hammered in the strips of thin copper that would supposedly repel the caterpillars. He hadn't seen how the webbing was spreading through the branches of the trees, rolling across from one to the next like mold, and I didn't have the descriptive powers or the authority to convince him. As my father and I argued about the situation, we were like a dueling duet.

Something is coming!
Something very bad!
It's creeping towards us slowly.
It's going to drive me mad!

I woke up one morning soon after, and peering out my bedroom window with the sheets clutched around my face, I saw nothing but an endless sea of white. Normally in our picturesque town, a lovely canopy of leaves and branches hung over the roads, and in the winter, there was nothing more beautiful than freshly fallen snow decorating that canopy. But this didn't look like that at all! The ground was still green with grass but the trees were all shrouded in a ghostly white that made it look as if they had been dipped into an oversized, white cotton candy machine from hell. And the worst was yet to come, for deep in all of that webbing were innumerable little specks of black that were now starting to grow and move.

Plop! Plop! "There goes another one!" *Plop! Plop!* "Look! They're falling everywhere!" My friends and I screamed as we witnessed the first waves of the massive birth a few days later.

Almost overnight, the trees, the yards, and even the streets of the whole town were completely carpeted in a living blanket of writhing caterpillars. It was unbelievable. It was clearly the result of some imbalance in the ecosystem; perhaps a poisoned species of bird that would have otherwise kept the now hated caterpillars in check. But I wasn't thinking about that then; I was too busy bemoaning the fact that nowhere was spared, not the streets and yards outside of our homes, not our front steps or patios, not even the public pool was safe from the disgusting and despised caterpillars.

I'm not exaggerating in the slightest when I say that the instant we stepped out of our front doors, our feet came down with a sickening squish. When my friends and I had to ride our bikes, there was not one inch of the road that offered free space to navigate through. As if we were riding in heavy rain, our back tires would shoot up splatters onto our backs as we pedaled along. Except instead of muddy rainwater, our backs were now being coated in green guts and slime. The best bet was to ride in the tire tracks left behind by cars, but even then the guts would splash onto our legs and shirts in an exceedingly unnerving manner. I felt betrayed. I felt like the boy who had been tricked into the child catcher's cage in the movie, *Chitty Chitty Bang Bang*, or one of the Pied Piper's hapless victims.

I screamed out loud, "This town sucks!" as I walked out the front door, forced by circumstance to ride my bike yet again. As I pumped the pedals of my bike with the resigned and dolorous rhythm of a galley slave, I would lament:

Oh why, oh why did you bring me to this place?
God doesn't live here, because even he couldn't face
All of these endless caterpillars!
I was tricked at first, by the cartoons and the beach,
But now all I want is somewhere out of reach
From these endless problems!
Oh why, oh why did you bring me to this place?
This God-forsaken place!

Again, not the best lyrics, I know, but let's face it – at least they're as good as the ones from *Urban Cowboy – The Musical.*

I remember being at my friend Jimmy's house during the infestation, and his father was vacuuming the driveway with an oversized, industrial strength machine. It whirred viciously as it sucked up pound after pound of living caterpillars, and the *schlurping* sound of the slug-like insects being pulverized very seriously threatened to make me physically ill.

"What are you going to do with all of that goop, Dad?" my friend Jimmy asked.

"Do? Why I'm going to make a pie, boys! A nice big Gypsy Moth pie! And all the neighbors are invited. But I'm going to save the biggest slices for you two, don't you worry!"

"Excuse me," I said, running off to vomit on the writhing mass of insects in my friend's front yard.

Clearly, we were all losing it. Yes, everyone in town was about to crack, and the depth of the carpet of caterpillars was growing. We used a ruler daily to check on the progress. I began to envision the mass of caterpillars rising to the level of our windows, spilling into our homes when the doors were opened. When it hit the three-inch mark, we decided we should call the governor to have him declare a national emergency. Someone beat us to it.

The next day, dawn broke early with the whir of airplanes. The entire town looked up to the sky, and our hearts gushed as I imagined those of the embattled citizens of Europe did during World War II when witnessing the Allied troops marching forth to free their people. Seeking to praise the machine of government at its most noble, we all spontaneously broke out into a patriotic hymn in voices not dissimilar to those of the Munchkins who, in the Wizard of Oz, come forth to praise Dorothy for the killing of the Wicked Witch of the West.

There!
Up in the sky!
The brave men of the air
Look at them fly
Flying in formation
Such a beautiful sight
Let's dance for joy at our liberation!

Ordinarily, I hated chemicals. I'd freak out when anyone in my family used bug spray in the kitchen, because it could possibly contaminate our food supply. For instance, just a few weeks before the caterpillars arrived, my father was spraying a pesticide in the flowerbeds around our house. He was being typically free and careless in the process when a splatter of these noxious chemicals came through the living room window and landed right on my face while I was watching an old Japanese horror movie during the *Creature Double Feature* on Channel 56. Coincidentally, the movie was about a guy who accidentally took a chemical bath that turned him into a walking human fungus. As I ran to the sink to scrub my face and gargle and spit and puke, I was exceedingly angry that my father could have done this to me. I didn't want to be a mushroom man, and, as a result, I learned to hate chemicals with a vengeance. But as the planes flew overhead, my friends still convinced me to run outside with them and dance in the spray raining down on all of us. Sure, everyone in town probably had a few years knocked off their lives by the previously illegal-strength pesticides, but no one was complaining.

Yes, the gypsy moth caterpillars' days were numbered. They began to convulse and gasp their last breaths. Their once fecund webbing was now rendered sterile, and their doom was assured. I can picture the glorious chorus of children ringing out in the maliciousness of vengeance achieved.

Die! Gypsy Moth, die!

Now you know you've outlived your welcome!
Die! Gypsy Moth, die!
We'll sweep up your bodies and laugh as you moan!
Because this town ain't big enough
It just ain't big enough,
No this town ain't big enough for you!
Or your brother, or your mother, or your cousins too,
So Die, Gypsy Moth die!"

Okay, so maybe that part's a little worse than *Urban Cowboy* . . .

It took a while for the ploughs and bonfires to destroy the remnants of our enemies, but by the time the heart of summer rolled around, everything was pretty much back to normal. Then one day, when the whole mess was… not exactly forgotten, but overcome, my friend Matt and I were riding our bikes back from the arcade on the seedy boardwalk of Nantasket Beach. Just as we were preparing to embark on the last leg of the journey towards my house, we came across a small 'one dollar sale' being put on by one of the many daughters of my Italian neighbors.

We stopped to look over Jenny's wares, and there on display, crawling around in an otherwise empty shoebox, balanced precariously on some nourishing leaves, was a lone, gypsy moth caterpillar. Jenny was a girl of our own age, and at nine years old, she should have known better.

"Her name is Rose, and she can be yours for only one dollar," Jenny quipped in her best, business-like manner.

We screamed our disbelief and struggled to crush the creature immediately, without, of course, paying for the privilege. But Jenny protected the horrible little thing, and insisted on her right to sell whatever she wanted.

Next spring, the plague returned for a second, and thankfully, final time, despite the assurances of the town leaders that such a thing *could never* happen again. Everyone was dumbfounded. "Surely the chemicals killed them all!" "How could they be back?" "Does God truly hate us?" they all screamed at the town hall meeting in bewilderment. *But not me!* I knew who was to blame, you see.

Ah! Gypsy Moth Rose!
How the trouble grows when you crawl my way!

OUCH!
-The Transmogrification Musical

BY LARRY ZEIGER

I have a weird habit of envisioning real life situations as Broadway musicals. While looking through the morning *Los Angeles Times*, I often brainstorm script ideas, musical themes, and lyrics for productions such as *Hillary and Newt – A Love Story, Will Success Spoil Sarah Palin?* or *Aliens from Mars vs. The Tea Party Express.* But today, I realize the best story to adapt into a musical is one based on my personal experiences. A tale so rich in character development and unexpected surprise twists that it could easily become the biggest Tony Award winning musical in history!

And so I present what will undoubtedly be a modern musical triumph of such power and scope that it will run longer than *Cats.* And like *Cats,* it will have a very simple title for all to remember, and that title is *Ouch! The Transmogrification Musical.* Glorious set designs, dazzling choreography, and a brilliant score will send audiences into the streets in a frenzy of exhilaration. Here is how I imagine this bold theatrical work will evolve . . .

Act 1

Scene 1

I receive a phone call at work from my friend, Ted. He tells me he wants to meet for dinner, because he has something important and personal to share with me. After I hang up the phone, I begin to wonder if Ted, like most of my friends, might be having financial problems, marital issues, or is on the verge of an emotional breakdown.

That night, Ted and I meet for dinner at Pasta Amore. Ted looks a bit uncomfortable, and after the appetizer is served, he tells me that he and his wife, Alicia, are breaking up. *Ted and Alicia? The two love birds? How could this be? They have a marriage made in heaven. They always look so happy together . . . so absolutely in love!* While eating my spinach salad with pomegranate seeds which occasionally get stuck in my throat, I listen to Ted as he tells me an incredible story about his life.

"As a child I felt *very different* and very much alone in the world. But when I met Alicia in seventh grade, well . . . Alicia and I . . . we fell in love, Larry. So in love, that I knew that one day . . . one day, we would marry."

"That's very beautiful, Ted. You two have always been lovebirds. And weren't you guys voted "Romantic Couple of the Year" in high school?"

Ted avoids the question and suddenly becomes quite solemn. "The problem is that I never have felt . . . *complete.*"

"I'm so sorry, Ted. I know this is a horrible thing to ask, and if you don't want to answer, that's perfectly all right." *I feel as if I'll put my foot in my mouth at any moment.* "Is there someone else?" I boldly ask.

"Well, yes, sort of . . ."

"I shouldn't have asked. What a fool I am."

"I know this is a bit awkward for you, Larry, but I think you need to know the whole story. Alicia is the one who wants to leave me!"

"Oh Ted, I'm so sorry. I had no idea."

"And I will be the first to admit that I still love her, but there is a major issue to consider."

"What's that, Ted?"

"Part of me wants to be with someone else."

Suddenly, I feel a song coming on. The words to the first verse with be something like . . .

"WANTING THE ONE YOU WANT IS NOT ENOUGH"

In the darkness of night I light a candle
How much can I handle?
In my world

That's spinning 'round
I feel upside down
Wanting the one you want is not enough
When you have too much love to give

The song will show the internal yearnings of Ted as he explains his conflicting dual nature to me while I sip a Jasper Hill Shiraz. After the song, we sit in silence as our dinners are served.

As in all great musicals after an introspective ballad, it is time for a rousing production number that entertains the audience but offers little or no information about the pivotal character. And so, just as Ted is about to tell me more about his conflicting personality, all the servers in the restaurant surround our table and break into a rousing rendition of *Pasta Amore*!

There's nothin' like noodles
Squiggly mass of doodles
A delight to eat
Do you catch the beat?
Asking for more-ay!
At the Pasta Amore
Amore! Amore!
When dinner is done
And you've had too much fun
With your generosity
And a good gratuity
We'll have no animosity
We'll dance a plié
And give you a bouquet
At you favorite hot spot
Where you eat more than a lot
And your spirits will soar-ay
And you will adore-ay
Because you can't ignore-ay
Pasta Amore!
Pasta Amore!
Simply fantastico!
SALUTE!

Additional verses will illustrate the delight of dining out and how good waiters make great tips by being pleasant and attractive while enjoying their jobs, unlike those who dine out who are over-stressed by their twelve hour work days and the frightening prospects of family obligations in a fragile economy. The servers finish their song with a tap dance that includes a Stomp routine with syncopated clinking of spoons on the heads of all the patrons that will surely delight audiences of musical comedy. The song also offers subtle commentary about the obesity of the American people from consuming too many carbohydrates and fats from pasta dishes served with heavy cream sauces.

Following the *Pasta Amore,* Ted removes some photos from his briefcase. They are photos of Madonna surrounded by several men. Another is one of Barbara Streisand, but it doesn't quite look like Barbara Streisand. I have no idea why Ted is suddenly showing me these pictures or why he is so attracted to these celebrated performers.

"What do you think?" Ted asks.

"I get it! It's a costume party!"

"It's *not* a costume party, Larry."

"Not a costume party? " I say with suspicion as I stare at the photos of Madonna and Streisand. "Then, what was the occasion, Ted?"

"No occasion really. These are pictures *of me.*"

"Of you?" I'm not completely grasping the moment.

"I just like dressing up as a woman. I mean, I thought you should know."

There is a long pause.

"Is this something new?" *How could I have asked that?* "No. I used to dress up starting in elementary school. I always felt . . . sort of . . . *different.*"

"Uh huh."

"And then as a teenager . . ."

"Uh huh."

"And then, as an adult, I . . . I . . . uh, just like *being a woman.* Like Streisand or Madonna. It's me, Larry. The *real me.*"

I'm momentarily speechless. I look into the eyes of my friend, Ted, and he looks at me as if he is waiting for a simple response, or maybe he's just looking at me, because he knows there is no simple response. "You know, Ted, you've been my friend for nearly twenty years, and you will always be my friend, but I'm surprised. I'm . . . well, more than surprised. What I mean is . . ."

Ted laughs and replies, "Face it man, you're shocked out of your gourd!"

"What me shocked? Are you kidding? Nothing shocks me, Ted. I'm a teacher. I've traveled the world. I read a lot. I have lots of diverse friends. Do you know what I mean? No matter what you say or do, you are still my friend, Ted. Nothing can change that!"

Ted agrees and we toast each other with a glass of Chianti and then a glass of Pinot Noir, and suddenly without warning, Ted jumps up on the bar, and to the delight of the patrons, he performs the song, *Switch Hitter in Love.*

I'm a switch hitter who's in the mood
In the World Series of love, hey dude!
I feel so tender
When I bend my fender
I'm just a Gender Bender
In love!

The song is performed in the Hip Hop style of Grandmaster Flash. Ted reaches into his internal soul to reveal his dual nature while the allegorical lyrics compare baseball to the complex nature of love and identity.

Scene 2

Several weeks later, Ted is honored for his philanthropic work, raising thousands of dollars for arts organizations in his community. I see him at the Artists and Models Ball at the classy Westgate Hotel where I learn that Alicia has filed for divorce. Ironically, Ted is with a knockout of a woman named, Melissa, who is one of the directors of the Sushi on the Rocks Art Gallery. I've never seen Ted happier, and Melissa looks at him with stars in her eyes. After he introduces me to her, she gives more than a casual kiss to Ted and runs off to the Silent Auction tables to bid on a painting called, *Breast of Chicken a la Mode.*

"Wow! Ted, she's something else!"

"I'm in love with Melissa, Larry."

"But Ted, we're friends, and you know, I mean, don't you think . . ."

"That I'm mixed-up? *A bit crazy?* No, Larry, Melissa knows everything about me. She loves me for who I am."

"That's wonderful Ted. I'm so happy for you . . . for both of you."

But after saying these words, I feel distraught over Ted's "identity crisis" and wonder if this new relationship with Melissa is simply a momentary flirtation. After all, Ted has a very unique and artistic personality.

Joining Ted after she has made her final bid, Melissa is absolutely exuberant. "I'm positive I will be the owner of *Breast of Chicken.*"

Filled with joy, she gently kisses Ted on his lips. He kisses her back, looks in her eyes, and whispers to her, "You know a good work of art when you see one," which leads to the charming duet, ingeniously titled:

"YOU KNOW A GOOD WORK OF ART
WHEN YOU SEE ONE!"

You know a good work of art when you see one
Even better in life - is to be one
It's great to be bold
And live life á la mode
And when the time is right
Take a bite
Of life and love
With stars up above
And become the work of art that you are!

Ted dances about the stage in wild abandon. At the end of the song, he steps on a chair and poses as Auguste Rodin's *The Thinker* to the delight of all the party guests who burst into applause. Ted is a hit and has cast a spell on everyone at this prestigious foundation event.

Ted and I keep in touch for the next few months, mostly by telephone. The subject of Ted's gender issues never comes up again until . . .

Scene 3

Summer arrives and I decide to take a vacation and fly to New York City. On a hot, steamy, night, I go down to the Village to see the musical, *Spring Awakenings.* After the final curtain I exit the theater into the lobby and run into Ted's friend, Melissa. "Hey Melissa, do you remember me? Larry Zeiger? We met at the Artists and Models fundraiser in San Diego."

"Of course, I do," Melissa says, "What a small world this is! Are you here on vacation or for business?"

"I decided I needed a break from work to catch up on the art and theater scene."

"I could live here!" exclaims Melissa. "There's so much diversity!"

At that moment, I hear Ted's voice calling out my name. I look behind me, but I don't see him. The voice becomes louder and louder and louder until . . . *no, it can't be,* a woman coming towards me, and her Chanel Glossimer coated lips are mouthing my name, "Larry! Larry! Larry!" It's as if Ted is doing some strange act of ventriloquism, but I don't see Ted anywhere.

Suddenly, the woman comes up to Melissa and puts her arm around her. My eyes bulge out of my sockets. Synapses and neurons shoot through my brain. *Am I having some sort of neurological disorder?*

I see before me someone I barely recognize. Long dark hair, heavy make-up, lipstick, dangling earrings, a low-cut, flaming red dress and boobs . . . boobs that I can barely take my eyes off!

"Ted? You're Ted? I mean . . . *the dress*! *You're wearing a dress . . . in public*?"

I am utterly confused. The situation is mind-boggling. I try to change the subject. "Hey Ted, can we talk in private for just a moment? I have some good news to tell you about (I make up any excuse I can) a song I've written!"

I push Ted into a corner of the theater lobby and boldly ask, "Are you sure you like dressing up like this? I know this is a theater crowd, but Ted, I'm your friend, and I'm worried about you."

"This is the real me, Larry! I feel absolutely liberated! This is the best I have ever felt since I was born!"

"And what about Melissa? She must feel awkward, Ted."

"Number one: my new name is Tedora"

"Ted! Your name is Ted!"

"No! It's Tedora, and Melissa loves me for who I am! That's what *true love* is all about. Isn't it Larry?"

I think to myself, *Should I be the one to judge*? I've been single all my life. Ted was married to the lovely and intelligent Alicia, and now he has Melissa who has loved him both as a man and now, as a man dressed as a woman, but this concept is just so alien to me. Seeing Ted in front of me with bulging breasts in a fashionable red dress causes me to have excessive heart palpitations, and not in a good way. And then Ted drops the next bomb

"Larry, there's something I have to tell you. It's time I update you on my upcoming procedure."

"*Procedure?* What are you talking about?"

"I'm having a surgical procedure in three weeks."

"Surgery?" I ask stupidly, "What kind?"

"Oh please, Larry. Do I have to spell it out to you?"

"Oh Jesus no! You're not going to be . . . to be . . . *castrated?*"

"Please, not so loud, Larry! We're in a lobby of a theater!"

My friend for more than two decades, the guy I joked with, the friend I drank beers with . . . is now about to become *transmogrified* into a *real* woman named Tedora! "Tell me, Ted . . . I mean, Tedora, that this is all just a bad dream!" At this point, the crowd in the lobby of the Atlantic Theater Company freezes, and I step forward into the spotlight and perform a musical soliloquy.

What's become of my best friend, Ted
I have no idea what's in his head
Is he dreamin' a dream
On a moonbeam
Or tranformin' himself
Is it good for his health?
He's turned on the light
And seen what's outta sight
For him that matters
To climb big ladders
And make a change
Maybe it ain't so strange
We have just one life
But is this masquerade right?
I'm goin' outta my head
'Cause I don't know
I don't know
I don't know –
What's become of my good friend, Ted!

At the end of the song, Tedora steps into the spotlight and sings -

What's become of my best friend, Lar
Lookin' shell-shocked

Like time has stopped his clock
It's not a bummer
That I beat to a different drummer
But maybe he'll adapt
To my different roadmap
Of takin' new directions
With my affections
And my new personality
So forget the absurdity
It's all about diversity
And acceptance, my friend
To the very end!

Following this poignant ballad, deafening applause will fill the theater as the lights come up for a fifteen-minute intermission.

ACT 2

Scene 1

ACT II is an absolute stunner with the revelation that Ted is going through with the surgical procedure that will change his life forever. Melissa travels to the hospital in Colorado and stays with Tedora during the surgery and the recovery period. With the backdrop of the snow-capped mountains, Melissa sings . . .

I can feel it in my gut
I love her – no matter what
She is everything to me
Everything a woman can be
That laugh
That smile
I'd walk the mile
I'd do anything I can to –
Stand by my wo-man.

Immediately after the surgery, Tedora, who is in superb spirits, surprises everyone by jumping out of the hospital bed, clothed in a spectacular Dior gown. She is more beautiful than ever with exuberance for life that could stop a clock. She even jokes with the doctors and interns at the hospital who form a kick line around her as she sings . . .

"PENIS FOR SALE"
I've paid the bail
I'm outta of my jail
I'm no longer a male
I've got a penis for sale!

The song, "Penis for Sale," brings the house down as all the doctors and nurses do phallic choreography in the style of a Busby Berkeley musical with acrobatics *a´ la Cirque du Soleil* added for good measure. A miraculously recovered Tedora joins the medical staff in a vigorous and exciting dance routine in which the interns and nurses lift her up in the air, forming concentric circles below her. They then join hands, circle within circle, and dance wildly around Tedora who is catapulted into the air for one last glorious lift. *There is a great deal of subtext in this number.*

Scene 2

The final scene of the production has a major revelation rivaling any of Moliere's romantic comedies. An elaborate party takes place at the San Diego Wild Animal Park to commemorate the grand opening of the new nighttime show, *Orangutans Gone Wild* and to also celebrate Tedora's *Re-Birthday.* Tedora and Melissa make a grand entrance, and the entire crowd bursts into a major song and dance salute to Tedora.

"SHE'S THE 'T' IN TERRIFIC!"
She's absolutely amazing
A sensation with all the right moves
She's the "T" in "Terrific"
So stylish and in the groove
Take her out on your big yacht
So tantalizing and hot
She can do a mean Foxtrot
That girl is simply top notch
Oh! She's the "T" in "Terrific"
And her fans are from coast to coast
Tip your hat to Tedora
And give the new girl a big toast!

"She's the "T" in Terrific!" should be choreographed by someone like Julie Taymor of *The Lion King* fame and will pay homage to different styles of dance including Salsa, Hip Hop, Stomp, and the *Horah*. The highlight of the number will be the dancing orangutans who jump off the stage, snatch women from the audience, throw them over their heads, and take them into their cages while performing Disco choreography in the style of the Village People as wild peacocks fly overhead. All the orangutans are men dressed in furry costumes except for one who is a real orangutan who has mastered the rigorous Julie Taymor routines under her tutelage.

Later in the evening, Tedora asks to speak to me and there is a look of urgency in her eyes. "Larry, I have something *unbelievable* to tell you – *unbelievable, but true!*"

"What could you possibly tell me now that I wouldn't believe?"

"Melissa and I are breaking up," Ted announces with a tremor in his voice.

"No way, Tedora. After all this? How could you?" I ask incredulously.

"There's someone else, Larry. Someone I truly love!"

"*Someone else*? Tedora, how could you do this to Melissa? She loved you as a man, she loved you as a man dressed as a woman and now, she loves you as a woman! And you're going to dump her? Why would you do this to her?"

And then the lights dim, and a spot shines on a stunning woman dressed in a low-cut sequined gown of gold who enters the ballroom. There is nothing left to the imagination as she and her cleavage approach center stage. She winks at me as if she knows me, and then blows a kiss to Tedora. All eyes are on this voluptuous creature.

"Tedora, I've missed you baby," says the mysterious woman in a *basso profundo* voice. My brain feels as if it will explode at any moment. *Is there yet another woman in Tedora's life?*

"Larry, I'm leaving Melissa. I've fallen in love with . . . with . . . Bobara, the *new* woman in my life!"

"*Bob-ara*? Don't you mean *Bar-bara*?

The tall voluptuous woman with broad shoulders standing next to me responds with great confidence, "BOB-ara! My name is Bobara!"

Suddenly, a group of waiters enters the ballroom and performs a lively musical dance number celebrating the new relationship of Tedora and Bobara.

The number will be a showstopper similar to the one in *Hello Dolly* and will have somewhat subtle references to Bobara's best assets.

Mountains of Love
Valleys of Gold
Moon up above
Time to be bold!
And to behold
Those Mountains of Love!

At the end of "Mountains of Love," Melissa pushes her way through the crowd, and all hell breaks loose. Tedora tells Melissa that the relationship is over, that life has taken a sudden turn, and Tedora has now fallen in love with someone else . . . and that Melissa should *try* to understand. Completely mortified with Tedora's decision to abandon her, Melissa departs from the party uttering a few choice words of her own. But Melissa, it turns out, is a very good actress. Just before she slams the door of her car, she tells one of my friends that her relationship with Tedora was about to end anyways, because she has fallen madly in love with the inventor of Wedge-Proof Underwear, and now has no excuse but to accept his offer to come and live with him in his spectacular multi-million dollar estate in Ahwatukee, Arizona. The biggest revelation of the evening, however, is that Bobara, the new love of Tedora, is actually a former football player named Bob who was a classmate of mine from my high school in Cleveland!

"Bob Abromovitz? The quarterback from the Class of '76 from Cleveland Heights High School? You've got to be kidding!"

Bobara intervenes and defiantly responds, "I'm not kidding, Larry. Although I enjoyed being the quarterback, those days are over. And today, I'm *finally* liberated! A man who becomes a woman who has fallen head over heels in love with a woman who was once a man who made the mistake of falling for a real woman! It's one delicious screwed-up romp even the French would love! I've found comfort and sexual healing with my new lover, Tedora! Could anything be better?"

I am ready to pass out when all of a sudden, Tedora hugs me and proclaims, "Life is just one great adventure after another!"

I look at Tedora, and I have never seen her as happy as she is tonight celebrating her "re-birthday party" at the *Orangutans Gone Wild* exhibit at the San

Diego Wild Animal Park. "And you, Tedora, are my most unique and interesting friend I've ever known!"

Amidst this personal revelation, Bobara reaches for me and hugs me in a tight embrace. "OUCH!" I exclaim as I try to conceal the pain I feel from Bobara's newly constructed breasts as she presses them into me.

"Oh, sorry," she says. "They're kinda like footballs. I hope I didn't hurt you."

"Oh no, just uh . . . uh. . . . a slight indentation in my chest . . . that's all."

The surprises never cease to end. At that moment, Alicia, Ted's ex-wife, enters the stage. Tedora initially is shocked to see Alicia at the party. Under an overhead spot, the two are initially silent for what will undoubtedly be a breathtaking, heart-pounding moment of musical theater history. And then . . . the silence is broken.

"Ted, you look so . . . so vibrant, happy and so absolutely elegant!"

"Thanks Alicia," Tedora says timidly and then adds, "I go by Tedora now."

"*Tedora*? Hmmm, I like it. A little bit of the old combined with the new. You are, just like I've always told you . . . *a work of art*." Changing the subject, she adds, "There's someone I'd like you to meet." She holds out her hand as a handsome Latino man approaches Alicia and puts his arm around her in a more than friendly manner. "This is my fiancé, Jesus Bustamante. He's an extremely successful Yoga and Healing by Touch therapist from Miami who has done wonders for my body."

"I do it all with my fingers, feeling the warmth of her soul, finding her troubled spots, and then healing her body with my touch. *Es muy bueno*," he says with a sultry Spanish accent.

Tedora is deeply moved to know that Alicia has found true happiness with such a good-looking, successful therapist and one with such talent. With great enthusiasm, Tedora proclaims, "And I too have found what I'm looking for. Bobara is my dream come true."

"And with Tedora, I've made . . . *a real touchdown!*" adds Bobara.

A lively rhythmic drum beat is heard and all the guests including Tedora, Bobora, Alicia, Jesus, and the orangutans jump on the dance floor and perform the final number of the show, a lively and moving tribute to everyone who makes life exciting and unpredictable. The stage is flooded with light and color as the entire cast sings . . .

"LIVING IN A RAINBOW"
We're suddenly all aglow
In a world tied with multi-colored bows
No need to take it slow
Oh no . . . 'cause
We're livin' in a rainbow
A rainbow of love
A world of opportunity
Of unity and beauty
And discovery
A world for you and me!
We're livin' in a rainbow
A rainbow above
In a world filled with love
For you and me
A new identity
It's all for you and me!

Confetti and multi-colored balloons rain down from the ceiling upon the cast and the audience. Everyone experiences a sense of exhilaration with this joyful, uplifting ending. The applause will be deafening as the cast takes its many curtain calls.

OUCH! is critic-proof and will play for years, and with characters like these, there is a myriad of opportunities for sequels.

OUCH!

THE TRANSMOGRIFICATION MUSICAL

Coming soon to theaters in your neighborhood!

Seven

Animal Houses

After a deadly dull high school faculty meeting where dreary speakers provide endless graphs about the lack of student achievement, Larry and Jack drive to Wine Steals, a wine bar in Point Loma where they sit outside overlooking a golf course and reminisce about their childhood pets.

To compliment Jack's "exquisite" tale, he selects a glass *of Cat's Pee on A Gooseberry Bush Sauvignon Blanc.* The wine, according to Jack, has an extremely "playful" taste and a "long racy body" with aromas that leap from the glass to his tongue. "This wine reminds me of my cat, and, his voracious appetite for furry creatures."

Larry's story about his pet duck, George, motivates him to select a bottle of *Mother Cluckers' Chardonnay* from the same Cooper's Creek Winery in Ontario as Jack's *Cat's Pee.* Larry enjoys the full bodied aromatic bouquet which reminds him of the waddling critter that brought so much joy to his young life until disaster struck . . . *big time!*

A Vegan's Nightmare

by Larry Zeiger

Barbara was everything in a woman I thought I had wanted. She was vivacious, witty, and she played the viola.

"My favorite restaurant is *C'est La Vie*," she announced. "I just love everything about it. The waiters all know me. The trendy decor fits my personality, and the food is *sumptuous*. Everything about *C'est La Vie* is right out of Edith Wharton's *Age of Innocence*. Have you read it?"

"No, I haven't," I said. She looked at me as if I were an illiterate. "But I intend to." *I lied.* "It's on my bedside table." *Another lie.*

"Actually, I haven't read it, but my aunt (pronounced *ahnt)* has a book about the making of the Martin Scorsese film adaptation which contains all these wonderful pictures of food. It's true culinary art! Each photograph looks like a painting. Scorsese and the art director worked tirelessly to make every morsel of food look like an art masterpiece. It's *so awesome!* And it's all like so . . . so completely accurate as to how Edith Wharton evidently described the food in her novel. You know, food is an art form. It's colorful, it has texture, and unlike a painting, *it's real* with the added dimensions of aroma and taste!"

"And you can eat it!" I added shamelessly in my most theatrical voice. We both laughed at this modest revelation. "Food as art? What a concept!" *I could tell it was going to be a long, boring night.*

"Oh yes!" she exclaimed. "Presentation is everything and that's why I truly love *C'est La Vie!* It's strictly *Cordon Bleu,* and everything is so *tres* elegant, and so *tres artistique.* It almost seems a shame to eat the food or even remove something on the plate as insignificant as the parsley which would obviously ruin the aesthetics of the creative expression of the master chef."

"I know what you mean." *I didn't, but I said it anyway.*

"I'm glad you understand. I love *haute cuisine nouveau*, and I can tell, you do too. So what restaurant are we going to tonight, *sil vous plait?"*

"C'est La Vie," what else is there?"

"Excellent choice, Larry, or should I say *tres magnifique?* You know it was during my junior year abroad in Toulouse," she sang out, "where I developed my passion for splendiferous foods in opulent settings paired with awe-inspiring wines!"

"You are *so* worldly, Barbara . . . so . . . so . . . *tres vivant."*

"And you are so absolutely right, my renaissance man! I have a zest for life and art . . . and fine dining. I can't wait for tonight's experience!" She then cleared her throat and with Valley Girl diction and exclaimed, *"C'est La Vie restaurant sert de bons petits plats."*

I assumed she meant that the restaurant was a pretty good one, and I simply nodded in the affirmative.

C'est La Vie, located in the beautiful seaside resort of Del Mar, had a view that was astounding. At sunset, light sparkled from the sea. A profusion of colors in the sky formed the perfect artistic palate for what I thought would be the romantic dinner of the decade. A classical guitarist was playing *La Vie en Rose* as we entered the restaurant. *Monsieur Maurice,* who looked more like an actor from Central Casting, immediately recognized Barbara.

"Bonsoir Mmme. Barbara," the tuxedoed host exclaimed as he wrinkled his brow, caressed his mustache, and then kissed Barbara on both cheeks.

"Bonsoir, Monsieur Maurice," she responded joyfully. "This is my date, *Monsieur Lawrence."*

"Ah, *bonsoir, bonsoir, bonsoir Monsieur Lawrence*! *C'est magnifique* to have you both here at *C'est La Vie, ce soir!"*

I knew this guy's French was limited to greetings so I just played along. "Yeah, *bonsoir* to you too."

"Soir! Do not pronounce the 'r'. The 'r' is silent in *soir* as in *bonsoir monsieur."*

Barbara and the waiter laughed at me and then exclaimed in unison, *"Bonsoir monsieur!"* For added laughs, they pronounced a long "r" in *soir* as if I were an idiot linguist. I could tell this was going to be a long night.

Monsieur Maurice then guided us to our table. At any moment, I expected tuxedoed waiters to break into passionate renditions of Edith Piaf and Cole Porter tunes as they danced from tabletop to tabletop. After a couple glasses of Barbara's favorite champagne, I felt more relaxed, ready to enjoy the evening. Maurice returned to take our dinner orders.

"Everything we serve is organic and cooked to perfection, and tonight's special is simply extraordinary. So distinctive and delectable, and it is the most popular dish on our menu!"

"Oh please, " Barbara exclaimed, "don't keep us in suspense! I can't wait to hear what the chef has in store for us in this awesome *restaurante du monde!"*

"Our special for *ce soir* is . . . *Confit of Duck!"*

I immediately began to tremble. *Confit of Duck! Confit of Duck! CONFIT OF DUCK!*

"And the duck is presented in a delicate sauce containing braised greens, turnips, *pomme maxim*, and green peppercorn, simmering in a red wine reduction. It will simply melt in your mouth! *Comprenez-vous?"*

The duck will simply melt in my mouth? My head was pounding. This was more than a migraine . . . it could be an aneurism!

Barbara's eyes widened. "It sounds wonderful! I won't even look in the menu. I know what I want. I'll have the . . . the *feet* of duck, *monsieur!*"

The waiter then turned to me. His words echoed in my head. "And you, *monsieur*, would you like the *duck confit* as well? It's an extraordinary dish . . . a *really* extraordinary dish! *Superblemente*, if you know what I mean!"

I began to feel dizzy, a sudden case of vertigo. Colorful spirals mixed with feathers began to swirl about me, and suddenly, I found myself falling down an abyss. I passed the waiter and Barbara. With enthusiasm, they replied in unison, "The duck will melt in your mouth! The duck will melt in your mouth!" And then . . . a duck flew by. He stopped in midair and looked at me. I stared back at the creature who uttered a helpless "quack-quack-quack" and then a tormented scream and, finally, a shriek of terror that I will never forget. The duck disappeared and then reappeared as a plate of *Duck Confit* with a huge turnip in its mouth. He spoke flawless English and pleaded, "Order the cow, order the chicken, order the turkey, or order the pheasant, but . . . *not the duck*!"

I continued to fall into the dark, deep hole of my past.

It was a warm, summer afternoon in 1954. My mother was taking my sister, Carole, and me for an afternoon drive to Chagrin Falls to hike the trails along the river. The ride seemed much longer than usual due to the fact that we were completely lost.

"Isn't it wonderful seeing the beautiful countryside? I never knew this road existed!" my mother exclaimed with nervousness in her voice. She scrambled for the maps, which were of no help. In the distance we could see a small farmhouse. "Oh look, I've found the farm I was looking for!" which translated meant, *I'm so lost. Maybe the owner of the farm will give me directions on how to get to our destination.*

The man and woman of the house were right out of a Norman Rockwell painting. While my mother asked them for directions, I wandered off to look around the farm. Near the barn, my eyes widened with excitement as I saw a tiny duckling who was making the softest quacking sounds I could imagine. He looked at me. I looked at him. And I swear to this day, he spoke to me and said in perfect English, "I want to be your pet, and your friend . . . *forever*."

In a matter of minutes, my mother was ready to depart, but I pleaded with her, "I can't leave without George!"

"Who's George?" she asked.

"George is *my duck*." I replied with charming innocence and determination.

She laughed a motherly laugh. "Oh no, Larry, the duck belongs to this man and woman. They don't want you to . . ."

The farmer interrupted. "Oh please, we have plenty of ducks on this farm. If the boy wants the duck, let him have it."

The very idea of having a duck in our house began to make my mother somewhat tense. "Oh, you are much too generous. But we couldn't . . . we just . . . couldn't accept this generous offer of yours."

Having the gift of artful persuasion, I opened my eyes as wide as I could as crocodile tears began to flow. "Please . . . *oh please, Mom!* This duck is so small. He won't cause any problems. Mom, I'm the only boy in the neighborhood without a pet. He won't take up any room. I'll take care of him . . . *I promise!*"

How could she deny a sensitive, tearful, loving, concerned, and mature six-year-old's heart-wrenching defense of the need for a pet duck?

One of the few times in her life, my mother was backed into a corner. The farmer, his wife, and my sister looked at my mother waiting for a response. I also looked at her with one final gigantic tear rolling down my face. Desperately wanting me as his new friend and longing for a new habitat, even the duck stared deeply into my mother's eyes, waiting anxiously for her response.

A moment later, she replied, "Well, I guess my son has a pet." I joyfully scooped George into my hands and hugged my new companion.

The ride home was one I'll never forget. My mother muttering to herself, "What will your father say? What will your father do? He hates animals." I didn't hear a word she said. I was in a state of pure nirvana with my duck climbing all over me making joyful quaking sounds.

When we arrived at our home in Cleveland Heights, my mother instructed me not to say anything to my father just yet. We would have to introduce the duck slowly into his rather conservative *pet-less* world.

"You did what?" my father screamed. "You bought the kid a duck?" My mother closed all the windows so the neighbors would not hear my father's ensuing rant. "Who's going to take care of this annoying animal?" he continued. "And what will happen when winter comes? Where will we put the damned thing?"

"We'll worry about that when the time comes," my mother answered back. "Leave Larry alone. He loves his pet."

"Why couldn't you get him another fish for a pet? Fish are small and easy to take care of!"

"Mickey, we tried that, and you know what happened!"

What happened was . . . when I was four years old, my mother bought me a small aquarium with six guppies (Barry, Carey, Harry, Jerry, Perry, and Snappy), and placed the aquarium on top of our old RCA Victor television set. Later in the day, I turned on the TV, and within thirty minutes, the fish were swimming exuberantly around in their new environment faster than any guppies I had ever seen in my life. Suddenly, to my amusement and to the music of the *Mickey Mouse Club Anthem*, my cute little fish began jumping out of the aquarium and then diving back into the water. *Wow! Circus Guppies,* I thought.

"This is incredible!" And then the glorious sight of watching this fish spectacle turned to abject horror, as one by one, the six guppies jumped higher and higher out of the aquarium reaching their final destination which was to fry to death on our television set. It was truly an ugly day for my pet fish and me. I buried all six of the critters under our rose bush and made tiny crosses and Jewish stars as markers for them. I was utterly devastated.

Considering the horrific incident, my father quickly realized that his comment about the ease of caring for fish as pets was a poor observation and was now resigned to the fact that I was going to be the only child in our neighborhood with a pet duck named George. And I was ecstatic!

As the summer months rolled on, I trained George to follow me everywhere, including Meithers' Ice Cream Parlor. For some reason, Mrs. Meithers would always usher George and me out of her ice cream shop with a stern warning that the older patrons came to her store for peace and quiet while they consumed their strawberry parfaits and chocolate phosphates. They did not want to hear the "annoying and grotesque sounds of a quacking duck." It became evident to me that the adult world could be a cruel and heartless place to live. But I kept on trying my best to show George the best parts of *my* world.

On warm sunny days, I would take George to Cain Park where he loved splashing around in the Children's Pool. Occasionally, a parent would caution me, that for "sanitary reasons," I should remove my duck from the pool, but I responded that George was "a very sanitary duck and rarely pooped in public."

One day in September, I hid George in my jacket and took him to school with me. Within a half hour, my first grade teacher discovered my little pet's legs protruding from my pocket and immediately sent me to the office for "bad behavior." My mother was called in for a conference with the principal, which made me feel as if I were some sort of weird delinquent. That day I learned that ducks did not have any civil rights in Cleveland Heights, Ohio. Still, I was always true to my boon companion.

About a week later, my mother had her Women's Book Club over for a discussion of Henry Morton Robinson's *The Cardinal.* All the women sat down for tea and pastries at our dining room table and talked about their kids, the sale at Higbees Department Store, the latest Hollywood scandals, and occasionally Robinson's novel. I had thought George was playing outside, but to my surprise, before the women had settled down in the dining room, he had crawled through the hole in the screen door, quietly making his way through the kitchen into the dining room where he decided to take an extended nap under the table where the ladies were seated. All of a sudden from my bedroom, I heard one lady scream, then another and another.

My sister, and I ran into the living room and witnessed the horrible spectacle. George had evidently made his way under the dining room table and had scampered across the ladies' feet, sending them into a screaming frenzy as they jumped on chairs to protect themselves from my little pet. My eleven-year-old sister, loving the role of "the drama queen," shrieked louder than anyone. Utterly perplexed by the bizarre reaction, George ran straight into my arms, and the two of us bolted for the front door. It took a while for the ladies to calm down, and I don't think they ever resumed their book talk about *The Cardinal.* Meanwhile, I took my pet down the street away from the commotion and had a deep, sensitive conversation with him.

"That was a close call! I worry about you, George, and I think I'm the only one in my family that really cares about you."

George looked at me with the sudden realization that I was right. He knew I would always be his friend and his protector. To show his appreciation, he jumped into my lap and rubbed his beak and feathers against my leg.

At the end of September a blast of arctic air off Lake Erie signaled an early start of winter. Using my superb deductive reasoning skills, I told my parents, "George will freeze outside!"

"Not a bad idea," my dad replied.

"Dad! How could you say that? He's just a tiny little duck and can't hurt anyone."

"I think he belongs on a farm where other ducks live."

"You can't take my duck away from me! You just can't!"

My compassionate mother intervened. "I have an idea. Maybe we can bring George inside for the winter. We can build a little home for him in the basement for those cold winter nights, and on warmer days we'll take him outside."

I cheered ecstatically. My mother's decision-making skills could have made her the first Woman President of the United States!

That afternoon, I created a room for George, which consisted of a large empty box, a donated pillow from my bed, and an aluminum pie pan for food and water. George was ecstatic. He quacked incessantly, showing me his gratitude for his new surroundings. It was a perfect arrangement . . . until the next morning.

The sun came up at the crack of dawn, and the quacking began. I was in bed and thought for certain that George would quiet down, but he didn't. I overheard my father yelling at my mother from the master bedroom.

"Son of a bitch! If that duck doesn't stop yapping in two minutes, I'm going to strangle him!" My mother tried to calm my father down but it was no use. He continued, "What kind of home has a duck in their basement? I'm going to kill the bastard!"

I had visions of my father with his hands around the skinny neck of my poor defenseless pet. I raced down to the basement to protect my feathery friend. I carried him upstairs, trying to comfort him until he finally stopped quacking. With tears in my eyes, I looked at my Dad and said, "You can't kill George, Dad. He's part of our family!" I cried profusely. Big tears flowed down my face onto the floor forming an actual puddle.

My mother defended me. "Mickey, look how you've upset Larry! All this talk of killing his duck is just too much for him!"

"So what's the alternative? Listening to obnoxious quacking on a daily basis?" my father bellowed.

I sheepishly responded, "I will get up each morning before the crack of dawn, Dad, and I will take care of George. I will take him outside so you don't ever hear him. Please Dad, please!" I looked up with that desperate heartfelt expression I was so good at. How could he say 'no' to this *perfect child?*

Realizing he had all but broken my six-year-old heart, my father gave in and hugged me. My mother hugged my father. And with her Kodak Brownie Camera, my sister took photos of all of us hugging each other. It was a magical moment captured on film forever. However, this family portrait of love, hope, and unity was not to last much longer.

The next morning at the crack of dawn George would not stop quacking – no, *not quacking* – this time he was *screaming!* Even I couldn't stop him. I tried talking to him, petting him, singing to him, but nothing worked. Again, my father yelled, "That duck is ruining our lives! We've got to get rid of the duck, and this time . . . *forever!*"

I did everything possible to protect George, but I began to feel it was lost cause.

My mother barred my father from the basement, and I heard her muffled words. "Calm down Mickey. I have a plan that will solve everything. I promise." I had no idea what my mother's plan was until later in the day when she dropped the bomb.

"You know Mr. Bedavecchia?" she said.

"Our really mean neighbor? Uh-huh," I answered.

"Well, his sister, who is a very nice lady, has a farm just outside of Cleveland."

I had a funny feeling I wasn't going to like this conversation. My stomach began to growl. My mother continued. "I spoke with Mr. Bedavecchia this morning, and he said that his sister would be happy to take George who could live on their farm for the rest of the winter."

"Oh No, Mom! No!"

"Just listen to me. George will be with other ducks just like him, and he'll be *very happy*! Trust me, he'll love his new home . . . and it will be so much better for him than our cold damp basement. And Larry, this is only a temporary home for George. Before you know it, spring will be here, the flowers will be in bloom, and George . . . he'll be back here with you, living in our own backyard! Larry . . . *I promise!*"

Nothing my mother could say or do would convince me, but I knew it was a done deal. A dark ominous thunderhead appeared over our heads. It began pouring rain. All I could think about was my impending farewell to my little pet.

The next day, my mother gave George to Mr. Bedavecchia, the scariest man I had ever seen. He always had a grumpy expression on his face and a raspy voice when he spoke. "Oh, don't you worry little Larry, my sister, Priscilla, will take good care of George. She'll take care of him *real good!"* he snarled.

As my pet waddled towards our neighbor's dented grey truck, George gave me one last mournful look and then opened his cute little beak as if to say, *Why are you doing this to me?* Bedavechia's then pulled out of his driveway, and I could hear the desperate muffled quacking of my duck grow fainter and fainter as the truck disappeared around the corner of our street.

Gone! My pet was gone! How could life be so cruel to a six-year-old and his small pet duck?

It was lonely, dark winter without my little friend. In December, I walked over to our neighbor's house and asked Bedavecchia how George was doing on his sister's farm.

"Your duck? Why your duck is getting *very big.* And, he's eating well."

"That's nice," I responded, but I couldn't imagine George any bigger than he was.

Bedavecchia then slammed the door in my face. He wasn't much for conversation.

The winter months flew by. I envied all my friends with their cats and dogs and couldn't wait for spring to arrive to get my unique pet returned to me. I continued to stop by Bedavecchia's house to get updates. He would always say the same thing. "George is getting *bigger.* He's a big duck now. You should see how big he's getting."

One day he told me that George was not a male duck. I was stunned. *How would he know this?* He told me that George's new name was Priscilla, the same name as his sister. *Why would anyone change the sex and name of my pet? What a sick, sick thing to do!*

Finally, the week after Easter, the weather turned warmer. The tulips broke through the ground, and hints of green began to appear on the maple trees. After nearly six months, I asked my mother if I could have my pet returned to me.

"I think that's an excellent idea. Why don't you go over Mr. Bedavecchia's and *politely* ask him if he'll bring your duck home from the farm."

I was ecstatic beyond belief and ran outside and began to jump around in puddles. The little bit of rain and the rainbow in the sky brightened my day. And then I walked up those cold stone steps to the front door of Bedavecchia's house. The exterior of the house was dark and drab, but I was floating on a cloud. I couldn't wait to see George.

I knocked on the door. *No answer.* I knocked again and heard footsteps inside. *Still no answer.* Just as I was about to knock again, Mr. Bedavecchia opened the door. He was a big man . . . in my mind, about eight feet tall.

"Can't you see I'm busy?" He held the sports page of the *Cleveland Plain Dealer* in his hands. "Why are you disturbing me?"

I could tell he was not in the best of moods and decided to get this over with quickly. "I'm here to get my duck, George." He stared blankly at me without saying a word. I thought that maybe he didn't hear me so I raised my voice. "My mother said it's time for George to come home . . . to my house . . . to live with me."

"I told you your duck is a female. He's not George. He's Priscilla."

"Well he was a *boy duck* when I had him!" I insisted.

"And I told you that female duck of yours grew up and got . . . *very* big!"

"What difference does that make? Can I have my duck? *Please!*" I pleaded.

"What do you want such a big duck for?"

"I want my duck!"

"Well, you can't have her!"

"Not a *her!* George is a *him!*"

There was a long pause. Even as a six year old, I sensed something was not right. I became more demonstrative. "Give me my duck right now!"

"Do I have to repeat myself? I said, 'you can't have her!' Your duck is far too big for you to take care of it. Now go away and quit bothering me!"

"Give me my duck!"

"You can't have the duck! My sister and I just figured you didn't want the critter anymore . . . so we ate the dumb duck . . . for Easter dinner!"

Ate my duck for Easter dinner? ATE MY DUCK FOR EASTER DINNER! I suddenly felt dizzy. It just couldn't be true!

I began to imagine George on a large plate with a golden apple stuck in his beak while Bedavecchia and his sister stuck forks and carving knives into him, and then, like the worst zombie movie I had ever seen, they were eating his foot, his wing, his breast, and his little heart. I couldn't bear it anymore!

"YOU ATE MY DUCK!" I screamed. No, it was more than a scream . . . it was a wail like a banshee! I'm certain you could hear it up and down the streets of Cleveland Heights all the way to Cincinnati! I turned and ran home amidst the sobbing sounds of my heart breaking into a million pieces. When my mother discovered the hideous truth, she too was appalled and went over to Bedavecchia's house and had words with him . . . words a six year old had never heard before.

I thought I would never stop crying as I learned that day how insensitive and cruel the adult world could be.

"I'll have the *Confit of Duck* . . . it sounds *delicious!*" Barbara proclaimed with excitement.

"Excellent choice!" the waiter responded. "And you *monsieur*?"

The server was waiting for me to speak, but I could not. Worse, the prospect of watching Barbara consume a cooked *Confit of George* just about put me over the top. I had to do something fast.

"Excuse me, I have a call." I took out my cell phone and began to speak. "Oh, it's a bit noisy in here . . . what . . . what did you say? Wait . . . you're breaking up . . . oh . . . say it again . . . huh? I can't hear you . . . " I turned to Barbara and the waiter and informed them that I was going to step outside to try to find better reception.

"But your order, sir?"

"Oh . . . uh . . . I'll let you know . . . in a minute."

There was no call. It was simply a ruse to get me out of the restaurant and away from the dinner special of the night. I left Barbara to enjoy her beautifully presented French cuisine of *Confit of Duck* by herself. It was the food that mattered most to her anyway, not me.

On the way home, I stopped by an Indian restaurant and sat at the bar and enjoyed a dinner of Vegetable Korma, Green Curry Tofu, and a glass of *Pinot Grigio* while listening to Ravi Shankar's music. Sitting near a window, I watched a light rain fall and reflect the lights of the city. As I ate my vegetarian dish, I was flooded with memories of my family, my neighborhood in Cleveland Heights, and my one and only pet, George, my duck.

THE DEATH OF THE EASTER BUNNY

BY JACK BEDDOWS

It had been a perfect afternoon for a group of small children in rural, upstate New York. The sun was shining and the grass was warm, thick, and green in the backyard where my friends and I were stumbling and laughing and marveling at how the long summer days seemed to last forever.

Little did we know the fun was about to end, as Justin Van Brackle appeared in the distance like a plague of locusts. The older neighborhood boy paused for a moment, as if in indecision, and then started his march over in our direction. My friends and I instinctively stopped what we were doing and gathered together at his approach. Justin could hardly wait to get within earshot before he spit out this poisonous and, given the season, most incongruous non sequitur: "Hey you little babies! Santa Claus isn't real!"

Enter the Snot-Nosed-Know-It-All, a character that has been plaguing the world since time immemorial. I can imagine a group of young children playing by the banks of some ancient river or other, happily minding their own business, until . . . "Hey you, little babies! Mithras, The Bull of Holiday Giving, isn't real you know! And the whole thing with Osiris? It never happened either!" No wonder ancient peoples used to stone blasphemers for their heretical crimes.

Like countless numbers of children before us, our first reaction to this shocking proclamation was to display our anger and denial, and if we'd had a large pile of stones handy, who knows how things would have turned out? As it was, the debate that followed echoed throughout the neighborhood long past playtime. Evidence was given, personal sightings and so forth, and then the evidence was contradicted. When it became obvious that we couldn't prove it *wasn't* our dads taking the cookies and milk, one of us yelled out what at first seemed the strongest argument possible: "Santa Claus *is too* real! My parents wouldn't lie to me!"

Almost immediately, I felt a slight itch of doubt, which then quickly grew into a lurking sense of betrayal that proceeded to grip my heart like a giant squid squeezing the wooden hull of a doomed Portuguese man-of-war. That afternoon, my friends and I argued tirelessly and admitted nothing, despite the increasingly overwhelming evidence put forth by our well-prepared opposition.

After Justin left, cursing our dumb obstinacy, we spent a few minutes bravely trying to bolster each other with affirmations. "That Justin doesn't know what he's talking about!" "Well, *I* still believe in Santa Claus!" But beneath the bravado of Santa's young defenders, the awful truth had done its work. When we finally dispersed, we did so full of rancor and confusion.

One boy, from a family of fairly recent Norwegian immigrants, walked off muttering, "If der Santer Claus is not real, den what of Fenris, the Wolf and the World Tree Yggdrassil?"

Over the next several weeks, as the once unshakeable notion of Santa Claus eroded within me, it became clear that he had been a cornerstone in the structure of my imagination, the bedrock of a fortress whose walls kept out a swarming abyss of doubt. Once Santa was gone, *all* of the characters that populated my childhood beliefs were doomed, including the second in command of all imaginary creatures, the Easter Bunny. Yes, with Santa gone, Peter Cottontail had no choice but to hop along towards the horizon in the Big Man's shadow.

While the commercial extremes of Christmas almost seamlessly replaced my childish wonder with a lust for gain, it was with a heavy heart that next April, I tromped out at the command of my parents to look for the multicolored eggs that I now knew couldn't possibly have been hidden by a magical bunny. But everything that dies, they say, comes to life again one day, and so my faith would enjoy a brief, but tragic revival.

Ten years later in our small section of wooded suburbia just south of Boston where my family had relocated, our Siamese cat had clearly established himself as something of a terror. A great hunter, who could run up a thirty-foot tree in the blink of an eye, Simon had all of the local birds and squirrels in constant fear for their lives. Master of all that was smaller than he, and faster and craftier than the hostile dogs of the neighborhood, Simon was undoubtedly king of his little corner of the natural world. He was proud of this fact too and delighted in showing off by bringing a stream of dead animals to our doorstep. He'd never deign to *eat* these poor creatures. He'd just leave them on display so that we'd understand what a mighty hunter walked among us. However, Simon made a tragic mistake that would cut his hunting career short by years. He refused to understand that it was a problem to constantly sharpen his claws on the living room furniture. I'm sure in his mind, this was a minor issue compared to all he'd done for us, what with all the dead birds and squirrels he'd given us. But my father thought otherwise. One day, in his mounting frustration at the sight of his new and newly ruined furniture, he pronounced Simon's fate.

"The cat," he said, "is to be declawed."

He soon enlisted my mother's support with an appeal to her own considerable domestic pride, and that was that. My brother and I, for whom childhood had preserved a natural predilection for the sanctity of any family member, furry or not, argued and screamed that it was wrong. But our arguments were soon crushed, and the decision was made final. Simon was simply not the same cat from that fateful day of surgery on.

Although he still went out occasionally, when our dog Golda patrolled the yard in his defense, Simon was a proud animal, and since he could no longer escape on his own into the trees, he mostly resigned himself to spending his time indoors, sitting in the windowsills looking wistfully outside or lying in patches of sunlight on the carpet or the couch. Years went by in this manner, without a single animal being deposited on our doorstep, and Simon seemed completely settled into this sedentary lifestyle.

But then, one Easter Sunday, something very special happened. It had been a pleasant enough holiday, one which was less about the active traditions we had enjoyed as young children—the Easter egg hunts and so forth—and more about the delightful combination of the pleasant slowness of Sundays, the soothing effects of chocolate, and the merest suggestion of religious piety, provided by the holiday cards displayed on the mantle. So imagine our surprise on this particular Easter morning when my mother started screaming from the front hall.

My father, my brother, and I rushed out to see what was the matter. My mother looked shaken and was pointing outside with a nervous finger. Crowding around the open doorway, we looked down to see Simon, who had a proud and mischievous twinkle in his eye and a very large, very white, and very dead bunny hanging by the neck in his mouth. In the discussion of the 'Holiday Miracle' that ensued, someone voiced the notion that perhaps it was the challenge of a mythical adversary that had lured Simon out of retirement.

"Well…we can never know for sure," I admitted in response.

But I did know one thing for certain—in an instant, my childhood faith had been rekindled and then just as quickly violated. And also, the Easter Bunny was dead. *Again.* This time though, there was blood on the front doorstep. It was then, as I stared down at the bunny's dead body that an idea stirred inside of me. I began to consider the possibility that I could actually be the steward of some type of holy relic, the authentic remains of the Easter Bunny.

I'll have to build a reliquary, I thought in my mounting excitement, *and I could get a little jewel-encrusted cross for the bunny to hold, and perhaps a cape and a hat for me. Perhaps Eastern Europe would be a good place to get momentum going before taking the display to more lucrative climates!*

One evening, several years later, I was taking off my top hat and riding boots, and pouring another small bag of coins into my traveling chest, when I suddenly realized a connection between what had happened to me as a child and what I had become. "Lost faith," I muttered to myself, as I dragged a hand over my chin while looking at my reflection in the small circular mirror hanging off a nail in the main supporting beam of my small attic room. As I bent over my basin of tepid water, splashing my face and preparing to shave, I considered how in the core of every good charlatan is a little boy who becomes bilked of his own credulity, and how this same charlatan then goes on to exploit others, not out of a meanness perhaps so much as an opportunity to live and breathe in a vicarious world of faith, if only for a moment.

I thought about shaving off my waxy mustache, as I meditated on how destroying that faith in others, while mostly incidental and seldom intended or even desirable, is still cruelly inevitable in the trade. Just after the stubble was gone, I set down the razor, patted myself dry, and mused to myself, At least I'm not a Snot-Nosed-Know-It-All!" After all, a charlatan, even with all his faults, breathes life into that which he most desires, if only for a little while.

And even with the occasional tar and feathering, hasn't he always been far more popular than that poor blunt instrument of misery, the one who is always so eager to tell you of the death of your dreams?

Eight

The Road to Vegas

After a tedious staff meeting on the subject of the "new" tardy policies and the confiscation of cell phones used during the school day, Jack and Larry drive to Little Italy where they select the Isola Pizza Bar for their next culinary and wine-tasting experience. The superb bartender, Roberto, pours them glasses of *Luscious Lips Red Wine* from the Falkner Winery in Temecula, California while Massimo, Stefano, and Alonso serve them fantastic Italian appetizers. To add to the ambiance, a floor to ceiling portrait of the sultry Oscar-winning actress, Sophia Loren, stares at them as they sip the *Luscious Lips.*

According to Jack, "*Luscious Lips* has a great bouquet and a delicate sweetness which reminds him of his first kiss with Lotta, the "really hot Swedish girl with the silky blond hair and hypnotic green eyes" he took to Las Vegas a few years back.

Larry adds that the wine has *nice legs.* He experiences a certain thrill while drinking *Luscious Lips* and staring at Sophia Loren which instantly reminds him of the wildest tale he has ever heard about two of his friends and their outrageous road trip to the City of Sin.

Viva Las Vegas

by Jack Beddows

On the night that I met Lotta Asplumb, the most beautiful Swedish nanny that ever lived, I felt like I was riding a streak of good fortune, which could only be compared to that of a high roller who's had Lady Luck herself blowing on his dice.

It all started a few months earlier. I was fresh out of college and had recently returned from a cross-country adventure with my musician friend, Sarah. That bizarre episode behind me, I was about to return to my regular routine of bussing tables and cursing the management of The Blue Parrot for failing to recognize my obvious waiter-like qualities. But before settling back into this mundane routine, like a bolt from the blue, my mom called to tell me that I had been left a tidy sum of money by a distant relative in England.

I was sorry to hear of the death of my great aunt, who, since she had no children of her own, had made her will by tracing the branches of the family tree, looking for the nearest male relatives to whom she could bequeath the sale of her modest home. *Let's hear it for old-fashioned gender bias!* I thought. Of course, I felt sorry for my mom, who did remember her well, but since I really had no idea who she was on any personal level, the fact that she ended up settling on my brother and me as the recipients of her largesse, was news that, overall, fell into the category of 'welcomed surprise.'

The first thing I did upon learning of my new found status as, while not quite rich, at least no longer dirt poor, was to go to a local clothing boutique and buy myself a swanky new shirt that I had looked at several times in recent months but never dared to even try on, in case I liked it too much. The second thing I did was to quit my job as a busboy at The Blue Parrot.

One thirty-dollar shirt aside, I've never been much of a spendthrift, and it was really the gift of time and leisure that was now temporarily afforded to me that I was so excited about. And so it was, that after a few indolent and happy months, I flew back to Boston for the holidays.

Christmas came and went pleasantly enough, and then it was time to face New Year's. This holiday had so often been a source of hype and frustration for me that I only looked forward to it in the most conflicted sort of way. But thankfully, instead of being herded into some expensive bar or hotel, or freezing my nuts off in Boston's albeit cultural, but mostly outdoors, First Night festivities, I found myself with a few compatriots, celebrating New Year's Eve at a friend of a friend's house party. This kind of low-key affair was right up my alley. And to make things even better, quite inexplicably, the best looking woman in the place, the aforementioned Swedish bombshell, Lotta Asplumb, to whom I had been introduced earlier in the evening, ended up hanging on my arm just minutes before midnight, waiting to ring in the New Year with a kiss. *Jackpot!*

What's more, since no one was in any condition to drive home that night, Lotta and I found ourselves sharing a couch in the living room as we prepared to go to sleep. As we cuddled up, Lotta scratched me behind the ear and said, "Tell me a joke, Jack!"

"You want me to tell you a joke, Lotta?" I asked needlessly.

"Yah! Please!"

"Well, I don't know too many."

"Just tell me one!" she said, seductively trailing a finger across my chest.

"Okay, but it's a little long."

"That's alright, I don't mind," she said as she nuzzled closer.

And so I told her my exhilarating tale:

Okay, so there was this penguin, and he lived in Santa Barbara. And one day, he received a phone call inviting him to take a new job skating for the Ice Capades in Las Vegas. He quickly agreed, and soon found himself packing up his things and preparing for a long drive through the desert to Vegas. There was just one problem: it was August, and his car was very old. So, just when he was on the outskirts of an isolated little town, still a few hours away from his destination, his car overheated and broke down.

"Aw, crap!" he said to himself. "No wonder my car broke down, it must be a hundred and twenty degrees out here! Now what am I gonna do?"

But happily, a tow truck drove by before too long. "Boy am I glad to see you!" the penguin said. "And lucky too! I thought I was going to be stuck out here all day."

"Not really lucky," said the tow truck driver, "You're not exactly the first guy to break down this afternoon. I've been driving up and down picking up all kinds of people. But I'll tell you what, there's a little town a few miles up the road, and my cousin owns the auto shop there. I can tow you over, if you like."

"Yeah, that'll be great!" said the penguin. "I've got to get to Vegas to start my new job!"

So the driver towed the penguin into the little town of Bullhead City and left him at the auto shop.

"I'll tell you what," said the mechanic, "you're not exactly the first guy to break down today, so it'll be a while before I can take a look at your car. I don't have air-conditioning here, so why don't you walk down to Main Street, get yourself an ice cream cone or somethin' and by the time you get back, I should be able to tell you exactly what's wrong."

"Okay," said the penguin. "An ice cream cone sounds pretty good right about now."

So the penguin walked into town in the brutal heat! It was like walking in an oven. But finally he reached the oasis of the ice cream store.

"Ah!" he exclaimed, as he walked into the air-conditioned shop, "I'd like a large vanilla cone please!"

"Well," said the man behind the counter, "It's been a real scorcher today, and we've been real busy, and unfortunately, I'm all out of cones. I can put your vanilla ice cream into a big Styrofoam cup for you though."

"At this point, I'll take whatever," said the penguin. "I just need to cool down."

The man behind the counter continued, "There's just one other thing. I'm all out of spoons."

"Fine! Fine! Whatever!" the penguin replied, perhaps somewhat impatiently. "Just give me the ice cream, man!"

So the penguin took his ice cream and started to walk back to the auto shop to find out what was wrong with his car. Just as he was finishing his frosty treat, he met the mechanic coming out of the garage.

The man wiped some grease from his hands onto his overalls and said, "Well, it looks like you blew a seal."

The penguin hastily checked his mouth with his flippers and said, "No, no! I was just eating ice cream!"

I smiled and waited patiently a moment or two for the burst of hilarity that was no doubt building up inside my lovely new friend, but instead all I got from Lotta was a dry-toned and disappointing, "I don't get it."

Oh well, I thought, *you can't have everything.*

Despite Lotta's obvious lack of appreciation for fine humor, in the week that followed, I took this Swedish beauty out and about with the express intention of impressing my friends with my lovely new catch. And apparently, I didn't give a damn how transparent my intentions were. The day after introducing her to every acquaintance I could track down, my good friend Matt called me on the telephone, and dispensing with any preliminaries, started in with, "You just had to do it, didn't you? Bringing a girl like that around here! What a show-off! You disgust me!"

"Matt? Is that you?" I replied. But he had already hung up.

The truth is though, that in the few weeks we spent together, not much more than a friendship ever developed between Lotta and me, despite the fact that I wouldn't have *minded* further developments in the least.

Not long before Lotta was slated to return to Sweden, I made plans with her to spend a few days with me in California before renting a car to go to Las Vegas for a last bout of tourism together. And this time, she was going to bring two of her young Swedish nanny friends along with her. *I wasn't at all against this idea!*

When I picked up the three young ladies at the airport, however, I was forced to accept the fact that not *all* young ladies from Sweden are candidates for the National Bikini Team. Not that these girls were bad looking, mind you, but they weren't like Lotta. So, my fantasy of carting three absolutely drop-dead gorgeous Swedish girls around, to the envy of all, was somewhat squelched. But what was more important than my ridiculous fantasies was the fact that both Jenny and Victoria were very sweet and always fun to be around. They were also very happy to have a guide in California, and that made me feel good about myself, as for the next several *exhausting* days, it was my full time job.

In the week that followed, I drove the girls up and down the coast, spending all of my time and energy trying to keep them entertained and showing them the California that I had grown to love. As we traveled up the 101 to San Francisco and back down the slower more scenic Route 1 to Big Sur and then back to Santa Barbara, we enjoyed the beaches and other natural beauties that the state has in such abundance.

Of course, I would be lying if I claimed I wasn't thinking about enjoying a *natural beauty* of another sort, but once again, Lotta and I never progressed much beyond a little kissing and cuddling. Perhaps that was part of the reason that as the last few days of their trip approached, I announced, "Well, girls, rather than you getting a rent-a-car, how would you like it if I drove you all out to Las Vegas?" They were very glad to hear my proposition. If nothing else, it would save them some money and provide them with a guide who could take them safely to their destination. And I was glad too, because this would provide me with a few more nights to share a room with Lotta, who seemed oblivious to the fact that she could not only have made it onto the Swedish Bikini Team, but she could, without a doubt, have been the captain.

Our first tourist stop on the way to Vegas was the Grand Canyon, which none of us had ever been to before. We didn't have the time to hike all the way to the bottom, a trip that usually requires camping at the base and a long climb back up the next day, and we didn't have the olfactory fortitude to deal with the donkeys and their guides. Instead, we decided to take a shorter walk into the great chasm.

About a half an hour into our descent, I got a bit of a bug to be mischievous, so I jogged ahead of the girls, claiming that they were moving too slowly for me, and then I hid around a corner. Just as they were approaching, I popped out and growled like a mountain lion. All three of them jumped so high that for a moment, I worried that a gust of wind might come along and blow them off the trail to certain death. Once they landed safely, however, I burst into laughter and proceeded to tease them mercilessly. Suffice it to say, my little joke cost me one of my last precious few nights with Lotta, as she preferred to sleep three in a bed with her friends, rather than to share one with a *vicious beast,* like me.

The next morning, we were up early for the last leg of our journey from the Grand Canyon to Las Vegas. A few hours after our departure, I commented to my passengers, "Hey girls, look at this! The car thermometer says that it's a hundred and seventeen degrees out there! Can you believe it? That's HOT! I hope the car doesn't breakdown." I said this last bit smiling, possessed with an inexplicable confidence that this could never really happen.

Just then, my car started to smoke, sputter, and lose power. "Shit! Shit! Shit!" I exclaimed, as the car quickly came to a dead halt on the side of the road.

"Oh no! What are we going to do now?" Lotta asked while Jenny and Victoria leaned forward from the backseat with looks of consternation wrinkling their brows.

"Well, I don't know about you," I started to answer while smiling at Lotta, "but I think *I'm* going to go get a vanilla ice cream cone."

"I don't get it." she replied dryly.

Like the penguin in the story I had told Lotta several months before, we were eventually towed into town where my own unreliable car was finally fixed for a fee that I hadn't figured into my travel budget. *Entertaining Swedish girls is expensive*, I thought with a hint of rancor as we continued on to Vegas later that day.

Before we knew it, looming ahead of us was that giant, money-sucking vacuum of a town. The only thing I had going for me was the fact that, besides the five to ten dollars I'd allow myself to squander on slot machines, I positively refused to gamble. This general policy of mine isn't due to any inordinate amount of good sense on my part, but instead stems from a simple acknowledgment that, when it comes to gambling, I'm a born loser. I never even get the fabled beginner's luck, which seems to grace most every other initiate into the games of chance. I go straight to losing every time. *So why bother?*

Instead of wasting time and money in the casinos, I was thinking that the girls and I would enjoy lounging by the pool, sipping cocktails, and eating buffet dinners, the affordable prices of which were subsidized by all the other suckers wasting their kids' college funds for another round at the craps table. *Let the chumps sweat while we lounge*, I thought, as we pulled into our hotel on the strip. What I didn't know was that the girls had other plans.

"I thought you told me that none of you wanted to gamble? This is our only night here, and I'd kind of like to relax a little bit!" I exclaimed as the girls attempted to drag me out of our suite so I could take them down to the strip to visit the casino next door.

"We *don't* want to gamble," Lotta said pleadingly, "but it's very important for us to get souvenirs to give to our friends and family back home."

Jenny and Victoria agreed, leaning their heads towards me and nodding plaintively, so that I found myself surrounded by a chorus of sympathy-rousing puppy dog eyes. *How could I say no?*

Before I knew it, we were out of the blissfully air-conditioned hotel and back on the filthy, hot, jam-packed Vegas strip. Pedestrians filled every inch of sidewalk, and cars were packed in both directions on the road spewing exhaust into the heat of a summer evening that lacked even a hint of a breeze to disperse the stench. We fought our way past some sort of outdoor pirate ship display, replete with fighting buccaneers and exploding cannons that further added to the noise and chaos.

All the girls really wanted were the free souvenir plastic mugs the casino provided. Each was embossed with pictures of happy gamblers under the names of the providing establishments and was just the right size for holding quarters for the slot machines or the pool of tears that would doubtlessly pour forth upon the realization that the money from your second mortgage had now vanished into Satan's a-hole in the form of a blackjack table or roulette wheel.

"Thank God that's done with!" I said. "Now you've got your souvenirs, and we can go back to the hotel and relax!"

Instead of saying anything, the girls treated me to another round of plaintive stares.

"Oh, for Christ's sake!" I exclaimed. In the end, I was dragged to a dozen different casinos over the next several hours, all for the sake of collecting souvenir mugs. "Not another one!" I moaned each time they would grab my arm to pull me out into the fray yet again.

"Just one more!" the girls would always plead, as we'd slog off for yet another battle with the foot traffic in our quest for plastic booty.

Perhaps it was some small echo of their long dormant Viking gene for conquest that kept them going, but whatever the source of their miraculous endurance, I couldn't keep up.

"Thirteen casinos is my limit, girls. I'll meet you back at the room," I finally said, despite the tearful looks they gave me. At this point, their puppy dog stares had no effect on me whatsoever. In fact, I would have kicked a whole basket full of puppies if it meant I could get back to our suite any faster.

When I made it back to our hotel, I breathed a heavy sigh of relief and couldn't wait to get back to our room to wash off the strip and maybe have a drink. On the way, I shared an elevator ride with an extremely inebriated middle-aged man who was accompanied by a younger, heavily made-up woman hanging off his arm. Her occupation I could only guess. This guy was so drunk he could barely stand, but whenever he started to lose his balance, he would secure his footing by reaching out and grabbing his younger companion's buttocks. To this, and to his occasional, garbled, lecherous comments, she would reply, "Oh George! You're incorrigible!"

That incongruously sophisticated phrase, Lord knows where she learned it, coupled with her heavy makeup and overly teased and processed hair, made this woman seem much older than she probably was. I stepped back into a corner as far away from them as possible and waited for the elevator door to open. As fate would have it, they were on the same floor as I was.

These two less than model citizens poured out into the hall in front of me, moving in a lilting fashion that the young woman's determination to get to the room could only slightly alleviate. I eventually became frustrated and made a break to pass them. As I looked back while getting ready to enter my room, the man fell against the wall while fumbling in his pockets trying to find his plastic room key just a few doors down. Suddenly, the door opened, seemingly of its own accord.

"George, where the heck have you been? Don't you know what time it is?"

Then this new character in the comedy partially emerged from behind the now fully opened door and noticed her husband's dubious companion for the first time. Her already elevated tone began to rise into a banshee-like shriek.

"What the hell is this? Did you bring a prostitute back here? You stupid son of a bitch! I can't believe you'd do this to me!"

"Naw, baby, naw! You've got it all wrong!" was all the man could think to shout back while his arm was still half-wrapped around the heavily made-up woman who was now trying desperately to disentangle herself.

"George, I hate you so much! Why did I ever marry you? I've never hated anyone so much as you! I HATE YOU! I HATE YOU!"

The wife continued to shriek while I fumbled for my room key to escape this scene. The last thing I saw was the young woman of dubitable employment shooting her own look of disgust at the befuddled, drunken man before she stomped off down the hall, muttering her own curses that were barely audible under the general clamor.

Not long after, when the girls had made it back to the room and were unloading their massive hoard of plastic mugs from hurriedly purchased tote bags, I exclaimed, "Holy Shit! You won't believe what just happened!" They *didn't* believe it, and since they approached our room from the other direction in the hall, they hadn't heard any of the ruckus which had been ongoing ever since. In order to convince them, I took them down to the room where, even through the thick hotel doors, the ongoing verbal abuse could still be heard.

"*No way!*" the girls exclaimed.

"See, I told you," I said triumphantly when we returned to our suite. We all had a good laugh about it, and then, because the girls had a plane to catch at noon the next day and they wanted to get up early for some pool time, we went to bed.

That night, I was far too tired to try to scale the icy Lotta Asplumb fjord from which I had been rebuffed countless times before. So instead, still giggling about the plight of our hapless neighbor, I laid next to my gorgeous friend and drifted off to sleep and dreamt of Swedish warrior women in horned helmets and furious Viking wives beating their husbands for bringing back ships filled with plastic casino mugs embossed with pictures of foreign prostitutes.

Meanwhile, somewhere in one of the few casinos on the strip that I hadn't been forced to visit that night, a penguin was completing a daring triple axel to the gasps of exited onlookers while backstage a somewhat rotund sea lion awaited him with a six-gallon drum of vanilla ice cream.

The party was just beginning.

You Forgot One Item

By Larry Zeiger

My well-educated friends, Tracy, an attorney at Maccarone, Machowski and Macandog, and Elliott, a CPA at Assman, Pitts, and Bacon, worked tirelessly packing their mobile home for their long-awaited trip from San Diego to Las Vegas. Their son, Alex, an aspiring actor, had landed his first leading role in a theatrical production, and they just couldn't wait for the opening night performance.

"I just love Vegas," Tracy exclaimed with delight. "There are so many great things to do like *numero uno* - seeing my adorable son as the star of a classic mystery – and a three way tie for second place – gambling all night, dining in gourmet restaurants, and let's not forget, shopping for designer clothing. That's my *real* passion! And speaking of clothes, Elliott, do you think I should take the Diane Von Furstenberg jacket or the Cynthia Steffle?"

"I don't think you'll need a jacket, Tracy. It's going to be 112 degrees in Vegas today, 114 tomorrow, and cooling off to a mere 111 on Sunday."

"But still, I'll need a jacket for the casinos. They're like refrigerators. I think I'll take the Von Furstenberg!" she exclaimed emphatically.

"I'm glad I could help." Elliott muttered. "And my nightgown! Which nightgown should I take?" Tracy had a habit of asking questions and never waiting for responses or caring what the responses would be. Within seconds she answered her own question. "I think I'll take the Lustrous Pearl Satin Bias Designer Nightgown. It's so sheer . . . so sexy and *so inviting!*"

Elliott, who prided himself on his organizational skills, wanted to get the show on the road. "Tracy, baby, if we leave now and drive all night, we can make it to Vegas before it gets too hot. And we promised our talented son that we would take him to breakfast at 9 a.m. Are you ready babe?"

At that instant, Tracy's lips became pursed, her eyebrows raised, and her teeth began to grind. Tracy hated being called "baby" or "babe." She was a sophisticated woman, a lawyer at a prestigious firm where no one would ever refer to her in such demeaning terms. Elliott's remarks annoyed her, but she must have thought, *Oh well, he's my husband. I won't say anything. Why ruin the trip!* She stuffed her Lustrous Pearl Satin Bias Nightgown in her suit bag, grabbed her Von Furstenberg jacket, downed one last cup of purified water, made sure all the windows were closed, and then exited their lovely home.

Finally, just after midnight, Tracy and Elliott were on their way to Las Vegas in their huge gas-guzzling mobile home that took up about three parking spaces. About a mile from their house, Elliott realized he had forgotten his cell phone. "What an idiot I am! I left it on the charger. How could I be so forgettable? Let's go back and get it."

"Don't be ridiculous, Elliott. We can live without it and simply talk to each other. We don't need a cell phone when we have each other."

"Whatever you say, honey."

"Can you stop calling me *honey* and *baby!* I'm a grownup with a name."

"Oh sweetie, I didn't mean it. I mean . . . Tracy, you know, I love you. And this is going to be a wonderful, fantastic, exciting getaway for both of us!"

Tracy smiled. She needed a little escape from the daily grind, and this trip was going to be just the right medicine for what she needed.

After driving about forty miles, Elliott noticed the tank was nearly empty and stopped at a Phillips 66 Station. Tracy turned to her husband with a bewildered look on her face. "Can't you remember anything? Not even an hour from our house, and we're stopping for gas? We'll never get to Vegas at this rate!"

"My mistake. Don't forget I was busy working all day on gardening. Planting those tulip bulbs takes time. Tilling the earth with that hoe. That's hard work, Tracy!"

"The ball game." She corrected him. "You were watching the ball game most of the day. Hurry up with the gas, Elliott!" For Tracy, it seemed like an eternity for Elliott to fill their monster-sized tank. "Now I bet we don't make it in time for breakfast with Alex!"

"Wanna make a bet, Tracy? I've never been late for anything. I told Alex I would be at his door by 9 a.m. and we *will* be there by 9 a.m. I even allowed time for us to take a two hour rest stop along the way."

"Okay, Let's not start an altercation," which was an odd comment for Tracy to make seeing that she was the one who initiated the argument. "I trust your judgment, Elliott," *even though she didn't.*

About 2:30 in the morning, Elliott started to get the nods and pulled off to the side of the road in what seemed like the middle of nowhere. He looked over to his slightly disheveled, but still lovely wife, and whispered in her ear, "Tracy, let's take a break now and sleep for a while."

Tracy's beautiful blue-green eyes cast a spell on Elliott. There was something so special about her . . . so hypnotic, so enticing, so sexy that suddenly, he found himself thinking about the porn movie, *Slippery Girls Gone Wild*, which he had secretly watched on his laptop earlier in the day during commercials breaks of the Padres-Giants game. The prospect of making love in their Palm Harbor Mobile Home in the middle of nowhere was becoming more than just an exhilarating thought for Elliott.

"Let's make love, Tracy. Let's stop here for a few hours. I want you. *I need you.*"

"But Elliott, you know how Alex would feel if we're late to take him out for breakfast. It's wrong, Elliott, *so wrong!*"

"No, it's right, Trace! I figured it out! Three minutes to change into that sexy nightgown, thirty minutes of lovemaking, one hour of restorative sleep, and then we're off to Vegas arriving according to my estimation at 8:37 a.m. That's twenty-three minutes early! Alex will be amazed by our timely arrival. Please, Tracy, *please*!" he pleaded.

Clearly, Elliott was a "master of seduction." The thought occurred to Tracy that a two-hour break from driving might do them both some good, not to mention, she would have an opportunity to try on her new negligee.

Before they retired for their thirty-minute tryst, Tracy filled a plastic wine glass with a 2003 *Beaujolais Appellation Controlee.* "Louis Jadot always puts me in the mood," she noted ecstatically. At first shocked, Elliott calmed down in seconds when he realized Tracy was talking about the brand of wine and not

Louis Jordon, the handsome young architect who lived across the street from them. Under the moonlit sky in the middle of nowhere, in their somewhat cramped mobile home, Elliott and Tracy made wild and passionate love for exactly twenty-nine minutes, and then went to sleep with Elliot setting a travel alarm to wake them in precisely ninety-one minutes.

Life, however, does not always run as smoothly as the ticking of a clock. Approximately fifteen minutes later, Elliott woke up feeling restless. He quietly exited the vehicle, and began his daily Yoga routine. He spent approximately six minutes alternating between poorly formed *Tree Poses* and *Standing Forward Bends*. Concluding his exercises for the night with *Downward Facing Dog*, he felt a sense of renewal and exhilaration. He then through on his clothes and quietly entered the driver's seat and started the engine. Being the sensitive husband, he decided not to wake Tracy. *She's had a long day*, he thought, *and she deserves a nice long nap*.

As the vehicle sped off, Tracy began to dream about flying through space on a *Beaujolais*-scented, silk negligee carpet. A few minutes later, the silk carpet ride began to collapse in her dream at the same time that Elliott gently touched the brake pedal, slowing for a red light in the town of Banning. At the point that Elliott came to a complete stop, Tracy felt the carpet landing. She woke up and noticed that her husband was not beside her. *I wonder if he's okay*? she thought. Unaware that Elliott was in the driver's seat, she got up, wiped her sleepy eyes, and opened the door to the motor home. She looked outside, and saw the Banning Adult Video Emporium. *That's odd,* she thought, *I don't remember this Porno Shop being here. Why would we stop to take a nap in front of a porno shop? That's just weird! And where is Elliott?*

At that very moment, the traffic light turned green. Trying to make up for lost time, Elliott hit the accelerator with a little more force than he would normally, causing Tracy to lose her footing and tumble down the two steps of the doorway of their mobile home into the streets of Banning.

Elliott sped off into the darkness, quietly humming *Peaceful Easy Feeling* by the Eagles, completely unaware that he had left his wife behind in a translucent designer negligee on a dimly lit street in front of an Adult Video Emporium in Banning, California.

"Damn it to hell! Where in the fuck is Elliott going!" Tracy stood up and noticed small cuts on her legs and arms. Her nightgown was covered with dirt from the littered street. A sticky Wrigley's spearmint chewing gum wrapper stuck to her hand. It was the sight of the gum wrapper that made her burst into tears. "Gum on my hand? Wrigley's stuck to me! I'm alone and cold. With gum . . . gum . . . gum on my hand! *Son of a bitch!*"

Calling her hysterical would have been an understatement. Within seconds, two men from the Banning Adult Video Emporium ran out to help her.

"Lady, what happened? Someone beat you up?"

The second man added, " Show me the douchebag! I'll take care of the mother fucker!"

For the first time in her life, Tracy was at a loss for words. Before she could even think of how to reply, a police car with its siren blaring pulled up beside her. A male and female cop exited the vehicle and approached the scene with caution. "What happened to you?" asked the male cop.

Never having been approached by police officers in her life, Tracy was at a loss for words as to how to reply to such a simplistic question. *Couldn't he see what had happened?* She was half naked, bruised, and surrounded by two men in long trench coats in front of an adult video store. *Wasn't that enough?*

Hysterical and confused, Tracy replied, "My husband left me . . . I mean, I fell out of my mobile home. He didn't know he left me here . . . no honestly, the light changed, and I . . . I fell out into the street . . . we were sleeping . . . I'm all bruised . . . my beautiful nightgown that I purchased at the Bloomingdale's Anniversary Sale and paid a good price for is . . . is . . . in shreds!" She was making no sense, and for the first time in her life, could not control the waves of tears that poured forth from her bloodshot eyes.

"It's okay little lady. We need to take you in for some help, *some counseling* and find out what *really* happened," said the male cop named Burt.

"First off, I'm not a *little lady*. I have a name. And that name is Tracy Ward. I'm a well-respected attorney from San Diego," she proclaimed while reaching for her driver's license, which she suddenly realized was in her purse in the mobile home with Elliott.

By this time, a small crowd of late night denizens began to form a circle around Tracy and whisper to each other phrases like "hooker beaten up and thrown into the street," "abused woman . . . case of battery," and "pimp threw out the bimbo."

Tracy was mortified and suddenly experienced acid reflux drilling gaping holes in her esophagus and stomach. Trying to regain some sense of composure, she attempted to explain what had transpired. "I opened the door of my motor home and fell into the street when the light changed. My husband took off thinking . . . thinking that I was still asleep. But really, he adores me! He would never hit me!" Tracy realized her defense was weak, and her case would be dismissed with no appeals allowed. *How could this happen to this bright, summa cum laude graduate of USC Law School?*

"Let's call the medics for an evaluation," said Rogelia, the female officer.

"Medics? It's just a scrape, a few minor bruises, like a kid falling off a bike," Tracy said desperately while covering her slightly exposed right breast and realizing no one was going to believe a word she said.

Minutes later, the Medics arrived and checked her over. "Just a few bruises and scratches," one of them said. "They should heal on their own."

How much did that cost taxpayers? No wonder California is broke! Tracy thought. "Now can you please release me?" After she said these words, she realized that with no identification, not a cent to her name, and half-naked, there was absolutely no hope that the cops were going to let her go anywhere but to a correctional facility. She was feeling cold and wished she had her Cynthia Steffle jacket with the fur lining. Tracy was placed in the back seat of the police car. The two guys from the Banning Adult Video Emporium waved "goodbye" and returned to the store to view the new release of *Cowgirl Hotties of Houston* as Tracy was taken to the Banning Shelter for Battered Women.

About the same time, Elliott was crossing the border into Nevada listening to the *Eagles' Greatest Hits CD.* He had the volume on low enough so he wouldn't disturb his wife, whom he believed was comfortably asleep in the back of their motor home. He tapped his foot on the accelerator to *Witchy Woman,* he hummed along with *Desperado*, and he had a hard time restraining himself from singing out loud to *One of These Nights.*

Meanwhile, a dumbstruck Tracy reluctantly entered the Battered Women's Shelter where she was forced to meet with an overly calm, ethereal psychotherapist named Sheila Bliss. Tracy was ready to attack Sheila at any moment but tried desperately to maintain her composure.

"I'm so sorry this has happened to you, Tracy. We're here to help you, but first you must give us the details of this horrible ordeal," said the therapist in a Julie Andrews *Mary Poppins* voice.

Shit! Shit! Shit! Tracy almost said. *This is the worst nightmare I've ever experienced! I'm going to kill Elliott! Maybe poison him or dope him up and when he passes out, I'll strangle the bastard!* "I would like to make a phone call to . . ." And then it suddenly dawned on her, Elliott did not have his cell phone. Her pulse pounding, Tracy took three controlled breaths and continued, " I'd like to call my sister in San Diego. I believe I am entitled to a phone call!"

"Of course you are. I'll dial it for you? Let me help," Sheila replied in a soft, therapeutic voice as she reached for the phone.

No! I am not an abused wife, I am not a hooker, and I am not a bimbo from Banning, Tracy thought to herself. *I can make my own phone calls!* But then Tracy realized the situation was hopeless. She ultimately relinquished her sister's phone number, and Sheila dialed for her. *Jesus! It's like I'm incompetent or some sort of freakin' idiot!* Tracy took three more deep breaths and closed her eyes.

Kathy had always been an early riser but could not believe anyone was calling at 5 a.m. Her immediate thought was to let the answering machine pick up the message. Placing the goose down pillow over her ears to block out the ringing, she was just about to fall back asleep when she heard the familiar voice of her sister screaming, "Kathy, get the hell out of bed! It's your sister calling from jail! Now answer *the fuckin' phone!*"

Kathy jumped out of bed and grabbed the receiver. "Tracy, what are you doing calling at 5 a.m.? Did you have an accident?"

"An understatement!" Tracy replied as she provided Kathy with the lurid details of her "descent into hell." Kathy assured her sister she would be on her way to Banning in a matter of minutes to rescue her.

Tracy had one more request. "Kathy, please call Alex and tell him to be waiting outside his apartment for Elliott. Otherwise, that dickhead will have a stroke when he discovers I've disappeared. No wait! Maybe that would be better!" Realizing what she had just said, she suddenly broke down in tears and screamed, "I didn't mean it! I didn't mean it! Honestly, I didn't mean it!"

At this point, Sheila, the therapist, reached for the phone and snagged it from Tracy's hand declaring that it was time for her to take a shower and rest in her room. Tracy wanted to respond, *Who are you to tell me when I should take a shower! I'm not a freakin' baby! I'm not some lunatic!* But instead she coolly responded, "Of course, Sheila. I do need to freshen up a bit. You are so thoughtful, so caring . . . so . . . *so helpful.*" But before Sheila could hang up the phone, Tracy leaned over and whispered parting words into the receiver, "Get me out of this creepy hell hole before I do something drastic!"

When Kathy arrived at the Banning Shelter for Battered Women at 8:30 a.m., Tracy looked as if she were on the verge of a severe breakdown as she provided her sister with all the gory details. "This was the worst experience of my life! The last few hours I felt like . . . like the *Girl Interrupted* living on *Shutter Island!*"

Tracy was a major cinephile, and asylum movies were her favorite genre.

Upon arriving at 8:47 a.m. in Las Vegas, Elliott was extremely proud of himself. Not only had he managed to avoid disturbing Tracy's restful sleep for the remainder of the trip, but he had also made it to Alex's apartment with thirteen minutes to spare. Pulling in the driveway, he began to sing, *Best of My Love,* his favorite song by the Eagles, as he thought about how it so aptly applied to his wonderful family. *My wife and son truly represent the very "best of my love!"*

And there was Alex running towards him looking, so excited to see his father - at least that's what Elliott thought. Before Alex could utter a word, Elliott jumped out of the RV and hugged his devoted son.

"Alex, my talented, handsome son, your mom and I are so excited to be here with you!"

"I have something to tell you, Dad."

"Wait a minute, let me go wake your mother."

Alex took a deep breath. "She's not in the RV, Dad"

"Of course she is, son."

"No she's not."

"Yes, she is!"

"No."

"Yes!"

"No, Dad! Listen to me! You left her in Banning!"

"I did *not* leave her in Banning! How absolutely ridiculous that you would even argue with me!"

"Dad, she fell out the door of your dumb gas guzzler in Banning. You left her on the streets of Banning, in her nightgown, half naked, *in front of a porn shop!*"

"I did no such thing!" Elliott opened the door of the vehicle to prove he was correct. With a smile on his face, he called out, "Tracy, come out dear. We're in Vegas! Alex is waiting to see you, baby." There was no response from the Palm Harbor Mobile Home. "Tracy, babe? *Please* answer me . . ." As he surveyed the empty vehicle, the blood drained from his face.

"She's in a Home for Battered Women, Dad! *That's totally fucked!*"

Elliott's legs weakened as he collapsed on the sidewalk. "I don't understand . . . how could this have happened? How could I have left Tracy in Banning? She was with me the whole time."

It was at that very moment that Alex's cell phone rang. After briefly talking with his Aunt Kathy and his hysterical mother, he turned the phone over to Elliott who bawled like a baby when he heard Tracy's voice. Elliott learned that Kathy had driven to Banning to convince the authorities that her sister's story was a valid one, that Elliott was *not* negligent or abusive - he was "*just oblivious*," and that they were indeed on their way to Vegas to visit their son. The authorities found the story truly bizarre, but they ultimately released Tracy, so Kathy could take her physically and mentally exhausted sister to Las Vegas to reunite with her family. At this point, Kathy thought it was entirely possible that her sister and brother-in-law might get an entire episode of the *Jerry Springer Show* devoted to them where Tracy murdered Elliott in a wrestling match watched by millions.

When Tracy and Kathy pulled into the driveway of Alex's apartment building in Las Vegas, Elliott and Alex were waiting outside. Tracy fell into the arms of Elliott who kissed her passionately on the lips.

"I love you more than life, Tracy. I'm so sorry. I can't believe I left you like I did. Will you ever forgive me? Please Tracy, baby . . . I didn't mean . . . *baby* . . . I meant, Tracy . . . *my muse!*"

"Eliott, *baby,* I do love you . . . I do! I do!"

Kathy and Alex applauded the scene, which was better than anything they had seen in any Tony Award winning production.

That evening they went to see Alex's performance as a devious small time criminal in Frederick Knott's suspense thriller, *Wait Until Dark*. Everyone loved the play, especially Tracy.

"Alex, you were terrific, and the play scared the *bejesus* out of me! Even the title, *Wait Until Dark*, sent chills up and down my spine.

"No wonder, Mom. Last night, you were really alone . . . *in the dark*. And it wasn't play acting!"

"Don't remind me."

Elliott decided to change the subject. "Honey, I've decided that we're going to get rid of our Palm Harbor Mobile Home and buy something more economical like a Honda Civic and for longer trips . . . you know, we can always fly or take a train."

"Hell, I'll even take a Greyhound!" exclaimed Tracy.

Alex brought his car around and the happy family went to Planet Hollywood to celebrate a day and night of great performances and endearing moments to savor forever.

NINE

EMBARRASSING MOMENTS

At the beautifully designed bar at Old Venice Restaurant in Point Loma, Jack is eager to tell his story about his somewhat less than mystical encounter with a ravishing college coed.

Larry's story is about the time he is an invited guest of California Senator Diane Feinstein at a luncheon in a fancy classic hotel in San Diego where absolute disaster lurks just around the corner.

Jack's tale is told while sipping a glass of the stylish, elegant, and delicious 2006 *Marilyn Merlot,* which reminds him of the girl of his dreams. Because Larry's story is about an event that nearly causes a major meltdown in his life, he selects a bottle of a 2005 *Basket Case Syrah*

Big Mouth Strikes Again

'Bad Boys, Bad Boys... Whatcha' gonna' do?'

by Jack Beddows

When I was a young man going to school at the idyllic University of California at Santa Barbara, there were so many beautiful young women all around me in such concentrated doses that it was like nothing I had ever experienced. I had *always* been an avid girl-watcher. However, growing up in a small North Eastern town with its long, winter months and heavy jackets worn everywhere, that trait was kept somewhat within its natural limits. But when I suddenly found myself experiencing the natural flora and fauna of the UCSB campus, as well as the densely populated college town of Isla Vista, nothing could then stop the wallowing sensuousness that began to swell inside me like a tidal wave. I could blame myself I suppose, for this increasingly pernicious trait. But being born a pleasure-loving Libra in the Year of the Pig no less, what chance did I have?

In those early months at school, I flirted with disaster on a daily basis as I rode my bicycle to and from campus. "Whoa! She's beautiful!" I'd blurt out loud, while staring wistfully at some lovely vision passing before my eyes, right up until the moment that I'd hear someone scream, "Hey! Look out!" from the oncoming bike lane that I would inevitably be drifting into.

"Sorry about that!" I would shout back, while zigzagging away, trying to regain my composure.

I wasn't the only one. Young men were constantly crashing on the winding bike paths, as they tried to squeeze in just one more moment of happy ogling before going down in a tangle of limbs and bike frames. And whenever I would see another boy suffer this indignity, it never took long to locate the source of his trouble, walking away in all her glory. I would pause and think, *There but for the grace of God go I.*

As time passed and I settled into my drunken reel of pheromones, I eventually became pickier when it came to the ladies. Not in terms of dating, mind you, as to be honest, I'd take whatever I could get. But as far as girl watching went, it wasn't long before I totally lost perspective and found myself on a manic quest to see who were the absolutely *most* beautiful girls on campus.

Occasionally, when summing up young women with the speed and ruthlessness of *The Terminator*, I made some slight notice of the near-total erosion of my character. But I would quickly forget about this each time that I walked by a world-beating stunner. I never dreamed, however, I would actually have a chance to go on a date with one of them. Then came Julia, like an answer to my prayers.

We were brought together on the set of a student film. I had done a little acting in high school, had taken a few theater courses on campus, and had friends in the film department, so I ended up being involved in a number of small projects over the years. Being a theory based film school, UCSB tended to crank out competitively out-there directors that would rather be making some kind of surrealist romp than producing anything that smacked of Hollywood. But for this particular movie, I wasn't going to be picnicking on severed body parts while a grizzly bear vacuumed up leaves in the background alone. No, this incomprehensible production was to be a romance.

When the director explained to me that I would have a female co-star (if the word *star* is even vaguely appropriate in this particular context), I couldn't help but wonder if my leading lady was good looking. As it turned out, she was more than just that. The two main characters in the film were supposed to be in love, and through her choice of actresses, the director made my job a particularly easy one. As we spent the next week or so working on the project, I wasn't at all bothered by the late hours or the inexplicable story line, as long as I was able to stare into the eyes of the beautiful, intelligent, and talented Julia.

During the production, I had ample opportunity to try and wrangle a date out of my lovely co-star, an endeavor which I fully surprised myself by being successful at. There must have been some sort of aphrodisiacal effect residually left over from filming together. That's the only explanation I could come up with for my good fortune. But regardless of how I got so lucky, it was all I could think about until the next weekend arrived.

That Saturday night, I wanted everything to be just perfect for what I hoped would be the first of many evenings out with Julia. After hastily trying on a few dozen possible combinations of shirts and pants, I settled on my Ross for Less hip outfit consisting of jeans, blazer and a t-shirt. It was then time to get my hair just so. Would it be mousse, gel, or *Tres Somme Sleek Finishing Cream?* I opted for the cream. It was just right for the almost-pompadour I had been cultivating. And then, in a mad panic, I decided to use my roommate's Old Spice aftershave as well. I didn't regularly use cologne and didn't know how much to shake out, and so I found myself splashing it on with a bit too much youthful enthusiasm.

Finally, it was time to drive over to Julia's apartment. As I walked to the door, I mentally prepared myself to meet not only my date, but also the fifteen or sixteen roommates she doubtlessly lived with in the high-priced student ghetto of Isla Vista. The closer the poorly built and maintained apartments were to the beach, the more roommates were typically needed in order to subsidize the outrageous premium put on living in a war zone of keggers and frat parties. As I suspected, my knocking at the door was greeted by one of a gaggle of young female roommates. They were downstairs watching television while my date was upstairs, finishing her preparations for the evening.

"Hi, I'm Jack. I'm here to pick up Julia." I introduced myself with as much suavity and sophistication as I could muster, in a practiced voice that was one part Cary Grant, one part Douglas Fairbanks Jr. and just a dash of Sean Connery.

"Hi! Come on in. I'm Cody!" the young roommate replied in a voice that was one part *I'm always bubbly and enthusiastic,* one part, *But I don't really give a shit*, and followed by a facial expression that was more than just a dash of *What the hell is that cologne you're wearing?* "Julia will be right down in just a few minutes," she said, her smile giving way to a crinkled nose.

"Thanks," I replied as I ducked into the room, wafting the front door back and forth several times before closing it, to lighten the load of Old Spice I had apparently carried with me like a sailor fresh from the docks.

"Everyone, this is Jack," Cody shouted out to the gang that proceeded to unglue their eyes from the television set just long enough to say "Hi," in unison.

Wow, I thought, *I've definitely got the right girl out of this bunch! I'll bet Julia doesn't sit around watching TV all night, especially not this garbage!* The girls were all watching COPS. Maybe if I'd spent any time with an officer of the law while he went on his rounds, I would have had a different perspective of this TV series, but probably not. This forerunner of the reality show craze that thrived on showing people at their worst was just kind of gross. And I was certain that my lovely and artistic-minded new friend would agree with me.

At last, my date walked down the stairs in a beautiful white dress, looking more than a bit like Marilyn Monroe. Her shiny blonde hair was bouncing, and her blue eyes sparkled as she greeted me. It was a moment full of romantic promise. But then, distracted by the sudden, blaring noise of commercials coming from the living room, my eyes darted for an instant back to the television, and it was then that my date started talking with her roommates. If only I had whisked her away before she had a chance to ask that next crucial question.

"Hey, what are you guys watching?" she asked.

"COPS," they all answered at once.

"Cool," Julia replied, in what I thought was a very diplomatic manner.

This would have been a good time to keep my mouth shut. Instead, I felt the need to impress my date with my intelligent social critiques.

"Man, I can't believe this show! Arresting people on camera? It's totally screwed up, isn't it?"

Now even if I were confident that my date would agree with me, and that her roommates couldn't hear me over the blare of the TV, this was still a dumb move. I was next to a roomful of girls who obviously all thought very much to the contrary of my needlessly expressed opinion, and Julia not only had to live with these young ladies she was also obviously trying to have a good relationship with them. So what was she going to say to this exactly? Nothing about what I had just done made any sense. But little did I know how bad the situation *really* was.

In response to my unasked-for social critique, Julia glared at me as she replied, "Really? You think that this show is *stupid*?"

"Oh yeah!" I answered. "It's totally messed up!"

And then in a sudden change of tone, she replied "It's actually *my father's* show. He both produced it *and* created it!"

"Oh…" I said, as the color instantly rushed to my face. I couldn't think of anything better to follow up with than, "Well, I guess we *are* pretty close to Hollywood and all . . . " I just stood in front of my date and the baker's dozen of her female roommates who, even if they didn't hear the full exchange, still were somehow instantly aware of the shift in dynamics between Julia and me. They all stared at me in dead silence. In the next few interminable seconds my blush intensified until I was glowing like a boiling lobster, a creature with whom I not only shared a color, but also a similar sensation of extreme discomfort.

Yes, things were bad. It was time to take stock in myself and in the situation. Clearly, I had killed my chances with this lovely young girl. That much was obvious. But I also realized in further horror that if it weren't for my stupidity, perhaps I could have ended up on one of the dozen or so reality shows produced by Julia's father. *Quality and redeeming social values be damned!* If I had a chance to be on television, I would have jumped at it!

Despite the bleakness of the current situation, Julia and I went out to eat anyway. Dinner was *not* a raucous and hilarious affair. I thought about trying to turn the whole thing around, but I could tell the nerve I hit was just too deep, and that the damage could not be undone. Things got even worse after dinner. I dropped Julia at her place, and we said our listless and final goodnights.

To top the evening off, on my short drive home I was pulled over by an overzealous cop who had been hiding around the corner of a four-way intersection.

"What's the problem officer?" I asked, after the blaring lights and the whoop of his siren brought me over to the side of the road.

"Whoa! Where's the fire?" he asked in return.

"I'm sorry. Was I speeding?" I was confused, and immediately mistrusted and disliked his disingenuous manner.

"No. You weren't speeding, but you stopped about ten inches past the line at that stop sign back there!" He said this as if I should have been shocked at my own recklessness.

"And? Is that a real big deal?" At that moment I was far too sad and tired to have to deal with the situation.

"*A big deal?* Why it's one of the clearest indications of drunk driving! Have you been drinking tonight?"

"No officer, I have *not* been drinking," I truthfully replied in a leaden tone. Having just come from the dinner where, not daring to do anything but follow Julia's example, I had had nothing stronger than a hot tea.

"Hmm . . . " the officer responded, "I think I'm going to have to ask you to get out of the car."

At this point it was all just too much for me. I began to seriously consider giving this guy the finger and taking off on a high-speed car chase. I imagined that it would be filmed by the pursuing officer and the soon-to-arrive police helicopters, and that while I was being stuffed into the back of a police cruiser at the inevitable end of my reckless run, I could scream out to the camera, "Julia! Julia, I was wrong! This show is the best! Just, give me another chance! And maybe you can talk to your father about me? You know like for some other television gigs . . . or something?"

But as the moments drifted on in shared silence, the officer must have noticed a focus in my reverie that had nothing to do with drunkenness. He blurted out, "Oh never mind! Just give me your license and registration! I'll be right back."

And so I waited, mild as milk, for the cop to run my ID and return with the perfect capper for my evening, a moving violation ticket that would end up costing me forty-five dollars! After that, I dragged myself home to drown my sorrows in a bottle of Merlot that I had bought to take to the beach with Julia after dinner, if things had gone a lot better than they actually had.

Perhaps it's all for the best, I later mused to myself, drunk and alone, and snacking on fake body parts made out of soy and wheat gluten, left over from the now less-seemingly surreal film that Julia and I had worked on together.

CAUGHT IN THE ACT

BY LARRY ZEIGER

As a child, I had a fear of public bathrooms. This neurotic tendency may have developed when my mother took me, a happy go-lucky seven-year-old, on a bumpy, claustrophobic train trip from Cleveland to Miami. The train was hot and crowded, and I was bored to death sitting still for so long, staring out a mosquito-spattered window while watching the world pass by.

On the way to the dining car on the first day of the trip, I stopped off to use the bathroom in the men's lounge, a dusty cigar smoke-filled room where five overweight guys who were playing poker, huffing and puffing on Phillies Panatellas. One man inhaled his cigar and began to cough profusely. No one said a word. Another man belched loudly and then spit into a napkin. I decided at that moment in my life that train travel was not for me.

The rocking of the train gave me a slight case of nausea. I entered the bathroom but could not figure out how to lock the door. Either the lock was broken, or I was just not mechanically inclined enough to figure out how to use it. Fearing the door would burst open at any moment, I grabbed the door-knob as tightly as I could. While sitting on the john, all I could think about was - *why in the world would anyone want to leave the comfort of his own home to take a two-day train trip to Miami?*

Who would have known on that hot summer day that about a mile away, an old beat-up Chevy had broken down on the train tracks? Suddenly, I felt the intense vibrations of the toilet seat underneath me, followed by a horribly jerky movement as if the entire bathroom were going to tip over, and finally, the piercing, screeching sounds of the brakes as the train came to a halt inches from the Chevy. In a matter of seconds, I lost my balance and watched in horror as the bathroom door flew open. And then I flew off the toilet, pants down, and slid across the floor under the table of the five cigar-smoking, Scotch-swilling poker players. They looked down at me with sickly grins. I stared blankly at them with a look of terror and ultimate humiliation. I cleared my throat and in a meek child's voice replied. "I'm sorry. I didn't mean to ruin your game." I then burst into tears over the embarrassment. I picked up my pants and ran out of the bathroom into the arms of my mother who desperately wanted to make sure I hadn't been hurt during the train accident. I, of course, never told her or anyone else what had really happened. However, for a good part of my childhood, I was consumed by fear whenever I entered a public restroom on any mode of transportation – buses, airplanes, cruise liners, and *especially* trains.

Forty years later, in the midst of teaching a high school English class in Point Loma, California, I received a phone call from the superintendent's secretary. Senator Diane Feinsten was to give a major address on the Global Economy at a luncheon at the elegant U.S. Grant Hotel in Downtown San Diego, and I was selected, along with Corey Hargrave, one of my top students, to receive special recognition from the Senator.

Corey was a bright, engaging young man who had scored a perfect 1600 on his SAT exam. Corey, however, could care less about his top score. He was more interested in filmmaking, theater arts, creative writing, and socializing with his friends. While most of his buddies had taken the Princeton Review classes to prepare for the SAT, Corey skipped all that. To him, the SAT was just "another boring standardized test, so why prepare?" He was told by his counselor as well as his parents to make sure he had a good night's rest before the rigorous exam, so Corey, who worked in the world of opposites, stayed up most of the night watching Quentin Tarantino and John Waters movies.

Three days before the event at the U.S. Grant Hotel, representatives of the Senator's office instructed both Corey and me about the proper protocol for his acceptance of the award at the luncheon. Corey was going to be called on stage after the Feinstein address and presented with a gift of one of her original paintings. He was to shake hands with the Senator and thank her graciously for this honor. Senator Feinstein would then acknowledge me as Corey's teacher, and I was to stand by my seat at the assigned table.

In the late afternoon, after I came home, I decided to rehearse for the luncheon and discovered several methods of standing that actually made me appear more polished, professional, and regal than others. Timing and posture were everything. I didn't want to rise too quickly and yet, I wanted to show a grasp of the moment.

I checked my closet and pulled out the one suit I owned. It was a bit dated, so I decided for this special occasion, I needed something more dignified and stylish. I was really getting into the swing of things. *Protocol* started to mean everything to me.

I drove to Nordstrom in Fashion Valley and met with a personal shopper who selected a Joseph Aboud pin-stripped suit, a Facconable shirt, a Michael Kors silk tie (with just the right amount of design to offset the pin stripes), and a pair of Mephisto dress shoes. I was determined to connect with the political elite at whatever cost.

When I got back to my condo after my impulsive shopping spree, I read the charge receipt I had signed at the store and nearly had a minor stroke. After a shot of *Tequila Anejo Sauza Commemorativo,* I relaxed and had visions of being offered a state job in the Department of Education or consultant to the next President of the United States. Later in the evening after my second shot of *Tequila Anejo Sauza Commemorativo*, I felt more comfortable with my wardrobe and was convinced I would make a positive impression as a stylish California educator.

The excitement intensified the day of the event. Television cameras and news reporters crowded the streets as the dignitaries entered the hotel lobby and ascended the stairs into the grand ballroom where the luncheon was held. Celebrated politicos were everywhere.

"Isn't that Gray Davis?"

"Barbara Boxer, she looks taller in person . . ."

"There's that rebel, Gavin Newsom. He may be our next governor."

"Isn't that Jerry Brown? He should be the next President!"

We walked slowly through the crowd. I felt quite dignified and smiled at everyone as if I had known them for years.

Corey commented, "Wow! Look at her! She must be somebody! I think she's John Kerry's daughter, the one who's making movies at AFI. I want to meet her!"

Corey, his parents, and I were seated at a table adjacent to the stage. An air of politeness and sophistication filled the room. During the meal, Corey accidentally dropped his fork on the floor. He looked over to me with a perplexed look. I could read his mind. *Should I pick up the fork? Is it permissible? Will someone bring me a new fork, or do I consume the breast of chicken with a spoon? If I fail in etiquette, will I still get my award?*

I whispered to him that it was permissible to ask the waiter for a new fork. My communications skills failed as he gracefully leaned over and successfully retrieved the fork and then proceeded to clean the utensil by dipping his napkin into his drinking water and wiping the fork clean. I must have had a look of horror on my face as the person sitting across from me at the table asked me what was wrong. I instantly made up something about my concern about Global Warming and how terrible it was that people waste so much water which could lead to major environmental disasters. Everyone agreed.

A woman from the mayor's office then changed the subject and turned to Corey and exclaimed, "How exciting to be selected for this honor . . . for being such an outstanding scholar! You must feel *so wonderful* to be here in this room with the Senator and all these dignitaries. How do you *really* feel?"

"Incredibly important," Corey responded in a sullen tone.

Another man from County Office of Education questioned the boy. "1600 on your SAT's, top scholar, aspiring filmmaker . . . *very* impressive! Is there anything you can't do?"

"Eat my lunch."

There was momentary silence, followed by brief laughter from everyone around the table.

"Oh, he's so clever!" replied the woman sitting to the left of me.

"And succinct!" added another table guest. "He is a born politician! We need people in Sacramento like Corey!"

Just as I was about to excuse myself to go to the restroom, the Master of Ceremonies asked us to take our seats and then gave a ten-minute introduction to Senator Feinsten. The senator received a huge ovation. She stood before the microphone and spoke passionately for forty minutes about the guest-worker programs, immigration laws, the mistake of having so many jobs go overseas, tax incentives for energy efficient homes, raising the fuel economy in cars, and conserving water.

The section of her talk on 'conserving water' reminded me that I really needed to go to the bathroom. During the course of the meal, I had consumed four glasses of iced tea due to the salty nature of the *not-so haute cuisine.* Trying to be as inconspicuous as possible, I rose from my seat to head towards the restroom. But at that very moment, she reached for the award to give to Corey. I quickly sat down and waited for him to receive his honor. He entered the stage and received a framed certificate and a small original painting by Senator Feinstein. I was asked to stand, and I did so with a sense of élan that, I was certain, transcended the look of every politician and political dignitary in attendance. The suit by Aboud, the tie by Kors, the shirt by Faconnable, and the shoes by Mephisto spoke volumes that I was a teacher with a sense of intelligence and class. On the other hand, I kept thinking to myself, *After the luncheon is over, could I return the clothes to Nordstrom and have my account credited?*

Following the presentation, several people surrounded Corey, congratulating him on his many accomplishments. I excused myself and quickly made my way to the men's room. To my surprise, after a lengthy lunch program, every urinal was vacant. With twelve urinals from which to choose, I selected the seventh one from the door (seven is my lucky number). After relieving myself for what seemed to be several minutes, I reached for the lever and flushed the urinal.

It was then that I understood that this was not going to be like any normal bathroom experience. Suddenly, a massive amount of water began to pour forth from the urinal. I jumped back for fear that the Aboud suit would be saturated with water, and I would become a prisoner of the men's room. For a moment, I froze in place. I couldn't believe what I was witnessing. Water splashed out of the urinal with such force that the floor began to flood. This horrific nightmare was like a scene from the film, *Titanic!*

Did I do this? Did I pull the handle too hard? Was I being punished for spending too much money on my fashionable attire? Was I a victim of technology gone wild? Did I drink too much tea? And after listening to Senator Feinstein's discourse on water conservation, what would the hundreds of dignitaries in attendance surmise if they knew what was transpiring behind the men's room door?

It was then that I heard a brief, but loud cracking sound. I couldn't believe my eyes as I watched the urinal split in half and drop to the floor with a thud! Even more horrifying, the pipes were fully exposed and water was gushing from the wall, like a hose from a fire engine. As I jumped back further from the ensuing flood, I noticed a pair of Amadeo Testoni shoes sticking out from one of the stalls. Some unknowing politico was behind that closed door. Could it be Jerry Brown? Arnold Schwarzenegger? Antonio Villaraigosa? Or . . . *Carlos Danger?*

"What's all the noise?" the man behind the door said in a gruff voice.

I had a hard time trying to find the right words to explain the situation. "Uh . . . a urinal has fallen off the wall, and . . . and the room is flooding!"

"You've got to be kidding!"

I took charge, like a real leader. "You must get out of that stall immediately! Now get up and get out!"

"Oh . . . how bad can it be?"

"*Very bad!*" I exclaimed.

The water suddenly began pouring into the man's stall. Instantly came the reply, "Holy Shit! What the fuck is going on?"

I didn't stick around to meet the distinguished gentleman behind the steel-grey bathroom door. I quickly exited to the lobby of the elegant ballroom and tried to look absolutely dignified amidst the crowd of well-wishers. *Was this incident a wake-up call or merely an example of political allegory?*

Carrying a large tray of dishes, a waiter passed by. I stopped him and told him about the disaster that was taking place behind the bathroom door. He casually responded, "I'll try to find someone after I drop off this tray in the kitchen. We're short-handed today so it might take a little while."

"You don't understand! There's a major flood in there!"

At that moment, water began to seep out from under the men's room door, soaking the elegant carpet in the lobby. The man I had alerted exited the bathroom. His shoes and pants had major water stains. He didn't look happy and quickly descended the staircase to exit the hotel.

"Whoa! That's *major* flooding, bro'!" the waiter exclaimed. "I better call maintenance right away!" He disappeared quickly.

The guests, whose brilliant minds would determine the future of our world, began to move away from the lobby area as the carpet became more saturated. I found Corey and his family and never uttered a single word about the cataclysmic bathroom incident that I had indirectly caused.

I learned an important lesson that day, and that is, we are living in an age where environmental disasters lurk around every corner and behind every doorway. Nothing, absolutely nothing, can be taken for granted. On the other hand, unlike my childhood experience on the train to Miami, I, fortunately, was not caught with my pants down. Instead, I exited the hotel with my Joseph Aboud suit completely intact.

Only the soles of my damp Mephisto shoes left footprints in the sidewalk as I strolled into the warm afternoon sunshine, unfettered, unscathed, and slightly more aware of the potential for global catastrophes.

Ten

Stolen Dreams

On a partly cloudy day in early May, Larry and Jack are late for their weekly storytelling and wine tasting session. Larry has misplaced the keys to his classroom but ultimately discovers them on his cluttered desk, while Jack thinks someone had stolen his beloved Ray Ban Classic Aviator sunglasses, only to discover them on the roof of his car where he had left them in the morning.

Both are definitely in need of serious storytelling and wine tasting and decide to meet at Zia's Bistro, an enchanting restaurant and bar in Little Italy. The setting is perfect. It almost feels like being in Tuscany as Daniele Spadavecchia, a local guitarist from Italy, serenades the customers with Gypsy Jazz standards and the incredible bistro staff including Vince, Ulises, Michael, Megan, Scott, Diego, Joey, Alex, De, and Tiziano argue over what bottle of wine Larry and Jack should consume.

Larry finally intervenes and selects a bottle of *Irony*, a wildly delicious and unusual *Pinot Noir* from the Russian River region of California. Larry immediately takes note of the flavor of mushrooms and bell peppers and the dark plum aftertaste. "Isn't it *ironic* how the taste just changes in seconds?" he exclaims as he swirls the wine in his mouth like the wine tasting connoisseur he aspires to be.

Jack agrees and offers metaphoric commentary that "this specific wine reflects the incongruity and immorality of life where nothing is held sacred." While the patrons at the bar and the Zia's Bistro staff eavesdrop on their tales of stolen objects and stolen dreams, Larry and Jack consume the flavorful *Irony*.

A Brief Encounter

by Larry Zeiger

One afternoon in 1981, after a grueling day attempting to teach 196 high school students how to speak and write English properly, I decided that I owed it to myself to escape into a late afternoon screening of *Time Bandits,* Terry Gilliam's satirical film about a young boy who joins a band of dwarves and travels from time period to time period for the purpose of stealing treasure. I felt so relaxed, sitting alone in a darkened theater, completely immersed in a celluloid world of outrageous fantasy in contrast to my afternoon class when one of my students, Albert, accidentally hit me in the head with the leftover remains of his Subway sandwich while intending to pitch it in the wastebasket behind me.

After the movie, I got into my car to drive home and suddenly experienced a major anxiety attack. *My wallet!* It was no longer in my back pocket. *Calm down,* I thought. *Maybe you accidentally put it in your front pocket.* But it was not there either. *Maybe it's under the car seat. But wait . . . what an idiot I am! If my wallet were under the car seat, then how could I have paid for the ticket, the popcorn and the diet soda? No, it must be on the floor of the theater . . . where I was sitting.*

I quickly returned to the box office and explained the situation to the manager. He could see I was upset and even offered to help me in my desperate search. We checked every row of the theater, the bathroom, and even the garbage cans, but the situation was hopeless; my wallet was nowhere to be found.

Reality hit me like a ton of bricks. I had been a victim of some deviant crook who had slipped his hand into my back pocket and robbed me. What kind of a creep could do such a thing to me in a movie theater and at a bargain matinee? Why would anyone steal from me? A school teacher with a miserable salary? A public servant who was barely making his first mortgage payment?

With tears welling in my eyes and anger eating at my soul, I came home and made calls to the bank, the credit card company, the Department of Motor Vehicles, and my health insurance company. But worst of all, my Genie Car Wash punch card was missing. I needed only one more punch for the Super Deluxe Wash and Wax. "One more punch!" I screamed. "One more punch!" I was devastated.

About a month later, just after I had replaced my credit cards and driver's license, the U.S. Postal Service delivered my wallet to me. Evidently, someone had tossed it into a mailbox. Everything was there - credit cards, driver's license, and even my Genie Car Wash punch card - everything *except* my money.

Being the eternal optimist, I wanted to believe that the unknown person who had mailed my wallet was actually the thief who, consumed by guilt about his immoral act, had decided to return my wallet to me with all the important forms of identification. In my wildest thoughts, I actually wanted to meet the crook to learn why he stole my money. *Was his rent behind? His car insurance? Did he need to purchase a gift for his girlfriend? Had he lost his job? Was he homeless? Or was he a schizophrenic thief who, after taking the money, felt compelled to return the wallet to the victim? Or was he simply a badass thief who stole for the thrill of it all?* I knew I would never know the answer, but I learned a lesson to always place my wallet in the front pocket of my pants, especially in movie theaters.

Several years later, I traveled to Italy for a summer vacation. Surrounded by centuries of art and culture I had previously only read about in history books, I fell in love with this spectacular country. It was a fantasyland of art masterpieces, statues, architectural triumphs, great music, fantastic food, and wonderful people. I decided to live lavishly for the last stop of my Italian adventure and booked a reservation at *Il Grand Hotel a Roma.*

The day I arrived in Rome, the streets around the hotel were flooded with thousands of people, and cameras were flashing everywhere. *For me?* I thought. *Those Italians, they certainly know how to make a guest feel welcome!* But then the crowd cheered for some other well-dressed man and woman who entered the hotel on a red carpet. As I followed them to the hotel entrance, another loud cheer rose from the crowd, but when I turned around to give them the celebrity wave, the cheers suddenly diminished to utter silence.

I quickly discovered that the man and woman who had entered the hotel before me were George Clooney and Julia Roberts who were filming a scene from *Oceans 12*. Obviously, the crowd must have thought I was Brad Pitt . . . until I turned around.

Once I entered the hotel, the manager graciously welcomed me. He then informed me that I could not have access to my room quite yet, because the movie crew was filming on my floor.

"How long do I have to wait?" I asked.

"About four hours," the manager responded.

"Four hours? Life simply stops for movies," I replied.

"*Si, l'arte e' molto importante.* Art is very important. We must respect it."

He thoughtfully offered me a free lunch in the hotel restaurant while I waited for my room, but instead, I decided to explore the city. I wandered about the streets and then stopped at a café and dined on mouth-watering *Rigatoni alla Carbonara* paired with a delicious *Pinot Griggio*. I decided that if I lived in Italy, my waist size would increase at least five inches.

After lunch, I took the Metro to check out Vatican City. It was late afternoon rush hour, and there were no seats, so I grabbed on to one of the poles near the exit door. At the first stop, about forty people entered the car and streamed by me. I was able to hold on but was now sharing the pole with about seven additional hands. The car was filled to capacity, and I felt like a sardine. At the next stop, about five people exited and thirty more entered, squeezing themselves into what had now become one large sweaty, body-against-body phalanx in which no one could move or breathe. I lost my pole position, but it didn't matter. We were so tightly packed into the car that even without holding on to anything, I couldn't move, crushed against so many bodies. A man behind me was holding on to my shoulders, probably trying to stabilize himself on the bumpy ride, or maybe he was just being helpful, making sure I didn't lose my balance.

People are so kind all over the world, I thought, completely unaware of this man's insidious intentions.

Five minutes later, I felt something in my pants. I looked down and there was a hand - not my hand - but the hand of the man standing behind me, unbuttoning my pocket with two of his fingers while simultaneously submerging his remaining three fingers deep into the recesses of my pocket . . . *reaching for my wallet!* For a brief moment, I was utterly mesmerized by the process. I had never actually witnessed a thief rob someone (let alone me) and his daring skill at manipulating his fingers in such blatantly choreographed moves was fascinating to watch. Suddenly, reality hit me like a swatter hitting a fly. I turned around and stared into the eyes of the perpetrator and then grabbed his arm before he could steal my wallet. In a bold, assertive manner, I declared, "What the fuck do you think you are doing?"

I had anticipated a scruffy, unkempt, gangster-like derelict, something out of *Reservoir Dogs,* but to my surprise, the guy turned out to be a man in his twenties dressed in what looked like an Armani suit, white shirt, striped silk tie, and Bacco Bucci dress shoes - the image of a young professional on his way home from a day at the brokerage. I was stunned.

He gave me an *I-never-get-caught-have-pity-on-me* stare and pleaded, "*Scusi! Scusi! Scusi!*" as if putting his hand in my pocket and reaching for my wallet had been a horrible mistake. "I no mean to do you harm. *Scusi! Scusi! Scusi!*"

"Don't *scusi* me! I know what you're up to! You're trying to *rob me!*" I countered.

Everyone on the train noticed something was wrong, and instantly stared at the thief, perhaps wanting to apprehend him, if they could move. He was panic-stricken. The train slowed to a stop. The doors opened, and the thief bolted, carrying a leather attaché case, probably bulging with wallets from unsuspecting victims who never in their wildest dreams would think this well-dressed sophisticate could ruin their day. He was the perfect archetype of the Hitchcock villain: the guy you least likely expect to victimize you in a public place surrounded by hordes of people.

I was lucky though. I had my wallet in my pocket and had outwitted the guy. I could see him tearing up the stairs of the train station, probably feeling victorious that no one was running after him.

But then, as an aspiring writer, I imagined how this story could have been different . . .

Before the doors of the Metro close, I squeeze through the opening and run up the stairs after the thief. He briefly turns and sees me gaining speed. Near the Coliseum, he tries to immerse himself in the mass of locals and tourists who crowd the plaza.

Thinking he will lose me, he makes a detour down an alley. He looks behind and sees that I am nowhere in sight. He breathes a sigh of relief. Quickly, I turn the corner, and to his horror, he runs right into me. Face to face, we stare at each other.

With a sheepish, pleading look in his eyes, the thief once again quietly pleads, *"Scusi, per favore!"*

"Don't *scusi* me, dude! It doesn't work! You tried to rob me! Why would you do such a thing? What did I ever do to you? I don't even know you!"

"Why you say this?" he says with pity in his eyes. "I do not take your money. I do not steal from you nothing!"

He has a persona of such downright innocence. Any moment I expect him to whip out a guitar and break into a rendition of *Piccolo Grande Amore.*

"You didn't take my money? You wanna know why? Because I caught you! You would have taken my wallet and my money, had I not discovered your hand in my pocket."

"But you see, I do *not* succeed. You have your money and I . . . I shall have my freedom. *Arrivederci, signore."*

"Not so easy," I respond. "Even though I was smart enough to catch you just in the nick of time, other people may not be so lucky. You're a thief! A thief! And . . . and just out of curiosity, I want to know why you would do such a thing. I mean . . . do you *enjoy* stealing? Does it really make you happy to turn a nice guy like me into your victim? Is that what gets you off?"

"Why you want to know this? Are you crazy person? Maybe I am dangerous man, and I kill you when your back is turned! Stab you with large serrated knife! How you like that? You be afraid of me!"

"In that outfit, I don't think so. You're not like some everyday thug! You look more like Cary Grant from . . . *Notorious* or . . . *To Catch a Thief!"*

"*Grazie,* you have good taste in cinema. I like that! As a *bambino*, I see this film and say to myself, I want to be like this man in *Thief* movie . . . like character, John Robie, that Cary Grant play. He is master thief! *E un bell' uomo* . . . handsome, debonair, and clever . . . like me!" He immediately changes the subject. "Sei un bravo ragazzo . . . you are nice guy. I like you. Can I buy you *espresso?*"

"You're a thief, and you're inviting me out for *espresso?*"

"*Si,* isn't this more . . . how you say . . . *civilized* way to get to know each other? Me, *uno ladro,* a thief . . . and you, the unsuspecting *turistico* from Canada."

"I am *not* from Canada. I am from the United States of America . . . from California."

"Oh no! First thing you learn *il mio amico,* my friend, is to always say you are from Canada. As unsuspecting *americano* I rob you, but as *turistico candadese* . . . *maybe,* but not so much. See, I give you good advice now. You like?"

We sit down at a café, a block from the Vatican, and order double espressos. "So tell me, why did you become a thief?" I ask.

"I am not *just* a thief! I am an *actor,* a street performer, and I direct myself! I perform and make good living . . . except for today."

"That's a morally ambiguous response. You're *not* an actor. You're a thief! And you make other people miserable because of what you do. Don't you see that?"

"You keep calling me 'thief,' but I do have a name."

"Oh, I'm sorry," I say sarcastically. "We should have formally introduced each other. I am Larry, an innocent tourist and *victim of crime* from San Diego who is paying big bucks for his vacation, only to get robbed on a metro by you! Go figure . . ."

"And I am Romulus, son of Mars, invader of Rome!"

"Romulus? There is no way your name is Romulus."

"I play *battuta* on you . . . I am just . . . how you say . . . *joking!* My real name is Maurizio. Honestly, I tell you truth."

"So tell me, Maurizio, what made you become an immoral "gentleman" who preys on innocent bystanders and ruins their vacations? You know in my country we lock people like you away!"

Changing the subject, Maurizio replies, "Italians . . . we are artists and dreamers. Sometime I want to live life of the great works of art I see in museums and in movies. Remember, I tell you I am inspired by Albert Hitchcock."

"Alfred . . . it's Alfred."

"Yes, *Albert,* I am sorry. I insult your culture with my stupidity."

"No not really. But his name really is . . . *Alfred!* But you know what? We have something in common. For many years, I used to refer to Vittorio de Sica as *Victorio* de Sica."

"Oh DeSica!" Maurizio's eyes light up like a Christmas tree. "You know DeSica? He is the one who inspire me more than anyone to be who I am today!"

At this point in time, I can't believe that Maurizio, a well-dressed Italian thief, and I, an unsuspecting American tourist who caught him, are sitting in an outdoor cafe sipping espressos and talking about international film classics!

"You ever see *Ladri de Biciclette*?" he asks.

"*Ladri de Biciclette*," I successfully make the translation. "Do you mean . . . *The Bicycle Thief?* It's one of my favorite movies. I saw it so long ago though. Isn't that the one about the poor guy who has a bicycle stolen which he needs for work, and then he and his son spend most of the story searching for the thief who stole it?"

"*Si*, e'giusto. That is correct. The reason I relate to this story is because . . . it all happen to me!"

"I don't understand."

"I had my *bicicletta* stolen when I was eight years old, and I never get it back. *Mio padre e mia madre* were too poor to buy me new one. When I see De Sica movie, I cry for days, and this start me on life of *small* crime, because I never want to be like poor, humiliated young man in *Ladri di Biciclette* because his . . . how you say . . . his *bicicletta* was stolen, and he has no *denero* to buy new one. When I see this film, I make up my mind. I never want to be like poor man in movie.

"That's so sad, Maurizio." I initially feel sorry for him, but then I think, *he is either a terrific actor, a prolific poet, or a talented con artist!*

"And when I dress in style, no one knows I am . . . *un ladro* . . . a thief.

"Your clothing is very stylish, Maurizio. How can you afford that fancy suit? Is it real Armani?"

"I use money I take from *portafoglios* . . . I mean, how you say . . . wallets and pussies."

"Purses. I think you mean P-U-R-S-E-S."

"*Grazie*, you nice man like . . . *como si dice, come il mio amico* . . . like my friend."

"That's so nice of you. I can't actually call you a friend though, because well, you know . . . stealing is wrong. It's immoral!"

"Who is to say what is immoral? With money I steal, and I buy things. I help out economy. I buy from poor people in market to help them. And, I make life exciting for people, just like I do for you. You live boring existence, but I add adventure to your life.

"But stealing *is* a crime!" I insist.

"Open your eyes! Look at world around you! *Everyone* lies and steals. What I do is . . . small tomatoes, in comparison.

I think you mean *potatoes,* like in uh . . . *small potatoes.*"

Maurizio avoids my comment. "And I bet when you go home to United States, you tell big story about being robbed to your friends, and everyone will listen with excitement."

"*Almost* robbed. You didn't quite succeed."

"Si, *almost* robbed. You are so clever too. You will make story about what happen to you in Metro even bigger and more *apassionante* than what really happen. You will *relish* the truth."

"Uh . . . *em-bellish*? I will *embellish* the truth? But I would *never* do that!"

"Oh *Si,* I bet you do. You will *embellish* to make story more exciting, as if you were in great danger from me, and then . . . and then . . . *una bella ragazza* . . .

"*A beautiful girl?*"

"*Si.* A beautiful girl puts her arms around you, and she whispers in your ear, *What hero you are to outwit dangerous thief! He could have killed you! You are so brave and daring.* She believes every word you say. And then she tells other people about your story. The story gets passed on many, many times until everyone wants to hear what happened . . . *to you.*"

Considering myself a moral individual, I defend my principled character, "Oh no! I would never do that! I would never lie just to get attention or even get the hot chick. I mean . . . *una bella ragazza!*"

"Ah, I am a thief, yes, but you will be the one who makes the most money," Maurizio declares confidently. "I bet you will write story and try to get it . . . *como si dice, pubblicato* in some big magazine in America, and you get more money from sale of story than I get from stealing your wallet!"

It is then I realize that Maurizio may be immoral, but there is something about him that makes him *logical* and more interesting than most anyone I have ever known. And so, I look him in the eye and declare with all honesty, "Maurizio, *grazie molte. Sei il mio amico.* I hope I said that right. *You are my friend.*"

"Are you sure you are not telling big lie?"

"No, Maurizio. Had you not attempted to rob me in the Metro today, I would have never had the opportunity to share double shot espressos with such a real honest-to-goodness *ladro.*"

"*Grazie molte. Sei il mio amico.* You are my *amico americano.*"

The bill comes, and I insist on paying. I mean how often would I ever again have the opportunity to be *almost* robbed, chase after my assailant, catch the *ladro,* sip espressos with him, and discuss the fine line that exists between art and reality, truth and lies, and enemies and friends, amidst the splendors of Rome in the shadows of the Vatican?

"I hope we meet again, Maurizio."

"*Si,* next year perhaps . . . in the Metro?"

"No, Maurizio, I much prefer the espresso bar. It's far more civilized."

We part company, and I go back to my hotel. The movie people have left the premises, and after relaxing in my room, I enjoy a pleasant evening listening to Italian music, dining on roasted vegetables and sipping a fine *Chianti Classico.* After dinner I drink an espresso and think how interesting it has been to have such a stimulating and creative encounter with a man dressed in fake Armani who had tried to rob me. My one regret is that I didn't encourage him to find a legitimate job as an actor, a director, or even an ambassador to the United Nations.

Several months later when I was back in San Diego, I was still sitting in judgment of Maurizio. Yes, he had attempted to rob me on the Metro in Rome, and in my mind, he had clearly crossed the line that separates morality from immorality. But my *imaginary* encounter with him at the espresso bar raised an interesting question. *Could I accurately judge the difference between truth and lies?*

I sat typing my fictitious story that would undoubtedly be discussed at elegant cocktail parties, published in the *New Yorker,* made into an Oscar-winning film to rival the international classic, *The Bicycle Thief,* and make me extremely popular with beautiful Hollywood starlets.

And then I took a break and wondered, *Could I ever be guilty of deceiving others? Is Maurizio any different from anyone I know?* And then I thought, *I could make a lot of money if I sold this story as an absolutely true account of my experiences as a traveler in* Rome *and my brief encounter with a clever and philosophical thief who taught me how to profit from my lively imagination by simply twisting the truth. It's just so easy to do . . .*

And then a feeling of extreme exhilaration consumed my every thought as I wrote my *absolutely true* account of my encounter with Mauricio on my trip to the Eternal City.

Thievery Corporation

by Jack Beddows

Several years ago, while back in Boston for the holidays, I was working out at Family Fitness with my brother Lucas, when suddenly the television positioned over the treadmills showed something that shocked me out of my routine and launched me into a world of confusion. Images leapt from the screen that meant more to me than they could to anyone else on the planet.

A jumping, dancing, and talking kangaroo in a letterman jacket appeared at the start of a movie trailer. The preview then cut to a shot of a regular kangaroo, happily hopping along until he tried to cross a dusty and empty-looking road and was suddenly hit by a Range Rover, driven, it turns out, by two hapless, small-time crooks. Presuming the kangaroo to be dead, the two comic crooks dressed him up in a letterman jacket in order to take funny pictures as a souvenir of their trip to Australia. But the kangaroo wasn't dead. Snapping out of unconsciousness, he quickly punched the crooks silly and hopped off with their jacket still on his back. To make matters worse, the jacket apparently contained mob money, which the two crooks must spend the rest of the picture trying to regain or else forfeit their lives.

When the movie trailer was nearly over, the film's title slammed onto the screen with the certainty of a comedic family blockbuster in the making: KANGAROO JACK! The title was accompanied by the return of the image of the personable kangaroo in sunglasses and jacket. Smiling with the insouciant arrogance of Bugs Bunny, the kangaroo casually smirked at the crooks whose efforts to catch him would be met only with mirth, and at the audience, who could never hope to be quite as cool as he. But when the kangaroo winked, I knew that wink was meant for me. My blood pressure began to rise, my heart began to pound like a drum in the outback, and I could hardly contain my excitement.

I scanned the gym for my brother, and then ran towards him, tripping over someone's discarded thigh master in the process. "Did you see that?" I screamed, while trying to recover from my spill and my excitement both. "They stole everything!"

"I know, I saw it," my brother answered with far less agitation. He was shocked by what he had witnessed as well, but he was trying to remain calm, to digest the information and to come up with the best possible solution. But there was only one possible solution, and I voiced it for both of us.

"We're going to sue those thieves and make a bundle!" My indignation at being robbed had instantly transformed itself into a joyous lust for wealth.

My brother started nodding, "Yeah, yeah, you're right, there's no way they can get away with this; it's too blatant."

You see, I was the *real* creator of Kangaroo Jack, and these rip-off artists were going to have to pay.

It all started several years before when my brother and I, both somewhat at a loss as to what to do with our lives, went back to school. Not to a great school mind you, or even a good one, but to an expensive "adult ed. university" designed mostly for working folks who just want to pay to get that piece of paper that says, "Master's" on it, so that they can get a bump on their pay scale or meet some bureaucratic requirement in order to move up the ladder. However, despite the school's lackluster reputation, at the time it was one of only two universities in the nation that was offering a master's degree program in Electronic Commerce, a degree geared towards those who wanted to enter the new and exciting world of the "Internet Economy." The other school offering a similar program being the slightly less accessible Yale University, we ended up at National.

At the time, Electronic Commerce was sweeping the nation, and you couldn't open a newspaper without seeing fantastic articles about the vast and apparently easy wealth being generated in the industry. My brother wanted in on it, and I was going along for the ride.

I would never have done this program if I had been left to my own devices, but it was good for me to take some business classes, and I ended up learning basic graphic design and website programming as well. Not to boast about the heights I would later scale within the industry, but this eventually led to me building several websites for friends. However, while I ultimately wouldn't get too much out of this program, it was tailor-made for someone like my brother, who likes to get an overview of how things work without being bogged down with too many pesky details that could only be mastered with actual extensive studying. Lucas represented the type of person the program ultimately sought to produce, which is to say, an entrepreneur who planned on coming up with a good idea and running the ship while finding other people to finance the whole thing and others to do all the actual skilled labor.

The year-long master's program came and went. Although far from being a school of good reputation or of particularly high standards, the classes and textbooks, many of which were the same as those from the Yale program, did give a good overview of the technologies and the current business practices involved in the world of dot com start-ups. More important, everything we learned in class reinforced in Lucas what he had hoped and suspected and dreamed about: that all you needed to make it big in this new economy was a talent for marketing, the guts to work for yourself, and the desire to make tons of cash fast. Unlike most of our classmates, his final project, Upstage.com, became the impetus for a very real business in the seemingly unreal world of the Internet.

Over the next few months after graduation, my brother managed to secure investors as well as recruit highly paid individuals out of finance, sales, and marketing companies; and find a fabulous office space, replete with giant vaulted wooden ceilings, dozens of work stations (mostly manned by interns from local colleges), and, of course,- some flashy dot-com paraphernalia in the front office, including a pool table and a fancy looking Harley Davidson. I was hired on to a separate website hosting and development company that was the outsourced producer of the code and design work for the site, and soon, Upstage.com was a reality.

Upstage was actually very similar to Facebook long before Facebook ever existed. The only difference was that instead of being geared to the public at large, this free hosting site, which allowed the user to post pictures, videos, and music clips, as well as personal information, was geared towards the artistic community. It was designed for musicians, artists, models, writers, filmmakers, and photographers who were looking to make names for themselves. Besides posting their online resumes, this community of artists could also join in discussion forums, connect with each other, and maybe even help each other out.

From the beginning, being a young struggling artist of sorts myself, I thought it was a cool idea for a website, though there were some downsides. In order to generate interest and excitement, the site would include some vague suggestions that this soon-to-be-giant database of online talent would be a launching place for new careers.

This was definitely possible, but certainly nothing that could ever be guaranteed to anyone. As it turned out, some artistic-minded, crazy end users took it hard when their genius wasn't instantly recognized by the world and compensated with immediately lucrative careers. The other issue was the question of how Upstage.com planned on generating any profits. That of course, was the sixty-four dollar question that neither my brother nor the vast majority of other Internet entrepreneurs could answer, except in the same vague terms that everyone involved in the industry was bandying about at the time.

This always bothered me, but it seemed as if the investors, themselves doubtlessly feeling the pull of easy dollars, only wanted to hear the appropriately in vogue line of bullshit told in a pleasing fashion and weren't really looking to be convinced of anything except that we were somehow all in this scam together.

Lucas' real plan, which the more savvy investors were certainly aware of, was not to find a way to answer this apparently insoluble riddle of how to generate profits, but rather to generate enough interest in the site to be able to then sell it off to a larger entity and let them figure it out—the quick flip business model that was becoming all the rage and which would soon go on to infect the housing market as well. Before the site was launched, however, we decided that it needed a mascot—a sample profile of a user to show people what Upstage was all about and how it could be useful.

That's where I came in. To that aim, I took a picture of a kangaroo reclining in a most human fashion and gave him the name, *Kangaroo Jack*. He wasn't a regular marsupial, however. According to the bio I wrote for him, he was a talking kangaroo who was launched to fame on a Discovery Channel special and soon escaped his provincial background of Alice Springs, Australia to become a famous model, dancer, musician, and writer. I used samples of my own music for the audio clips, and for an example of Kangaroo Jack's writing abilities, I included a story that was strikingly similar to what would later become the screenplay of a major Hollywood movie.

Despite having a talking kangaroo named Kangaroo Jack who goes through adventures extremely similar to the ones I wrote about for the launching of the website, I suppose it might still be possible to voice the doubt that the makers of the film ever even saw Upstage or its marsupial mascot. Well, to keep adding nails to the coffin of my dead dreams, I can also relate how my brother, in preparation for the big launch of the site, spent many tens of thousands of dollars in advertising in the Hollywood trade magazines, and you can bet that if the producers of that film didn't see the site right away, someone who works for them did, and quickly told them, "Hey! Here's a cute character, and a good idea for a film that we can steal outright!"

At least I'm about 99.99% sure that's the way it happened. After all, besides using the same name, the same character, and the same basic story, the film even used the same hometown for Kangaroo Jack that I had posted on the splash page of his then prominent and well-advertised website. Yes, in the beginning of the movie, the two main characters even drive past a sign that reads, *Welcome to Alice Springs!* It was as if the makers of the film were taking the time to give me, the real creator of the character, a special little, "Hey! Thanks for the idea, pal! We're going to make millions off of it, and you can pretty much go ahead and screw yourself! Oh . . . and happy holidays while you're at it!"

What also may have led to the blatant thievery, if this was the case, was the fact that Upstage.com was not long for this world. As quickly as it came into being, it faded right back out again. What made the evaporation of Upstage particularly poignant was how close we really came to achieving escape velocity from the black hole of economic disaster that was about to open up in the financial universe. You see, right before an investor was about to make a truly massive, life-changing infusion of cash into the business, his mother died. He went into mourning observances and so could not do any business for several days.

It was then, just when the check was written and ready to go, that the entire Internet economy collapsed, dragging most of the rest of the economy with it. Soon, Upstage.com, and the vast majority of other dot com businesses that had been enjoying a ridiculously easy ride up to that point, found that the white waters of commerce had taken them past the fun and exciting part of the trip, straight towards the cliffs. Soon, there was nothing but chaos and regret, people abandoning ship like sinking rats, executives desperately trying to get rehired (mostly in vain) at their old jobs, interns loading up on the free Cokes from the soda machine and making off with all the staples and rubber bands they could cram into their backpacks—*madness everywhere!* And Kangaroo Jack it seemed would become nothing more than a forgotten byproduct of an economy that no longer could take care of itself, let alone worry about the plight of talking marsupials.

So, perhaps it was the crash that fueled the brazen intellectual property theft that led to *Kangaroo Jack* the movie. "There is no more Upstage.com," the thieves may have reasoned, "so who's going to come after us?"

We were! Weren't we?

However, over the next several months, after that day in the gym when the secret plotting of a group of blatant thieves was finally made public, it became painfully clear that suing a major Hollywood movie company is not as easy as it...well yeah, never mind all that, it's just not easy. They have the best lawyers and limitless supplies of cash, and all we had, was the truth on our side, which sadly, is not very much in a world filled with the machinations and tyranny of evil movie executives.

We tried for months to find a lawyer willing to take the case, but without massive amounts of cash of our own, we had no takers that would even have had a marginal chance of success against the legal juggernauts we would be facing. Sadly, we had to give up, and for the next several years, whenever I would see copies of that very successful children's film in Blockbuster's display aisles or at friends' houses who had kids that loved the movie and would run around screaming, "Kangaroo Jack! Kangaroo Jack!" I would have to pause to cry a little tear for what could have been.

So now I leave the thieves with the following curse: may your dreams be haunted by the giant, stamping feet of a monstrous marsupial that will chase you eternally down the desolate and dusty roads of hell! Unless of course, you might be interested in taking a look at some other screenplay ideas I have, in which case, we can forget about the curse and should definitely do lunch sometime. Seriously…call me. I'm in the book.

Eleven

Life as an Outlaw

Jack and Larry drive to Little Italy to a new restaurant called, Monello, which is an Italian word meaning 'naughty little boy.' They are greeted at the door by Guido, Valentina, Alex, and Daniel who inform them they have arrived just in time for the celebrated *aperitivo*, a special Italian Happy Hour where such exotic dishes as beetroot gnocchi, lupini beans, and octopus salad are served.

While feasting on Chef Fabrizzio's delicious appetizers, Jack and Larry contemplate serious moral issues that have had lasting impacts on their lives. Jack reflects on a real life incident of hardened criminality, while Larry's thoughts turn to an investigation of one of his favorite students.

To compliment their stories, Jack selects a 2006 bottle of *Dynamite Vineyards Merlot*, noted for its explosive flavors. Larry's memories of his story agitate him so much with the narrow-minded characters he once encountered while teaching high school that he chooses a bottle of the earthy *Fat Bastard Cabernet* followed by a bottle of the tasty *Bitch Grenache*.

The choices of wines along with the mouth-watering appetizers enhance the telling of the tales to fever pitch.

Breaking the Law

-An Epic Tale of Heroes and Villains

By Jack Beddows

You know, Danny, I've sent boys younger than you to the gas chamber. I didn't want to do it. I felt I . . . owed it to them."
-Ted Knight from the film, *Caddyshack*

Now, I'm no Winona Ryder. Yet, I *have* been caught shoplifting...twice in fact. But who's to blame ultimately? My parents? My peers? Society? Advertisers? Am I leaving anyone out? All I can do, I suppose, is present the facts and let you decide who's truly at fault.

It all started back when I had two overriding passions, one of which was video games. The arcades on the boardwalk of nearby Nantasket Beach were frequent haunts for my pre-juvenile friends and me, and if any of our parents were looking for us, a quick drive by the bike racks of those establishments was always a good bet. And no one's bike spent more time in those racks than mine.

These were the days when classic video games roamed the earth like dinosaurs, games such as Asteroids, Pac Man, Donkey Kong, Zaxxon, Spy Hunter, Centipede, Tempest, Dig Dug, Defender, and Galaga, to name just a few. These games *kicked ass!*

As great as these games were, however, one thing's for sure, they weren't cheap. Not when you had a habit like mine. I was popping quarters into them like a gerbil hitting a feeder bar, and it never took long for my five-dollar weekly allowance to evaporate, which leads us to my second obsession: comic books.

It was a golden age for this form of entertainment as well. In stores all over this great nation of ours, comics like Spider Man, the Incredible Hulk, the X-Men, Dr. Strange, and the Fantastic Four all beckoned to geeky twelve-year-old boys just like me. Of course, not all of these geeky twelve-year-olds lived in such close proximity to an arcade. Since I couldn't resist blowing most of my limited budget on video games, when I'd later look over the many comics in the Cohasset News Store that I wanted to take home with me, I was always saddened to realize that I could only afford to buy one or two at the most with the scrapings that I had left after my latest gaming spree. I thought about trying to control my video gaming habit, sure. But the simple truth was that even if I could manage to spend less at the arcade, which, let's face it, was purely a hypothetical supposition, at sixty cents a pop, there was still no way that I could possibly afford all of the comics that I wanted… *or was there?*

It was a bright, winter afternoon, and I was at home in our living room playing cards with a friend. Since my parents wouldn't be back from work for another few hours, we had the house to ourselves, and Matt and I were making the most of this opportunity to just hang out and relax.

Suddenly, this blissful peace exploded when my older brother, Lucas, came home with a friend of his. They walked right into the living room without even taking off their muddy shoes, which to me was almost an unfathomable flouting of house rules, and then they proceeded to unzip their winter jackets. Instantly, a flood of comic books and candy bars spilled to the floor like manna from heaven. I couldn't believe what I was seeing.

"How did you get all those comics?" I asked.

"We stole them, you retard," my brother answered, "What did you think? We put them in our jackets to keep them warm?"

This spectacular display both impressed and made me extremely nervous. What they had done was clearly wrong. Yet, there on the floor was a hoard of comics piled up like gold, and my heart cried out like a miserly dwarf. And while I would not be ready for a long time to attempt such a daring criminal feat myself, a seed of evil had been planted in my soul.

Over the next several months with every visit to the downtown Cohasset News Store, my mood steadily shifted from sad to obsessive. As I would gaze lovingly at the colorful comic book covers I held in my hands, I would stand paralyzed for what seemed like hours. I felt like an impoverished mother forced to choose between her children. Finally, teary eyed, I'd place back a newly orphaned edition, walk to the counter to pay for its sibling, and then run back to make sure I really had made the right decision. *How could I be forced to choose?* It was just too cruel.

While lost in these fits of indecisive anguish, I would see in my mind's eye the image of an endless stream of comic books falling from my brother's unzipped bomber jacket. Eventually, it simply became too much for me.

One more pivotal event occurred, however, before I crossed that line that separated me from a world of juvenile criminality. My mother took me along to her job one school holiday in the fall, and although I liked the quiet and the view from the Boston skyscraper she worked in as an office manager, there wasn't much else to do but read, and it wasn't long before I finished the relatively thin fantasy book I had brought with me. Fortunately though, there was a bookstore down on Washington Street, not far from her building, and she let me go down there and gave me an extra five dollars, so that I could get myself another book.

I immediately went to the fantasy section, which was the most common source of reading material for me, ever since I had devoured *The Hobbit* five years earlier. I was glancing at several of Robert E. Howard's *Conan the Barbarian* novels, wondering which of those that I had not yet read would prove to be the most epic when a young voice broke me from my reverie.

"Yeah, Conan's cool, huh?" the voice said as I spun around, immediately feeling a little defensive about my overt *geekiness* and wondering if I was being made fun of. But when I turned around to see two young black boys my own age, there was nothing sarcastic in their smiling faces to indicate I was the object of ridicule.

Then the second boy spoke, more or less repeating what his friend had said while nodding his head at the book in my hand, "Yeah, Conan's cool, I like that shit."

I was surprised for several reasons at this point. For one, although I had been to Boston plenty and seen lots of African American kids on the subway, I grew up in a town that was about 99.9 percent white. And besides one black friend I made on a trip to Florida a year or two before, I had had very little direct experience with black kids. So frankly, I was surprised that they were interested in talking to me at all, as I didn't really think of myself as being particularly cool or otherwise interesting enough to justify crossing what I perceived as a mild if unspoken color line. The other thing that surprised me was that they would be interested in reading Conan books, as I was almost certain, that unlike me, they probably had better things to do with their time. But instead of expressing any of my questions or doubts, I merely answered, both shy and flattered, "Yeah, Conan's pretty cool, I guess."

"Tell you what," the first boy replied, "how much is that book?"

I looked and read out loud, "Five ninety-five. Why?"

"Well," he answered, "you meet us out front in a couple minutes, and I'll give it to you for three dollars."

With this, I started to suspect that maybe these two weren't fellow fantasy fiction lovers after all, and I became nervous and excited and unsure if I shouldn't end my conversation with them right away. But on the other hand, they had been so friendly, and made me feel so accepted in what was undoubtedly more their neighborhood than mine, that this seemed a somewhat ungrateful choice of action to take. Not to mention the lure of a proposed arrangement that seemed risk-free for me and that would leave me more than enough change to go get a candy bar and a drink before returning to my mom's office. *What else could I do but accept?*

They immediately suggested that I go wait outside, and just a few minutes later, while I was standing there wondering if this whole daring escapade was really going to happen, the two boys walked out of the front of the store. They started busting up laughing as they came over to me, and the first boy pulled out of his jacket the exact book I had last been looking at and handed it over to me. In return, I gave him the three dollars we had agreed on, which I had already separated from my total wad of seven singles.

"Thanks, man," he said, "Have fun reading your book! See you around!"

Then they started to jog down the street laughing, I hoped not at me, while I stood there, still a little overwhelmed and excited from the whole transaction. But there I was. Book in hand, a few extra dollars in my pocket, while my two new friends were off with three in theirs.

Win! Win! I thought. But then, the question inevitably arose in my mind, *Why didn't I just take the book and keep all of the money for myself?*

Previously, it had been one thing to know my brother stole from a store; he was five years older, practically a grown man a whole world of experience away from me. But these two had been boys of my own age, and I suddenly realized that whatever invisible barrier separated me from the world of theft, it would never be crossed simply through the process of getting older.

When the winter returned and the wearing of heavy coats again became the norm, I made my first foray into the criminal world. I was standing outside the News Store, mentally preparing myself for what I was about to do. I was with my friend, let's call him Jimmy, who although not a comic book fan really, was always ready for delinquent behavior. He seemed happily excited about what we were going to do, but me personally, I was scared shitless. My heart rate was soaring, I was sweating profusely, and we hadn't even gone into the store yet.

"Are you sure you want to do this?" I asked my co-conspirator.

"Don't be such a *wuss*!" Jimmy answered, and just like that it was settled. We were going into the News Store to steal.

Despite my extreme nervousness, our plan worked perfectly. Jimmy successfully distracted the older couple that ran the store while I stuffed three comics into the waistline of my pants under my jacket. It was then, when I was adjusting my coat to make sure everything was properly concealed that I again started having second thoughts. *Is this something Peter Parker would do?* I asked myself. *Wait! This is wrong!*

But then, immediately after that twang of conscience, my lust for comic books reasserted itself, and a devilish voice whispered to me, *If the store-owners really cared, they'd have the comic rack near the cash register where they could keep an eye on it. They probably wouldn't even mind! Go ahead! Just take the comics!*

As I walked up to the counter, my great nervousness apparently went unnoticed as I purchased a single issue of the Fantastic Four, in order to keep up appearances. As I handed over my dollar, the other issues hidden beneath my fluffy ski jacket burned my stomach with shame. The cheerful old woman behind the counter merely bent over to hand me my change and said, "There you go, deary. Have a *wonderful* day!" Her general pleasantness only made me feel that much worse about myself.

We were hardly out of the door before we burst into nervous laughter; no doubt a side effect of the quick burst of adrenaline our larcenous activities produced within us. But it wasn't until later, long after the excitement subsided and we were sitting around eating chocolate bars and looking over Captain America and Batman comics, that I knew for sure, that we would steal again.

One day, not long after, while playing at my friend Brian's house, I started to brag about my growing comic collection and my daring method of acquisition. I waited expectantly for his reaction, which I figured would range from moral outrage to sheer disbelief. Instead, he kept doodling calmly and didn't even look up as he replied, "Oh sure, I've been stealing comics all winter."

He then proceeded to open his closet to show me his own considerable stockpile. I must admit, I was rather crestfallen about my apparent lack of originality. Now that I started to think about it, I realized that Brian, who had an older brother the same age as my own, probably traveled a very similar path down the road to perdition. And since almost all of my friends had older brothers about the same age as mine, I began to wonder just how many of us were in on this illegal enterprise. *And if the thieving really is that widespread,* I thought to myself, *how long could it be before even the kindly but oblivious proprietors of the Cohasset News Store would catch on and crack down?* There was, clearly, only one logical conclusion to be made . . . *I'd better grab as much as possible while the grabbing is good!*

So the stealing continued at an accelerated rate. Caution was thrown to the wind, and as a result, my comic book collection was achieving a truly impressive magnitude. I had to squash most of my clothes into a single drawer in order to make room for all of the comics in the others. Many were the afternoons that like a dragon with his hoard, I would gaze over the alphabetized rows of my collection, and had a single issue been out of place, I would have smelled it.

Finally though, as it inevitably must be, justice was served. And as usual, pride was there before the fall. Once again, now nearly a year since our initial theft, Jimmy and I set out towards the Cohasset News Store. When we arrived, we left our bikes leaning against the wall outside and then entered the store in to do our evil deed. It was much the same as it had been on all of our previous jaunts, except that this time we didn't even bother to flee the scene of the crime when we were through. Instead, we went around to the back of the store where Jimmy had the bright idea of climbing up on the roof.

"Are you sure we should do that, Jimmy?" I asked

"Sure, why not?" he replied.

I looked down at the stolen goods in our hands and back at Jimmy, but I *still* couldn't think of a good answer.

So we left our comics and candy bars by the bikes and climbed up the back wall. The roof was flat-topped and graveled, with air vents that, in retrospect, were probably the agents of our undoing. We really weren't being all that loud, but the vents likely amplified our voices and footsteps on the roof, and it was certainly enough to alarm the old couple below, and they called the police. As the station house was only two blocks away, it wasn't long before we were shocked to see a cruiser pull up into the parking lot, giving a quick blurt of a siren wail as it did so.

We didn't wait to be caught on the roof. Like a pair of spider monkeys, we leapt off and ran down the back alley in a flash. Cohasset, Massachusetts being one of the cushiest assignments conceivable in the world of law enforcement, the officers on the scene weren't even close to being in the kind of shape that would have allowed them to catch us, even if they wanted to try. However, our brains were certainly not equal to our feet.

We not only left our bikes behind in our mad dash but also the evidence of our recent thievery. But we weren't thinking about that last crucial detail when, two minutes and as many miles later, we sat huddled in a secluded, wooded cranny, regaining our breath and debating about what we should do next.

As we sat in the woods reviewing our situation, we felt truly stuck. Our bikes, the very soul of every northeastern suburban boy, were doubtlessly waiting for us at the police station by now. We were going to have to go claim them. At first, we snuck back to the store to double check on what we already knew would be bad news.

"Yup, we're screwed. They took our bikes. Shoot! Maybe we should just tell our parents they were stolen," I suggested.

"Screw that! I'm getting my bike," Jimmy answered. "Besides, how much trouble can we be in? All that the police know is that we climbed up on a roof. Big deal!"

"Yeah, I guess you're right, it won't be that bad," I concurred.

How wrong we were. The truth is, when the police were trying to deduce the identity of the roof-climbing culprits, they wheeled our bikes around front and brought our discarded comics and candy back into the store.

"Yes, we remember the two boys riding those bikes," the older couple answered, "but they didn't buy any comics, just a single candy bar."

Busted!

When we walked into the station to apologize for climbing on the roof and to humbly ask for our bikes back, the short, bespectacled officer behind the reception desk didn't acknowledge anything we said. Instead, much to our shock and horror, he immediately started in with, "So, you two think it's cool to steal?"

Damn you, Jimmy! I immediately thought. *It was your stupid idea to climb the roof! And to come back for the bikes! Why do I listen to you?*

While our parents were called at work, the policeman's lecture began. With topics such as poor morals, lack of character, and shame of the community, the sermon was thorough if not wide-ranging. When the officer asked my last name and realized who my older brother was, I learned that my fraternal forerunner had been caught several times for stealing. Again, I was asked if I thought that was "cool." I gave a teary-eyed, "No," in reply, wondering why my brother had never mentioned that side of the story to me before.

Meanwhile, guilt welled up inside of me, and as the tears started to flow, I felt true remorse for my crimes, even if that guilt was only brought to the surface by my being caught. Jimmy and I both admitted that we had upset the nice old couple that ran the News Store, and we also admitted that we had let our families down. And although the police let us go home with our bikes, we both knew that that evening we would go through hell facing our angry parents, and we both knew that we would suffer some long standing punishments as well. *We were right!* Allowances were stripped, curfews were reduced to the level of house arrest, and chores were increased for a month. By the time the whole ordeal was over, I had completely learned my lesson. *Or almost . . .*

The years passed, and not only had I not stolen a single thing since my comic book days, I had been pretty darn good overall. At the age of nineteen, I seldom got into any trouble, focused as I was on exercise, artistic pursuits, and at times, academics. And like the vast majority of my classmates from Cohasset High's class of '89, I had always been completely drug-free. This didn't seem to hold for older or younger grades at Cohasset, but somehow, those of us caught up in the Nancy Reagan, *Just Say No* years, really did seem to have been heavily influenced by the campaign. Of course, this didn't apply to alcohol, which was drunk in copious amounts by almost all of us reared in the northeast.

Yes, with my love for learning and for keeping fit, I was, in my own small way, trying to emulate the habits of a Peter Parker or a Batman, although not having any superpowers or any particular sense of bravery for that matter, I studiously avoided any unusual displays of heroics.

But as my time in college continued, my rigid discipline living a healthy lifestyle began to compete with a widening awareness of the variety of experiences available to me. As a result, my defenses were down when I went out for a drive with my friend Matt, back home on a wintry Cohasset evening. As we sat in his car, looking out over the moonlit water past Rocky Beach, he suddenly lit a match. Soon, I smelled an odor that whisked me back in time to a distant memory of the late seventies, when I was a small child walking hand in hand with my mother, wandering around in a field of music fans in the aftermath of a Styx concert. He passed the joint my way, nodding his head while little wisps of smoke escaped his puffed-out cheeks.

In no time at all we were talking about the possibility of whole universes existing in our fingernails and other such heady topics. The more we talked, the clearer it became that we were perhaps the most intelligent and insightful people on earth. We were certain that if we wrote down our thoughts, we could publish several essays that could immediately earn us honorary PhDs in philosophy from any school in the nation. But then we got hungry and decided to drive to the local Stop & Shop instead.

As we wandered under the harsh fluorescent lighting, I decided in some sort of half-assed spirit of Marxism picked up in school that all those who were hungry should have food, regardless of how little money they may or may not have in their designer Levi's. To tell the truth, I did have a dollar on me, but I knew I was going to need to buy some water or juice with that, because, *Gosh, my mouth was really dry for some reason!* So I began to open a package of Peanut M&M's I had picked up from the candy display aisle.

"Jack, I don't think you should be doing that," Matt replied.

Obviously, Matt lacked the true fervor of the proletariat. Either that or he had more experience with pot than I had and was not quite as befuddled as me. After I scoffed at his warning, he decided to wander off elsewhere, safely out of my proximity while I continued munching on my delicious treat.

Meanwhile, I noticed that there was a very large, red-haired gentleman, who, like me, was also not carrying a shopping basket and who seemed to be having trouble locating the item of interest that had doubtlessly brought him to the store. *Probably getting something for the wife,* I thought. As I wandered on, nibbling on Peanut M&Ms, I couldn't help but notice that he was almost always poking his head in the same aisle that I was in, apparently struggling in vain to find that missing item. I didn't think too much of it.

As I wandered and snacked, I eventually decided that I should neatly fold the remainder of the bag of M&M's and place it back on the shelf for the next hungry worker who might come along. Suddenly, I felt a shadow looming over me and the now furious, red-haired giant grabbed my wrist and spun me around to stare into his contorted visage.

OH SHIT! He works for the Stop and Shop! I suddenly realized, now that it was far, far too late.

A second later, I found myself being dragged through the store and up a flight of stairs by this in-store detective who was roughly the size of Sasquatch. He was shaking with rage and adrenaline, making the trip a bumpy one. His level of extreme excitement led me to think that perhaps this was his first interaction with such a dangerous criminal like me. He pushed me down into a chair at one end of a long table in a shabby looking meeting room. At the other end sat a wispy old man with a gray mustache, a gray comb-over, and a cheap blazer and tie that were also mostly gray. He sat looking at me narrowly through his thick, black-framed glasses without saying a word.

I immediately began to apologize.

"I'm so sorry about opening that bag of M&M's! I know what I did was wrong, and I'd be happy to pay for the bag right now."

I paused for a reaction but received none. *What's this guy thinking? Am I screwed?* I wondered to myself before continuing.

"In addition, I'd be happy to write the store a formal apology letter, if that would be acceptable to you." The old man still said nothing. "I can certainly appreciate your feelings in this matter, and you have every right to be angry with me. And although it *was* just a handful of M&M's, I understand that there are principles involved here as well, so perhaps in addition to paying for the item, might I suggest a six-month ban of me from the store? Or perhaps any other time frame that you might feel is appropriate?" I may have spoken like a lawyer, but I reeked of fear.

And again, in return, I received nothing but a stony stare from the old man.

So I continued blabbing at an even more accelerated pace, "Well, I understand completely. My mother shops here regularly, and has done so for over ten years, and I wouldn't want her to think this is the kind of place where riff-raff are running around stealing and creating an un-safe environment!"

Although still silent, the old man then leaned forward in a way that I interpreted as positive body language. *Wait!* I thought to myself, *I think I'm winning him over! Just give him some money, and you're safe!*

I hurriedly got to my point. "So please allow me to make restitution for the package of M&M's right now." I began to pull my lone dollar out of my pant's pocket, and the old man began to shrug his shoulders, while holding out his palms in a universal gesture of forgiveness and understanding. I was going to get away with it. Thank God!

Just then, two hairy, ugly police officers buried in thick winter gear entered the room. Without a word, they grabbed me and wrenched my arms behind my back rather painfully. Doubtlessly, while I was pleading with the manager, the police station had received a phone call from the angry store detective about a *serious* criminal on the loose that he had heroically captured single-handedly.

Before I knew what was happening, I was being dragged out of the store in handcuffs in front of dozens of shoppers, several of whom were mothers of high school classmates of mine. It was then, as the officers threw me into the back of their cruiser to drive me down to the station that I finally saw Matt standing in the crowd that had gathered to watch the proceedings. He shook his head sadly from side to side while my eyes pleaded with him behind the glass and wire of the cruiser's back window, *Please! Help me!* I mouthed as we pulled away.

I had always suffered from a touch of claustrophobia as a child, and riding handcuffed in the cruiser quickly sent me into a panic. It didn't help that as I stared at the backs of the heads of the two officers, I noticed that their beards and body hair were so prevalent that loose strands were popping out all around their necks past even their thick winter coats. *Jesus,* I thought, *these two look like a couple of crazed werewolves!*

I then realized they had been speaking to me while I was drifting off into my fantasy about lycanthropic law enforcers. *What did they just say?* Something about an easy solution to this whole problem? *Wait! Are they soliciting a bribe? Holy Shit! Did they just proposition me for sex?* Suddenly, I was desperate to get out of that car. I think I nervously muttered something like, "Tee hee hee. Take me to jail then! Jail's the place for me!"

Once we arrived at the station, however, I recognized a familiar face, which managed to calm me down some. It was the same officer who all those years before, had lectured me on the evils of stealing. *Maybe he'll just lecture me again and let me go*, I thought. *That wouldn't be so bad!*

Apparently, he didn't remember me, but unlike his fellow officers, he exuded the warmth of a genuinely friendly fellow. He calmly requested that I fill out a form or two, and made no attempt to lord it over me. *It's all going to be just fine*, I started to think with increasing confidence.

"There we go," he continued, "if you could just sign here and here. That's it, and uh . . . thank you very much. That about does it. If you could just step this way, the officer will show you to your cell."

Suddenly, his friendliness became meaningless as I recognized the looming reality that was waiting for me. I was about to be locked up. It was then that I was hit by an even bigger wave of claustrophobic paranoia than I had experienced in the cruiser.

I don't want to go in there! I screamed inside my own head. But there was no way around it.

Once I was locked inside the tiny cell, the bars of which were plated with a wall of Plexiglas that made me feel even more restricted, I thought to myself, *Wait! Even if I really want to get out of here, even if I ask them really, really nicely, they just won't let me out! I'm trapped like a rat!* It wasn't a pleasant situation for a sheltered young teenager, still stoned off his ass for one of the first times in his life, and the next couple of hours really sucked. The minutes dragged by, accompanied only by a rising and falling but continued sense of panic, until I heard something from the depths of my incarceration.

It was too vague to distinguish at first; I could just make out distant but boisterous voices that even the walls of the jailhouse couldn't quite quell. And though I couldn't make out the words when I first tuned in to the far away screaming, within seconds, accompanied by the screech of tires as someone's car careened wildly up to the station, I could clearly hear someone yelling, "WHOOH! YEAH! We've gotta bust Jack out of prison! WHOOOH!" Right away, I knew it was Matt with a whole gang of my inebriated friends stuffed into his car, coming to bail me out.

Thank God they came for me! I thought. *But wait,* I then asked myself, *why would Matt bring a whole gang of drunks with him?* At first, I considered the possibility that he just wanted moral support on the trip to the police station. But I soon arrived at the much more likely conclusion that he simply wanted to share my humiliation with as many people as humanly possible.

Ironically, while I had just spent hours in a jail cell for eating a half a bag of M&Ms, the police didn't seem too worried about releasing me into the care of a gang of drunken teenagers. I suppose Matt was acting sober enough, though I suspect he had had a few beers while rounding up our friends to come get me. But this was also back in the days when drunk driving was still being treated like a misdemeanor, when in any but the most extreme cases, usually the worst thing that would happen if you were pulled over, was that your beer was confiscated after which you merely had to promise to drive straight home in order to be released to your own recognizance. In any event, I was soon freed and stuffed into the car with the rest of my friends, and we headed off to see what else the night might hold for us.

We went over to our friend Ian's house whose parents were out of town, and there I recounted my adventures to any and all that would listen, highlighting, of course, the injustice of the system and my own personal nonchalance throughout my ordeals. For the rest of the night, I had a lot of fun pretending that the whole experience had been nothing but a light-hearted adventure for me, which I suppose is generally the best way to deal with something hideous.

What wasn't fun though was the thought of going to court to sort out the final charges brought against me. The whole week leading up to the court date, my stomach was in knots. I didn't want to have shoplifting on my otherwise spotless record, and I didn't want to have to pay any sort of fine, and I *really* didn't want my parents to ever know what had transpired. I was feeling extremely unhappy as I drove myself to court and waited in line for my turn in front of the judge.

"Hey, Jack!" I was suddenly surprised to hear my name being shouted so casually in the Quincy District Courthouse, and I turned to see Polly Ledman, an attractive girl who had been in the grade above me at Cohasset High. She was with her older boyfriend, Cody Maltz, a friend of my brother, who stood off to the side looking tired, bored, and likely hung-over.

"Hey, what are you doing here?" she asked in a friendly upbeat manner.

Suddenly, I got the feeling that my being in court that day had upped her estimation of me from non-entity to possibly interesting personage. If so, this would certainly explain her attraction to Cody who was constantly in trouble.

So we chitchatted about our various misdeeds like best friends until our court appointments took us apart. As I watched her very pleasant figure walking away, I was left to consider some of the fringe benefits of a criminal lifestyle.

After being admitted to the courtroom, I had to sit and wait while the judge in session was plowing through his busy caseload like a factory worker on an assembly line. I didn't envy him, as everyone in front of me that morning was either a rough criminal type, there to set trial dates to address their antisocial behavior, or at the very least, an annoying, petty ne'er do well that clearly had whatever fine they were about to pay coming to them. They all lied and justified themselves to him aggressively with the maddeningly circular logic of three year olds. Despite the fact that my current situation might have inspired me to feel some sympathy for them, I was mostly just glad the judge had the power to put his foot down and shut these idiots up. I did note rather nervously though that all of this was clearly taking a toll on his patience. When the judge got to me, and my crimes were read out loud, I felt more than a bit apprehensive. But after looking over the details of my crime, coming as it did on the heels of a stream of drug abuse and domestic violence charges, the judge merely looked up with a disgusted sneer and exclaimed, "What! This guy's in here for eating a half a bag of M&M's?"

He dropped his weary head into his hands and shook it from side to side, as if to ask, *Why? Why am I being bothered with this nonsense?*

He sighed deeply and asked me, "Would you like to plead no contest?"

At this point, I was terrified of saying the wrong thing, "Uh...I'm afraid I don't know what that means," I finally managed to sputter out.

At that point, despite the fact that no one was supposed to give me any advice, the court translator whispered to me, "Just plead no contest, and get the hell out of here! There won't be anything on your record." This breach of protocol was no doubt committed less with the intention of helping me out as preventing the judge from popping a blood vessel.

"No contest!" I said victoriously.

The judge banged his gavel, "Case dismissed!"

A few weeks later while back in California, my mother called to tell me that she had discovered, by religiously reading over her checkout receipts, that the Cohasset Stop & Shop had a cash register that through some mechanical fault, consistently overcharged customers several dollars at a time. My mom related how she had pointed out this fault to the gray-haired, wispy manager who admitted that the machine was faulty and needed to be repaired. But she noticed over the next several months that nothing was ever done about it and that the machine continued to overcharge. At a few dollars a mistake and with probably hundreds of customers a day going through that particular machine, the store that had me thrown in jail over a half a bag of M&M's was knowingly ripping off its loyal customers by many thousands of dollars a week.

After getting off the phone, I smoked a joint with my roommate and thought about the ironic news. I soon found myself fantasizing about that overzealous store detective and the wispy old manager being dragged into the center of Cohasset for a public hearing at the conclusion of which they would be forced to ride backwards on donkeys in the middle of the freezing cold winter with their hands tied behind their backs and wearing nothing but dunce caps made out of used M&M wrappers.

And after having experienced that particularly vivid image, I decided it was time to stop smoking marijuana for a while. As a substitute to help me relax, I thought I might start reading comic books again, especially as one of my roommates had shown me a couple of cool new titles that were a bit edgier and more mature than those I had grown up with. But it had been a long time since I had last purchased a comic book, and when I went to a local news store,

I was shocked to notice how the prices had jumped from the sixty cents I used to pay as a kid all the way up to a ridiculous two dollars and twenty-five cents per issue.

There's no way, I thought, *on my meager student's budget, that I could ever afford to start buying comics again . . . or was there?*

The Big Cheese

by Larry Zeiger

I fell asleep and quickly found myself immersed in a suffocating nightmare. Parents, administrators, and high school testing coordinators surrounded me. Sitting in a chair in the center of a circle, I was forbidden to speak. A strobe light flashed in my face. As each person spoke, the circle became tighter and tighter until I felt I was being strangled.

"My daughter is a gifted student. She was born that way. How could you give her a B+? She's never had anything less than an A."

"Why are you allowing food in the classroom? I saw one of your students eating nuts of all things. *Do you allow nuts in your classroom*?"

"Not once have you called security about students using cell phones in your class! And they're text messaging! And listening to IPODs! Don't you care at all about school protocol and district procedures?"

"I hear that your students don't give a damn about the Golden State Exam, the AP Exams, the Exit Exams, the No Child Left Behind Exam, the SAT Exam, the Achievement Exams, or their Final Exams! Is this because of you and your *anti-testing* views?"

"One of your students at the Youth Leadership Conference was caught smoking Marijuana. It was one of YOUR students . . . YOUR students . . . YOUR students. *Do I see a pattern here?"*

"Your students were on the roof of the theater being more than intimate! How could you let this happen? Do you know what your students are doing?

Are the films you show in class and the books you make them read causing this disgusting behavior?"

"My son swore to me and my wife that he would never ever look at a naked woman until his wedding night, but you had the audacity to take my son to the Getty Museum where he saw a completely nude statue of a naked Greek woman which you called *an antiquity*! You've ruined my son for life! Look at him! It's all because of you! Because of you! BECAUSE OF YOU!"

I woke up sweating profusely. My heart was ticking like a time bomb. I took several deep breaths to calm myself down. I then got ready for work to teach the 192 students in my overcrowded classroom, hoping that it would be an exhilarating experience – and not one of anxiety-producing stress.

In my 29th year as a public school educator, I was always getting into trouble, often being viewed as being far "too liberal" and "too student-oriented" by the more conservative members of our staff. On my most recent teacher evaluation, the vice principal, Stinky Roquefort, stated: "Mr. Zeiger is an effective teacher in spite of the fact that he seldom follows rules set forth by the school administration." The first six words of the evaluation were accurate, but the last sixteen words made me nauseous and were simply untrue (for the most part). As a result, I refused to sign the evaluation.

Ultimately, the principal, Oscar Saganaki, had Stinky rewrite his assessment for fear that I would write a letter, an article, or maybe even a short story about the American teaching experience that would one day be published and expose this repressive academic institution to the world. I had a desk drawer full of notes and outlines but never the time to actually write the story. And besides, at this point in my life, I had to focus on the upcoming musical theater production I was directing at the school and the fourteen-hour work days ahead.

The development of an original musical featuring a cast of nearly one hundred creative and talented students was exciting, inventive, and well received annually by thousands of community members. Students loved looking for story ideas, developing scripts, designing sets and costumes, and promoting the musical. And when, I brought in a copy of the *L.A. Times* one day and read them the article about Winona Ryder's infamous shoplifting experience at SAKS Fifth Avenue, the class was ecstatic about the topic for the 2003 musical. What a perfect mix of story elements: celebrity, shopping, pop culture, and *thievery!*

The students did their research bringing in news and entertainment magazines as well as Internet articles to develop their own unique musical libretto blending elements of drama, comedy, and a heavy dose of fantasy. We contacted SAKS Fifth Avenue who donated display items and hundreds of shopping bags to add authenticity to the production. The student marketing directors wrote their own press releases and contacted all the local and national media. The title of the production the student directors decided on was -

STICKY FINGERS

-A Tale of SAKS, Lies, and Videotape

Who would have thought that a real life drama about theft and false accusations would develop behind the scenes of what was to become one of the most highly publicized high school musicals in history? It all started two months before the show's opening on a warm day in late March when most Southern California high school students would much prefer to be at the beach. The excitement of this quirky theatrical production was building, and nothing was going to stop my cast members from making their show the best ever.

The student art designers couldn't wait to get started on constructing sets including replicas of SAKS 5th Avenue, Grauman's Chinese Theatre, and a Los Angeles Court of Law. Due to cutbacks, the school had eliminated the woodshop class as well as the technical theater and industrial arts classes. As a result, I thought it would be difficult to find students who had the knowledge needed to design and construct the sets. When I asked the students if they could produce diagrams of what they were going to build, Tyler, the set director, responded, "Hey man, that takes too long! You'll see . . . no planning is necessary. It's all in our heads and our imaginations. All we need is a hammer and nails, and we'll have the best sets you've ever seen!"

After four laborious weeks on set construction, using Tyler's "trial and error" method, we were not meeting our deadline. Because of this, I told the entire cast they had to show up on the last weekend before our dress rehearsal to finish the set or, very simply, we would have no show. I was a master of *Jewish Guilt.*

That Saturday, I was amazed that nearly the entire cast had assembled outside the theater, and many of the students, so excited about the rapidly-approaching opening night, were actually practicing dance steps in the entranceway to the performing arts center when I arrived. I opened the door, and the set builders and artists streamed down the aisles of the theater to the scene shop, ready to complete "the dream sets of a lifetime."

I opened the door to the scene shop and was shocked to see that the cabinet where all the tools were stored had a combination lock on it. The blood drained from my face, as I had no knowledge of the combination of the lock or even where the lock had come from. All I could think about was that I had made seventy students come on a Saturday to build a set, and someone had obviously tried to sabotage my efforts. *Who could have done this? And what could the culprit's motive be?*

"Oh, that's Mrs. Asiago's lock!" exclaimed Jenish, one of my most observant students. "I saw her put it on the cabinet Friday, after school. I told her we were coming here to work on sets, and that's when she ran into her class, got the lock, and snapped it on the cabinet door. She then began to utter some words I couldn't understand. I had no idea the tools were stored in there, or I would have said something. Now why in the world would she do such a thing?"

"I know why!" said Miguel, one of the lead actors in the production. "Asiago hates you, and she hates your shows! It doesn't take a rocket scientist to figure that one out. I mean like . . . *duh*."

"Now why would you say a thing like that?" I asked while trying to conceal the burning rage that was building inside me. But then it became clear to me that Velveeta Asiago, the drama teacher, had intentionally sabotaged my day and made me look like an idiot in front of my students. I tried to remain calm, but the perspiration dripping from my forehead in buckets was a dead giveaway. "Why would she lock up the tools that *I had purchased* for the theater? That's very odd."

"I just told you . . . she hates your ass!" Miguel responded articulately. "Your show sells more tickets than hers. Don't you see what's goin' on, dude?"

"I am not 'dude,' Miguel. My name is Mr. Zeiger."

"If I call you 'dude' it's a sign of respect. Now be coo'."

I calmly responded, "Thanks Miguel for the brilliant lesson in semantics."

"*Whatever* . . . just lighten up, *Zeigman,* before it's too late."

"I have an idea," said Matt Schneider, a brilliant student with a sharp analytical mind who loved mathematics and physics and was more than capable with a screwdriver. "We don't need the combination to the lock. All I have to do is just unscrew the latch; the lock falls off, and *voila!* We're in!"

Within seconds, just as he had predicted, Matt unscrewed the latch. The lock fell to the floor, the cabinet door flew open, and Matt was proclaimed "hero of the day" by the entire cast. As a result of his ingenuity, the students worked diligently for several hours constructing the remaining sets. In the late afternoon, the group of students began to slowly disappear, leaving me with the chore of putting all the tools away and cleaning up the backstage area.

"Hey, Zeiger, why don't you just leave the stuff where it is?" Matt suggested. "We're going to be working on the set all next week. We can clean up during class on Monday."

Why was it that most of my students had greater logical thinking skills than I had?

Agreeing with Matt, I turned out the lights, locked the doors, and went home to enjoy what was left of the evening. I was in a terrific mood until Monday morning when I pulled into the parking lot at 7:20 a.m. and noticed two police cars in front of the Administrative building. *Must be students smoking pot behind the math building again, or was it the graffiti gang who always tagged the foreign language building?* I opened the door to the main office and was greeted by the vice principal, three policemen, and two campus security guards.

"Zeiger, follow us," said Gouda, the campus police officer in a commanding voice.

"Why? Why should I follow you?"

"Just follow us."

"Any particular reason?"

"Just follow us."

"Could I have a possible clue as to what this is all about?

"In the conference room . . . yes."

An atmosphere of dread and doom consumed the mildew-infested room. Something awful had happened, and I was being treated as if I were a suspect in some insidious crime. Everyone took a seat around the long table and stared . . . at me.

"The theater was broken into this weekend!" exclaimed Stinky Roquefort, glaring at me as if I were concealing valuable information.

"You're kidding," I responded. "I was here all day Saturday. I didn't see a thing. What time did the break-in occur?"

"We thought *you* would have that information for *us*!"

"What 'information' are you talking about? I locked the door when I left the theater and turned on the security alarm. Or does the security alarm in the theater not work?" I inquired.

Office Fundido responded, "Stinky thinks it was one of your students."

"And why does Stinky think that?" I asked.

Ever since Stinky Roquefort was appointed vice principal of the school, I had one major altercation with him after another. Stinky was one of those hard-nosed, left-brain guys, while I, on the other hand, was a creative right-brain spirit. Stinky hated people involved in the arts. He thought the fine arts department was comprised of nothing but weird freethinking nutcases. His major concerns were tardy policies, confiscation of cell phones, and male and female students caught in passionate embraces behind the sex-ed classroom. I just knew Stinky was making up these accusations for lack of anything more exciting to do with his dull, over-paid position.

"What damage was done?" I asked. "Was anything stolen?"

"Someone broke into the room in the back of the scene shop, where the tools were stored. Stinky believes it might have been one of your students who did the job after you left on Saturday." Officer Mascarpone replied.

Stunned by this accusation, I responded, "You've got to be kidding! I can't believe you would think one of *my students* would do such a thing!"

Mascarpone continued, "According to the drama teacher, Velveeta Asiago, when she arrived at work early this morning, she noticed that you had left the door to the tool room wide open, and the lock to the cabinet which contains *her tools* had been broken off. And, she claims that many of *her tools* were missing! And furthermore, she insists that you would have knowledge of the identity of the culprit. So give us the name, Zeiger! We suspect you know who did it. Now tell us everything you know! EVERYTHING!"

What I knew was that nothing had been stolen. That deceitful, incriminating Velveeta woman had it in for me! She was worried that *Sticky Fingers* would outdo her version of *Annie.* I hated *Annie,* and she knew it. If I heard one more tone-deaf Annie-wannabe sing, "*Tomorrow! Tomorrow! I love you tomorrow,*" I would undoubtedly go insane.

"Now just a minute! Velveeta was the one who put her combination lock on the cabinet that houses *my tools!* Velveeta is fully aware that I generously purchased nearly all the tools for the theater and, furthermore, I am absolutely certain nothing . . . *nothing was stolen!*"

With sweat pouring forth profusely from his brow and most likely knowing he had stretched the truth about a mile point five, V.P. Stinky Roquefort shouted, "Nothing was stolen! Nothing was stolen! How could you possibly say that? The evidence speaks for itself. The lock was broken off the cabinet door! And you say, 'nothing was stolen'? Tools were strewn all over the theater, and many of those tools, according to that sweet Velveeta woman, are missing! And you, Mr. Zeiger, you were alone in the theater . . . alone with your students. You were . . . the adult in charge! *Nothing was stolen?* Shame! Shame! Shame on you!"

"What tools? Name them! Give me a list!" I demanded.

Like a CIA agent discovering a cachet of missing nuclear weapons, Stinky screamed, "A power saw! A drill! Two hammers! A Bostitch stapler! And . . . and . . . a jar of nails!"

"Oh please! Why would anyone take a jar of nails? And a Bostitch stapler is *not* a tool!"

"We know you know who broke the lock off!" echoed Havarti, the school police officer.

"The lock was *not* broken off! Two tiny screws were removed from the latch. That's it!" I declared, immediately thinking I had said too much.

"Oh! Then you do know!" Stinky exclaimed with a look of malicious delight. "Tell me Zeiger, WHO DID IT?"

I felt as if I were under a hot light in an interrogation room. And what about Matthew Schneider – that brilliant scholar with straight A's who had fed the homeless on weekend . . . a saint disguised as a high school student. This could ruin his chances of getting that scholarship to Berkeley! I had to think fast.

"Tell us, Zeiger! We know you know!" Stinky Roquefort was salivating at the mouth at the prospect of bringing this kid to justice. He leaned towards me. "Don't protect your students! We know what a pushover liberal you are! We have to apprehend these kids! They're destroying our school! And our community! And in the future . . . the world! We have to teach these *gangbangers* a lesson!"

There was no way in the world I was going to turn my student into these vultures. I had to protect him. The creative juices began to flow through my brain, and in a matter of seconds, I arrived at the decision that was to have a major effect on the life of Matthew Schneider for the rest of his life.

"I . . . did . . . it! *I did it!*" I proclaimed.

There was a long pause, and then Fromage, one of the school's security guards, pointed his finger at me and shouted "You did *what?*"

"I removed the screws and broke into the cabinet with the lock that someone maliciously placed on the door to prevent me and my students from using *my tools* to construct the sets for *my show!* While every tool may not have been put away in the cabinet, I am certain by taking a brief tour of the theater, every tool in question will be found, including the jar of nails and the Bostitch stapler . . . which is *not* a tool!"

I had to catch my breath after my nothing less than superlative response.

Stinky Roquefort was as red as a stop sign. At any moment I expected him to explode on impact. "Oh I get it," he said sarcastically. "You're trying to cover for one of your students! Trying to protect the thief, *are you*?"

"No, I did it! I stole *my own* tools! Now according to what I've read in books and seen in movies, you have to handcuff me." I looked at the officers who appeared baffled by my declaration of distorted truth. "Oh, but I think I am entitled to one phone call. I'd like to contact Anderson Cooper . . . oh yeah, and Larry King . . . so they can put me on CNN as you take me down to the jail and book me in front of a live TV audience! You harass me all morning with preposterous accusations and then expect me to go back and teach my five overcrowded classes, grade papers all night, rehearse all day after school, build sets, arrange music, choreograph dances, and direct over 100 hormone-crazed teenagers by myself! I want CNN to cover this story! I'll even settle for FOX! I want the world to know that I . . . I am a victim of Public Education!"

To further emphasize the absurdity of the situation, I stuck my hands out in front of Officers Gorgonzola and Mascarpone and shouted, "Handcuff me! I want to become a national news item! I want to write a book and retire as a filthy rich, fucking educator!

Stinky Roquefort was speechless, but I felt at peace with myself as I was ushered out of the office and told to go back to my class to teach as if I were given the ultimate prison sentence.

"Is the case closed?" I asked.

"No way," Stinky responded. "I'll be talking with your students to get the information I need that will lead to justice and retribution at our sacred academic institution!" And then with a sickly grin, he uttered, "Now back to class! You have a job to do!

How could I possibly teach after this interrogation? I asked myself. A few minutes later, when I entered my classroom, the security guard, Mozzarella Tillamook, who had been watching my students, gave me the evil eye as if I were some top-notch criminal from *CSI*.

"Your class was unruly," she said. "One of the kids gave me his copy of *Y Tu Mama Tambien* to watch in class, but because it was unrated, I let them watch live coverage of the war in Iraq instead."

"Oh, that makes sense." I knew it was going to be a very long day.

By lunchtime, I had learned from one of my colleagues that Velveeta Asiago appeared to be joyful, almost ecstatic, over the tales of my persecution she had heard through word-of-mouth from other faculty members. That afternoon I received an incendiary note from her.

Mr. Zeiger –

As you know, the tools of the theater are owned by the Thespians who are the backbone of the drama department. Your students, who are NOT Thespians, broke into the cabinet and stole from us. I am buying new tools today and sending you the bill for everything including the Bostitch Stapler, which I've owned for more than two and a half years!

Everyone knows that as a teacher, your passion is being on stage in the spotlight while my passion is WORKING THE SPOTLIGHT and helping my students to succeed in theater – and in life!

You are a disorganized mess who cares little about your fellow staff members and your students.

Warmest regards,

Velveeta Asiago

-Woman of Deep Moral Convictions

I wrote back immediately and left the following note in Velveeta's mailbox:

To the Woman of Deep Moral Convictions:

Nothing was stolen from the theater. It's all part of your hyper-imagination. I realize it was your means of trying every which way to degrade my reputation as a professional who works countless hours for the betterment of humankind. As I have told you repeatedly, almost every tool in the cabinet was purchased through my charitable fundraising efforts long before you were ever hired at this institution. I let you use these tools out of the goodness of my heart. Now be a brave soul and DROP THE CHARGES or forever be haunted by nightmares in your depraved mind.

If you check in the scene shop, you will note that every tool is in the cabinet including your prized possession, the Bostitch Stapler, which, by the way, is NOT a tool.

With deepest gratitude that you finally come clean and tell the truth,
The Man in the Spotlight

At the end of the school day, Vice Principal Stinky Roquefort and Officer Havarti came to my classroom with the good news. After a careful investigation of "the crime scene," they discovered that there had been . . . *no crime!* All tools were accounted for including the Bostitch Stapler. Havarti added that the stapler was even "full of staples as if it had been recently loaded."

A stunning revelation of remarkable findings! I thought to myself. *This guy needs a real job!*

Havarti left the room, but sadly, Stinky Roquefort remained. "There's just one more item that I'm still puzzled over."

"What's that?"

"Who broke into the cabinet? Who unscrewed the screws?"

"I told you Stinky, I did it. Now leave me alone! I have a show to rehearse."

"I'm not done with this investigation, Zeiger. Some *sicko* gangster kid violated a school policy, and you're protecting this teenage malcontent! And let me tell you something. When this kid grows up, he will always know that his early teenage crime was just the beginning of something more sick and disgusting. When you read about *Jòe Shmo* on the front page, that he robbed a 7-11 or a Bank of America or ran off and joined a Somali pirate brigade, I hope you take great satisfaction in knowing that you gave him his first big break!"

Stinky glared at me as if I were some sort of deviant educator lacking any sense of moral fortitude for the job.

"You will never find out who unscrewed that latch, Stinky! The case is closed!"

"*Shocking!*" he exclaimed. "You A.C.L.U. guys are all the same! You destroy what is good about America with your petty idealism!"

"Uh huh yes, of course. Thank you for your continued support," I said sarcastically, "and your insightful commentary."

I will never forget the piercing look in Stinky Roquefort's eyes and that cynical smile as he turned towards the door and proclaimed, "I'll find him! And he'll be punished accordingly . . . with or without your help!"

Later that day, I told Matt never to utter a word to anyone about "our little secret," and I also congratulated him for being such an expert at problem solving.

In a matter of days, the sets were done and the show's opening night was a smash hit with a lengthy standing ovation. No one had any idea that *Sticky Fingers – A Tale of Saks, Lies, and Videotape* would cause such a stir and so much nationwide publicity! Thanks to my students' exceptional marketing skills and the fact that nothing much was happening in the news world the week we opened, we were bombarded by media – the *Los Angeles Times* did a full page story, CNN did a live hookup, *Warner Brothers Celebrity Justice* did a feature story, the BBC interviewed my students via telephone during one of my classes, and my students were on almost every local and national TV news station. Ultimately, this high school show became such a hot new item, that a TV news commentator remarked, "This must be the most famous high school musical in the history of the world!" When the story appeared in newspapers and magazines in China, Japan, Jordan, and on an Italian porno website, I began to believe it! The talented, ambitious, creative cast was thrilled with the attention they had received. Their hard work had paid off with memories for a lifetime.

Meanwhile, Velveeta and Stinky avoided me like the plague. Once in a while, Stinky would pass me in the halls and say something like, "Hey Zeiger, I think I know who did it. I'm going to get him by the end of the semester. You'll see!" And Velveeta would simply utter, "Your kids are anything but

Thespians. You've taught them only to care about publicity, not about the art of *real drama*!"

Two weeks after *Sticky Fingers* closed, hundreds of parents gathered in the school's gymnasium to celebrate the accomplishments of their sons and daughters in academics, sports, community service, and extra curricular activities at the annual Senior Awards program. Before the event began, smarmy Stinky Roquefort approached me and said, "Well, we made it through the year, Zeiger. Are you sure you don't want to give me the name of the evil perpetrator?"

"No," I said, "but I'm surprised you haven't figured it out yet." If it were possible, the guy would have punched me in the face, but there were too many witnesses, so he simply gave me that evil administrative stare and walked over to his seat of prominence – at the front of the stage with all the other administrators.

After a record-breaking three-hour ceremony, the final and most coveted award of the night was to be announced. Teachers, counselors, and administrators annually voted for one student who was ultimately proclaimed the Citizen of the Year, an award for hard work, dedication, commitment, and honesty; an award that most certainly would be a rite of passage for a potential CEO of some major corporation, a state senator, or perhaps even something greater.

Vice Principal Stinky Roquefort approached the microphone, cleared his throat and in perfect diction proclaimed, "It is my honor and privilege to announce the winner of the Citizen of the Year Award, the most prestigious award we give this year." He reached for the sealed envelope as if this were the Oscars of the Academic World. "And the winner is . . . the winner of the Citizen of the Year is . . . MATTHEW SCHNEIDER!"

To the sounds of tumultuous applause from students, parents, and staff, Matt entered the stage as I witnessed one of the great ironic moments of my teaching career. Stinky Roquefort shook Matt's hand, then patted him on his back, and with heartfelt emotion uttered the words, "Good job, son! You are a model for your classmates and your community!"

Instantly, the audience gave the Citizen of the Year a standing ovation. Even Velveeta Asiago was on her feet and remarked, "What a wonderful boy! I know no one more deserving!"

Matt looked over to me with a worldly look of a young scholar and humanitarian who would always reach out and lend a helping hand to anyone who needed assistance. If I could have directed this awards program, I would have had thousands of flower petals drop from the ceiling with a huge spotlight on Matthew Schneider as a choir of school administrators and police officers sang a rousing rendition of *We are Family*

Four years later, while dining on an exquisite selection of cheeses at Wine Steals, a local eatery near my home, I received a phone call from Matt. He wanted to let me know that he would soon be graduating with a degree in Criminal Justice from the University of California at Berkeley, that he was president of the leadership fraternity, and that he had also developed a passion for social and political psychology. At the end of our conversation, he thanked me for giving him the opportunity to perform in the production of *Sticky Fingers* - and for saving his life.

That night, the Asiago, the Gouda, and especially the Stinky Roquefort were delicious paired with a glass of the *Bliss Schoolhouse Red.* The depth and richness of the wine, the succulent taste of the cheeses, and the phone call from the Citizen of the Year made this night a teaching memory to savor forever.

TWELVE

GAMES PEOPLE PLAY

On a warm, sunny day in early June after grading hundreds of essays and exams, Larry and Jack meet at the Courtyard Marriott located at Liberty Station in beautiful Point Loma. Located in a park-like setting overlooking the bay, the hotel bar provides the perfect ambiance for relaxation and serious story- swapping. Because Larry once stayed at the hotel for three months while his home flooded, he knows everyone at this resort. Kurt, Ashley, Chelsea, Stephanie, and Chris welcome him back to the hotel and usher Larry and Jack to the bar where Jim, the celebrated bartender, tries to convince them to change their drink of choice to margaritas, claiming that he makes the best ones in the world. But because consistency is a major part of both Larry and Jack's lives, they decide to consume wine to keep their stories flowing with the proper style and wit.

The conversation of the week focuses on the exhilaration of winning verses the scars of defeat in two unusual competitions. As a result, Jim recommends a bottle of the tasty *Numero Uno Sangria* from the Miramonte Winery in Temecula. After his first sip, Larry notices that the flavors of blackberries, raspberries, plums, citrus, and melons seem to compete with one another, thus inspiring Jack and Larry to tell stories of victory and defeat and the coveted prize of being *Numero Uno.*

After their stories are told, Jack and Larry break the rules and sample Jim's magnificent, award-winning margaritas, an excellent compliment to a late afternoon exchange of stories about winners and losers and the games people play.

How I Beat the Champ

by Jack Beddows

While many people know that I am a somewhat underweight, vegetarian guitar player/school teacher, few are aware that I am also a fearsome figure in the world of martial arts, as the following story illustrates . . . As I squared up for my long awaited re-match with Saulo Ribeiro, one of the all the all-time greats of Brazilian Jiu-Jitsu, I thought to myself, *This is it! My chance for payback! The victory of the underdog will soon be mine!* It was long overdue, as far as I was concerned.

The last time we had competed, I had been soundly beaten, and Saulo had not been at all gracious about it. In the first place, Saulo, who doesn't like to waste his time, only considered accepting that initial challenge after I beat one of his strongest students, long-time black belt and highly esteemed competitor and instructor, Paulo Guillobel, an event of which the outcome was doubtlessly surprising to everyone but me. Immediately after my victory, Paulo wanted a re-match, but I didn't think I could afford to risk it. *Why should I give him another chance?* I thought. *Now's the time to keep moving up through the ranks.*

I heard Saulo ask Guillobel incredulously, "How did he beat you?" In response, Paulo merely hung his head in shame. I couldn't help but smile. Then, after taking an appropriate rest and feeling full of confidence, I approached Saulo and issued my challenge. He accepted with a smirk that clearly communicated what he thought of my chances.

From the beginning, it was a complicated struggle, and for a while there, it seemed a very even match. But once I made my first thoughtless blunder, the reality of the situation quickly became clear, and my confidence turned into dismay. It was obvious I was not ready.

The instant my concentration lapsed, Saulo positioned himself one step closer to ensuring my total defeat. He sensed my frustration and in response he goaded me to try and even further unbalance me mentally and thereby hasten my demise. "Yes, you are right," he snarled, "You should just quit now! Just give up!"

But others on the sidelines, clearly sensing the psychological struggle accompanying the match, shouted support. "Don't give up! It's not over yet!" It was nice to hear, but they were wrong.

"I do so love to win!" Saulo said in his gravel-filled voice when I conceded my defeat, and after the match was done, his admirers immediately flocked to his side, while I was left to lick my wounds in silent consternation. It was a grim moment. But I swore it would be different the next time that Saulo and I tangled.

After two months of extensive preparation, I again issued my challenge to the now bemused champion. He agreed with a scoff, and as we sized each other up before commencing, Saulo started in again with his verbal attempts at disheartening me, hoping to see me defeated before we even began.

"You are too tense!" he said, "That's why you rush and make mistakes!" It almost could have been mistaken for good advice, except for the accompanying ironic smile that seemed to add, *Yes, I can afford to tell you exactly what's wrong with your game, because it won't matter. I'll beat you just the same! Just like last time . . . remember?*

I was scared. Who wouldn't be? But I refused to let it show. When we started with our opening moves, I maintained my composure. Soon, I noticed that once again, Saulo was slightly tentative and far less aggressive than I had imagined he would be in his opening game. But the last time I hoped to capitalize on this, it turned out to be a trap. I reminded myself to stick to my game plan. *Work for small gains, keep improving position, and resist the temptation to go for a quick finish.* Once more, Saulo sought to distract me. "Yes, I can see how this is going to end. I told you, you are way too tense!" Again, this was accompanied by a grim smile with threatening undertones.

My only response was to keep calm and wait for my big chance. And then I saw a clear opening. For a millisecond, I considered that it could be some sort of trap. But no, in his continuing attempts to distract me, Saulo had really distracted himself.

As I made my move, he immediately realized his mistake and scrambled to recover. But he was too late, and I was like a python, tightening my grip and leaving no room for escape. I could feel the frustration in my opponent change to burning anger. It was then that I spoke. And although I tried to keep an even tone, my excitement was no doubt hard to miss. "Knight to B5. I don't think your queen is going to make it alive out of this one." I paused for a moment to let it all sink in before adding, "Looks like chess isn't really your game after all."

"God damn it!" Saulo swore. I had taken out his most powerful offensive piece, and one that he relied on the most heavily. And since I refused to let my concentration lag for the rest of the match, he was never able to recover. A few moves later, he threw down his king in disgust. The metal monarch bounced against the marble board with the sound I had longed to hear: *Tap, Tap.* And that's how I beat Saulo Ribeiro, one of the world's great martial artists at chess.

While in reality, I'm just a hobbyist in the world of martial arts, I do study with Saulo Ribeiro and his younger brother Xande, two of the greatest Jiu-Jitsu practitioners in the world. When they moved to San Diego, they partnered up with my brother Lucas, who runs a judo school, and soon after, we all became good friends. Being at one of the centers of the subculture of Jiu-Jitsu, there is always a stream of visiting students and competitors from all over the world. And in typical Brazilian fashion, there's often a lot of music and fun and socializing including Sunday barbeques, playing guitar and singing, and occasionally, a friendly game of chess.

Go for the Gold!

by Larry Zeiger

The most coveted trophy of the competition was the slightly less than perfectly designed nude male body of a Greek athlete made from plaster of Paris. As Seth looked in the mirror, he could think of nothing but winning this kitschy sculpture and placing it in a prime location for all to see. He struck the pose of an Adonis about to toss the discus on the verge of becoming the godlike champion he was born to be.

"I'm going to win this year, no matter what!" he exclaimed adamantly as he threw some last minute items into his suitcase.

"Even if you lose, Seth, it's the spirit of the competition!" exclaimed his psychologist wife, Carolyn interrupting her husband's vision. "Your cousin, Joe's got a great pitching arm, and when he tosses that thing, it really takes off and sails away. He's won the trophy the last two years. You've got to admit, he's pretty good . . . and he's won medals in the Olympics!"

Seth looked as if he were going to implode due to Carolyn's misguided remarks, but he held back. Instead, he just turned a bluish-red color and screamed, "Olympics! *Shla-lympics!* He won in bobsled racing! Who in the hell cares about Bobsleds? What kind of sport is that anyways?"

Carolyn tried rephrasing her words only to dig herself deeper into her own little abyss. "What's wrong with second place? It's only a game! "

Seth's eyes widened with horror, reminding Carolyn of many of the victims in the *Saw III* movie she had recently watched on Pay4View. She decided not to say another word.

Meanwhile, in another part of town, Joe was eagerly anticipating the big event he had been preparing for the entire year. Seconds after he pulled out of the driveway of their lovely Pacific Beach home, Joe turned to his wife, Marla, and asked, "Did we forget something?"

With a sudden look of realization, she responded, "The kids, Joe! We forgot the kids!" She exited the car and found Alex and Ian in the backyard tossing a Frisbee back and forth. "Come on boys, your dad doesn't want to miss the bus. This afternoon is the annual tournament he's been waiting for all year!"

And so it was, throughout the city of San Diego, fifty-seven lucky people were packing their bags and getting in their cars to ride a Mexicoach tourist bus which was to whisk them south of the border to Rosarito Beach, Mexico where for nearly three decades, my friend, Mary, and I had celebrated our birthdays at our *Fiesta de los Cumpleanos*, a weekend of revelry including a dinner party with Mariachis, a *Ballet Folklorico* show, Salsa dancing, and Karaoke. But the cornerstone event, and definitely the most exciting part of the trip, was hands down, the Tortilla Toss Competition, a *major* contest in which party guests would compete to see who could toss a tortilla the farthest off the pier at the hotel.

The hour-long bus trip to the hotel was a highly spirited one. Our friends including doctors, lawyers, university professors, public school teachers, counselors, actors, musicians, and aspiring *American Idol* rock stars, delighted in escaping to Mexico for two days and acting like college students on spring break. The masks of maturity were shed aside on this spectacular fiesta day in Mexico.

After we checked into our oceanfront hotel rooms, Mary and I shopped at the *mercado* to purchase five hundred corn tortillas. We always made a point of supplying the tortillas for the competition due to the one year when Cynthia, one of Mary's daughters, came up with the "brilliant" idea to secretly freeze her own tortillas, thinking that a frozen tortilla would fly significantly faster than an unfrozen one and ultimately provide her with a victorious first prize trophy in the tournament. However, as luck would have it, just as she was about to make her toss, a seagull swooped down and snatched the tortilla out of her hand. The crunching sound made by the bird devouring the frozen disc was enough to alert the judges that Cynthia had committed a horrible transgression and was ultimately banished from all future tortilla-toss competitions.

Surprisingly, our friends took this unique competition quite seriously, and as a result, many of the participants had proudly developed highly original tossing techniques. The more experienced throwers would employ basic physics and hold their fingers up in the air to determine wind direction and velocity. Others used fancy choreographed moves, rotating their hips and flicking their wrists with great force. Others claimed that a dance move such as a vigorous *pirouette* or *hip hop* form of *popping* prior to the toss of the tortilla would definitely enhance their chances of winning the "spectacular" first place trophy of the plaster of Paris model of *The Discus Thrower* or the runner-up prize of the statue of a cigar-smoking hooker which we had purchased for $2.00 while waiting to cross the San Diego border one rainy night in 1987. The winners of each competition were responsible for painting their winning names on their respective trophies and returning them the following year for the next set of prize-winning champions.

This year's tournament promised to be a hard-fought battle between Seth and Joe, the two cousins who would brag at every possible moment about their "incredible" past performances.

"Did you see my arm? I have an incredible pitching arm, Joe. And it's *all* natural, *not like yours*, with all that Whey Protein you eat morning, noon, and night. I don't need any of that! I was just born with superior strength and the talent to be a winner!"

"Oh really, Seth? We'll see what happens this afternoon. And it's *not* Whey Protein – it's *natural protein* from things like fresh tuna, skinless chicken breasts, and organically grown salmon. I don't need any of those fake powders."

"Oh sure, Joe, and let's not forget a little Human Growth Hormones thrown in for good measure!"

"I don't do illegal substances of any kind, Seth! Oh, and one more thing . . . do you recall that I'm the only one in the family with a gold medal? And that's *Olympic* Gold. Not some cheesy plaster of Paris dime store trophy, Seth! In my proud possession in my trophy case is *real* Olympic Gold!"

"Hey Joe, why don't you remind us all again and again and *again* that you won a trophy in bobsled racing in the Olympics? *Big Deal!* And how many years ago was that anyways?"

At which point, their Aunt Helen piped in, "Will you two just shut your big fat mouths, and let me enjoy my double shot of *Patron* in peace!"

At 4 p.m. after a gentle rainfall, the clouds disappeared, and the tortilla toss contestants, minus Cynthia, joyfully ran out to the pier. Hundreds of tortillas were distributed to all the party guests. Practice tortillas were thrown with wild abandon. Some wavered in the wind and flopped down to the sand, but other more accomplished contestants waited for that perfect gust of wind to send their tortillas soaring into the stratosphere. Each contestant was allowed three practice shots and then tossed what he or she hoped would be the *Tortilla Ultima*, the one that would sail out into the blue Pacific, and provide the winner with first place gold. Judges were positioned on the sandy beach to make sure no one cheated. Whenever a tortilla was tossed further than another, a judge would stand next to that tortilla as a human marker, so there would be no discrepancies at the end of the tournament as to the identity of the lucky winner.

Even Zenobio, the bell captain, and Julio, the general manager of the hotel, entered the competition, but on this windy day in February 2006, no one tossed a tortilla further than Seth. The party guests and workers at the hotel cheered ecstatically. Seth gave high-fives to everyone, and danced around the pier as if he had won the California lottery.

"Oh man! I've won! I've won!" he proclaimed. "It just *sailed away*! I couldn't even see it land! I tossed it so far . . . it just disappeared in the horizon! Carolyn, did you see it land, honey?"

Carolyn played along with her husband. "I've never seen any toss like that in my life, Seth! I'm so proud of you, baby!"

"And I'm the last contestant! What a fantastic toss, and it went even further than the one Joe tossed last year. I'm sure of it!" He then went up to his cousin to rub salt in his wounds. "Joe, did you see it? Did you see it? Amazing! Incredible! Clearly, man, mine is the winning toss! This is so awesome! I mean like it's *really, really awesome*! It's better than any toss you ever made in your life, Joe! *Admit it!"* It was these last words spoken by Seth that changed the course of the spirited competition.

"But my dear cousin, Seth, there's nothing in the rule book that says that last year's winner can't enter again . . . *is there?* Maybe I can surpass your toss or maybe I can't, but I think I deserve to try!" And then in a commanding voice, Joe proclaimed, "Bring on my lucky tortilla!" Suddenly, everyone became quiet on the pier, waiting breathlessly for a response from Seth.

"You can try, but if you watched my tortilla, just seconds ago, sail off into the sunset, you would realize that your chances of surpassing my superb toss are practically nil . . . but go ahead . . . do it, man! Do it, just to get it out of your system! If you must, *you must!"* Seth said with a smile on his face knowing full well that Joe could never match his incredible toss.

Thinking the tournament had ended with Seth the proclaimed winner, some of the guests started leaving the pier. But Joe suddenly felt a gust of wind coming from the south. He grabbed a tortilla, turned his body to the left, took three steps forward, and with the grace of a Baryshnikov, he artfully tossed the tortilla off the pier.

At first it looked as if it were about to land about thirty feet away, but a second gust of wind lifted the tortilla into the air, causing it to sail upward towards the sky. And then to the horror of Seth, Joe's tortilla sailed over the heads of the judges on the beach and continued to fly past the point where Seth's *supposedly* winning toss had landed. Those who had the opportunity to witness this staggering feat of athleticism, technique, and "luck" released audible "oooos" and "ahhhhhs." The vendors on the beach selling toy parachutes began to scream out, *"Estupendo! Maravilloso!"* Applause rippled though the pier and the beach. All the party guests surrounded Joe and patted him on the back and gave him high fives. Everyone was ecstatic, everyone that is, except Seth.

Mortified and feeling utterly defiled, Seth turned as white as a ghost and mumbled, "Joe should *not* have won! It's totally unfair!"

Overhearing her husband's comments, Carolyn tried to comfort him with her overly simplified rationalization she used when talking to small children on playgrounds. "It's no big deal that you lost, sweetie. It's just a silly game!"

"*Silly game? No big deal?* I won the toss fair and square. Joe should be disqualified! How could you say this to me? And you're my wife? I can't believe we're related. You know, he only did this to make me look bad."

"There's nothing wrong with second place, Seth," Carolyn noted, "and furthermore, there are more competitions tonight, including Karaoke! Why not try Karaoke? You always loved to sing in high school."

The suggestion of performing Karaoke made Seth's blood curdle. In high school, he thought he had a good voice – no, not a good voice, a *great* voice – so he auditioned for the Men's Chorus and sadly, was rejected. Every one of his buddies was accepted, but not Seth. It was the ultimate humiliation, and now as an adult, he resigned himself to the fact that he simply couldn't sing well, but then again, he knew he was a better singer than his cousin. In fact, he could really get the crowd going, especially if it were a slightly inebriated crowd, with his rendition of *Sweet Caroline.* That song always sounded great when he sang in the shower with the cool hollow reverb bouncing from the tile walls. *But what if he lost?* Losing at Karaoke after losing the Tortilla Toss Tournament would break Seth's heart into a million pieces. He simply couldn't bear the thought.

And so in front of everyone, he announced that it was simply unfair for Joe to win the trophy two years in a row and that Joe's toss should not be counted. Furthermore, he proclaimed that he should be declared the official winner and that Joe should be disqualified due to possible injections of HGH – human growth hormones – and for paying thousands of dollars to participate in the Cenegenics Medical Institute "to regain his youthful strength and agility!"

Joe paid no attention and held the trophy up in the air, as all winners do. He was the victor and nothing Seth could say or do would change the judge's decision. Marla kissed her husband, and the crowd, except for Seth, cheered.

Things got worse as the afternoon progressed. Fifteen minutes after Joe had been declared the winner of the Tortilla Toss Competition, a letter appeared under Joe's door smothered with 100% Fire Roasted Salsa. He opened the soggy letter and read the following:

Hey Joe –

Okay, you won fair and square. Isn't that what you want to hear EVEN IF IT'S NOT TRUE! I know that you are an Olympiad – so I still believe that you may have used Performance Enhancing Drugs to help with your post competition win. But fine, keep the trophy, man! JUST KEEP THE DAMN THING!

And by the way, I will be forwarding pictures for all to see of your children drinking *Coronas* and shooting off illegal fireworks from last year's trip to Rosarito. And you call yourself a winner when you can't even control your own kids! Oh and you might think twice about peeing off your balcony as you did seven years ago at this annual event, because you never know who could be under that balcony with his camera with crystal clear photos to post on Facebook! I think when we get back to San Diego, a blood test will most likely prove that you should be disqualified from all future competitions!

For now, I can only bask in the glory of the upcoming Karaoke competition where I will win the most coveted award of this trip - the velvet painting of the naked hooker, "Gloria," the one you always wanted to hang in your garage. And next year, I aspire to win the Tortilla Toss trophy and the Karaoke Award. You will be no competition for me!

A Winner for all Seasons,
Seth

Minutes later, a response was delivered to the hotel room of Seth and Carolyn. Seth read the letter from his cousin while his blood pressure soared to 210 over 154.

Seth –

The controversy my latest championship has caused and the hostility I have had to experience are well beyond the bounds of respect and decency that any honest competitor should be forced to endure. Fortunately, I have been blessed with a limitless spirit and an impervious attitude that enable me to ignore the negative bravado of this competitor's lesser opponents. I AM THE WINNER, because I am simply better than you. And I CAN SING!

Tonight, I'm planning to perform the Village People's hit song, "Y.M.C.A." to thunderous applause in the Karaoke competition. Who knows – I may be a two-trophy winner by the night's end! Give it up!
Your lovin' cousin,
Joe

After completing the letter, Seth wondered if he was having a hormone issue, a testosterone boost that was causing him such anger and jealousy over a dumb loss in a sport no one outside of the people attending this party had ever heard of.

That night after dinner, Seth summoned the *Gods of Confidence* and decided he was ready to win the Karaoke competition at all costs. He would sing his heart out, get down on his knees to the audience, and do back flips if necessary to win the coveted velvet painting. He would outdo any "American Idol" in the history of the world. Being humiliated in front of his entire family and friends during the afternoon Tortilla Toss was just too much for him, but tonight would be a different story . . .

The hotel bar was packed with party guests and locals. Everyone was in a festive mood as those who thought they were going to be *The Superstars of Tomorrow* sang one pop song after another. There was, however, a noticeable absence of Seth. Joe suspected he was probably walking the beach preparing for his breakout performance. Suddenly, the double doors of the bar flew open and Seth, dressed in a sequined denim jacket he had purchased from a local street vendor and with hair slicked back with almost an entire tube of *Got2b Glued,* entered the bar and moved with an air of suavity and coolness no one had ever noticed in him before. Silhouetted by light from the stage, he walked up to the DJ, selected his song, and then sat down next to his wife. All eyes in the crowded bar were upon his newly created rock star persona.

Carolyn placed her arms around her husband, looked in his eyes and whispered, "Honey, I know you want to be a winner, but you are already *my* winner! Isn't that enough? Are you sure you want to sing tonight . . . in front of everyone?"

"Carolyn, tonight, you will see 'the new me.' I am going to be the next David Cook, the *Idol Champion* of the Rosarito Beach Hotel!"

"Please, Seth, I'm begging you . . . don't do this! I love you more than anything but you simply can't sing!"

"Just wait until you hear me, sweetie. I've got it down. Neil Diamond would go crazy if he were here!"

It was at that moment that the DJ, Julio Torres, called Seth to the stage. Everyone at the party knew this was going to be a devastating and pathetic attempt of this disco- glam star-wannabe to show up his cousin. With confidence, Seth walked up to the stage. Carolyn prayed for a sudden power outage, but the music came on, and her husband boldly stepped up to the microphone. He opened his mouth and sang . . .

Hands
Touching hands
Reaching out
Touching me
Touching you
Sweet Caroline

Seth not only sang *almost* on pitch, but he belted the lyrics out with confidence and bravado. And he didn't just stand at the microphone; he had the entire number choreographed. His hands were reaching out towards the audience, seductively touching his body, and when he got to the *Sweet Caroline* chorus, he jumped off the stage as his adoring fans swayed their arms in the air reaching out for him! Seth, in turn, began touching everyone's hands in the cantina. When he got to the end of the song, he reached for Carolyn, swooped her up in his arms, and planted a lengthy kiss on her lips. The frenzied crowd went crazy, jumped to their feet, and gave Seth a rousing standing ovation.

At the end of the evening, not even Joe's enthusiastic performance of "Y.M.C.A." could match Seth's stellar interpretation of "Sweet Caroline." The judges were unanimous with their praise. One of the first to congratulate Seth and give him a peace offering of a shot of *Anejo Tequila* was Joe, who hugged his cousin exclaiming, "I wouldn't dare try to challenge you on this one. You were *fantastico!* What a talented family we have - me with tortillas and you with that voice!" Seth downed the Tequila and hugged Joe. The crowd responded with tumultuous applause. *Champions forever!*

The next morning, we all boarded the bright red Mexicoach for our one-hour return trip to San Diego. As we passed through customs at the border, Joe proudly held his plaster of Paris Tortilla Toss Trophy above his heard, and

Seth, holding his prize, stared lovingly into the eyes of the enchanting velvet painting of the naked and incredibly buxom "Gloria," while the customs officers looked on in bewilderment.

When the bus dropped us off in front of my condo in San Diego, we all hugged each other and vowed to return to next year's wildly anticipated *Fiesta de los Cumpleanos – The Festival of Birthdays,* where we would all have the opportunity to sing and dance, and experience the golden moments of our lives.

THIRTEEN

STORMY WEATHER

It is that rare day in San Diego where it is actually raining, not the simple drizzle that most Southern Californians label as "downpours," but a rain where you actually might want to use an umbrella. From the eastern mountain slopes, you can hear the faint rumble of thunder, if you listen carefully.

Jack and Larry meet at Caffé Calabria, a charming wine bar, coffee house and award-winning roaster located in North Park. Arne Holt, the charismatic owner, ushers us in, and immediately we are given the royal treatment by his staff including our server, Beat, the pizza chefs, Leo and Eric, and the baristas, Anton and Max.

But it is wine Larry and Jack are after, wine to compliment their stormy weather tales. As a result, Larry selects a bottle of a 2005 *Dracula Zinfandel* from the Vampire Vineyards of Paso Robles. An alluring, mysterious flavor stimulates Larry's imagination and causes him to recall a horrible nightmare he had as a teenager. In a matter of a few seconds, he finds the aroma of the wine enticing and hypnotic, and feels he is becoming possessed by the magical flavors.

Not in the mood for a red wine, especially one that so overwhelms the senses and the palette, Jack selects a bottle of a 2006 *Twisted Chardonnay*. The crisp green apple taste reminds him of a Thanksgiving dinner that turns into a family disaster.

The faint sounds of thunder rumble through the dining room, followed by brief flashes of lightning, which add to the mood of the exchange of these dark and forbidden stories.

The International Thanksgiving Day Thriller

by Jack Beddows

I was with two friends of mine, Sabine and Wolfgang, a lovely German couple I had known for years. Wolfgang was a research scientist with a doctorate from Oxford, doubtlessly the best educated of all my acquaintances. Sabine was a fellow schoolteacher and my first good friend from when I entered my then-new career enriching the lives of the various ne'er do wells collectively known as America's youth. The three of us, collectively too cheap to pay for parking at San Diego's Cabrillo National Monument Park, a sightseeing stop not far from the neighborhood to which I had recently moved, were now trudging along the road, hoping to make it there before sunset.

The park is situated at the top of an isthmus with a harbor inlet to one side and the Pacific Ocean to the other. It is a lovely spot. But that particular afternoon, there were dark storm clouds rolling in as the daylight began to wane. We had to park a good jog away from the promontory jutting off into the ocean, where Juan Cabrillo, Spanish conqueror and explorer, had landed centuries before. Old Juan had used the height of the point to survey the land and, if I had to guess, to decide how best to squeeze all he saw into profit. As for us, it seemed doubtful that we would be able to make it all the way to where the cream of imperial Spain once stood before we were rained on for our presumption. After all, he risked crossing the world in a wooden boat, and we weren't even willing to put up eight bucks for parking. But still, we would trudge on. That's the German way, and who was I to argue with that?

As we continued, wide swaths of sloping grass began to open up on either side of the road. It would have been unalloyed pleasantry, if not for the ordered rows of graves in the military cemetery that had commandeered much of the otherwise lovely real estate. It was then that I turned to consider my friends. Sabine was tall, beautiful, and pleasant, and my only criticism of her was that she liked to wear very thick-heeled boots, which made her temporarily taller than me at social gatherings. Wolfgang was also pleasant but very intense. It wasn't long after we met that he was gripping me by the shoulders, so excited and glad was he to find someone as sympathetic as myself to any of the wide range of political and environmental issues that he considered so important, and yet so ignored by the average person that he thought he might go mad at the lack of reason surrounding him. And it was hardly a rare occurrence for him to be seen wrestling with intense thoughts and emotions in a manner to do Goethe proud. He also more than justified Sabine's wearing of thick heels, as at a strapping six-foot-four, Wolfgang was the largest scientist I had ever met. In short, the defining characteristics of the pair were that they were statuesque, well-educated, and most of all, exceedingly nice. It was because of their extreme pleasantness that I was hesitating.

You see, for the last twenty minutes or so, Sabine and Wolfgang had been dropping periodic hints about how they really had no plans for the upcoming Thanksgiving holiday, and it was obvious they were hoping for an invitation. On the one hand, I was flattered. Yes, it was true that many of their other acquaintances were leaving town to be with their own families, and their relatives weren't likely to come all the way from Germany to observe Thanksgiving. I knew they considered me a good friend and honestly wanted to share in the warmth of my family, which tugged at my heartstrings a little, no doubt. But then again, *they didn't know my family.*

"Ooh! It's starting to come down a little now!" Sabine exclaimed, breaking me out of my reverie. The rain hadn't really started yet, just a speck or two, but I could feel the tension building. It's funny how when you know a couple, you can really understand what each has to deal with in the other, like the private scenes that must be so much more intense than the public versions of the conflicts inevitable in any relationship. And if Wolfgang's public displays of intensity signaled occasional moodiness at home, Sabine's sticking point was a tenacity that bordered on the obsessive once she had her mind set on something. In short, I knew that if I didn't answer the unspoken question soon, she was going to decide that I was missing their holiday hints due to some vague cultural barrier, and that she was going to have to be more direct.

"So Jack, what are *you* and *your family* doing this Thanksgiving?" she asked, thereby confirming my fears as I started to feel there was really no way around it. If I had known what was to come, I would have risked the inexplicable rudeness of refusing to invite them, rather than face the frightening scene ahead. But of course, the future's not ours to know, and at the time I reasoned with myself that perhaps it wouldn't be so bad after all.

"Oh hey! I have an idea!" I said, as if I only then had put two and two together, "Why don't you and Wolfie come to Thanksgiving with my family and me? I'm sure it will be really nice!"

Immediately after I spoke, the thunder cracked like an exclamation, the lightning sparked across the sky, and the rain started to come down in buckets.

As we ran back to my car, about a quarter of a mile down the little traveled road, I glanced back again at the cemetery sloping off the side of the road and hissed to myself in a whisper, "My God! What have I done?"

No matter how well dressed they are come the holidays, there's no way to hide who your family really is. Though I love them dearly, as a child, back in Massachusetts, I had lived in embarrassment for as long as I could remember.

One habit of my father's that often led to ridicule was giving advice to my friends and me whenever we were about to leave the house and ride off on our bikes.

"Watch out for traffic! And if you see any cars coming at you, just jump into a ditch! Jump into a ditch!"

Where to start? I would wonder, my brow wrinkling in consternation, as my friends would suppress their various guffaws and chortles.

"You know, not every street in the world comes with a ditch, Dad," I often thought about saying, but I knew it would be pointless. My father's heart was in the right place of course, but this strange offshoot of over-protectiveness was a source of boundless amusement for others, and often, my friends would sneak up behind and then startle me, shouting, "Look out, Jack! Jump into a ditch! Just jump into a ditch! HAHAHAHAHAHA!!!"

"Yeah, ha! That's a good one! Well, I gotta get to class guys . . . "

But my father wasn't the only one on my mind. There was also my brother, Lucas, to worry about.

"'The Jew is using the Black Man as muscle against you!' Ha Ha!"

Sure, I liked the *Blues Brothers* movie too, but who knows when this sort of unexplained quote could spark an international incident? It seemed like just the sort of thing my brother might unleash at a holiday gathering.

The only other guests scheduled to appear were Andrew, a friend of my brother and me, and his lovely mother. Andrew was a nice guy, but in recent years, he had become completely addicted to a certain stimulating substance typically produced somewhere in the South American region of the world. Sadly, I was counting on him to be one of the stabilizing influences in the trial to come.

Before my friends arrived, I decided to calmly and maturely approach my family to discuss my concerns. First, I talked to my mother.

"Mom! You have to help me! Don't let anything bad happen, I beg you! You have to stop them! You have to help me!"

One would think this sort of un-prefaced pleading would be met with confusion and questions. My mother, however, knew exactly what I was talking about. But unfortunately, she had developed over the years her own coping mechanism for conflict, which was to pretend nothing was happening until the problem went away.

"Oh! Stop exaggerating!" she chided me.

Meanwhile, my brother overheard this snippet of conversation from the other room and sauntered over saying, "What? Are you worried about embarrassing *Ze Germans*? Do you think we're going to start making Hitler jokes or something? Maybe do the John Cleese scene from *Fawlty Towers*?" This last question was a reference, for those that don't already know, was to a British television show in which John Cleese, one of the stars of the Monty Python crew, portrayed a small hotel owner named Basil Fawlty who suffered a head injury and decided to entertain his German guests by goose-stepping around the room impersonating everyone's favorite Teutonic dictator. I used to think that scene was hilarious. But when my brother brought it up, the mere mention of it made me cringe.

I looked at my mom one last time with pleading eyes, and then the doorbell rang like a *Poe-ish* knell of doom.

"Oh what a lovely home your parents have!" Sabine cooed, as I opened the door.

"Ha! Ha! Lovely, yes!" I responded, laughing for no particular reason except my extreme distraction and nervousness.

But as the next hour or so before the meal passed, nothing too unpleasant happened. I stretched out the house and grounds tour as long as I could, trying to engage in lengthy conversations about the orange tree, but even back in living room, nothing went too out of control. Our friend, Andrew, who besides the modern day snuff habit, had also in recent years adopted the curious trait of talking like a character from an old western picture. He came up with a few bemusing comments, but otherwise, he was on his best behavior, as he typically was in the presence of his no-nonsense mother. My dad may have coughed once or twice with a bit too much enthusiasm, causing the occasional cringe, but the Californian climate he had retired in had indeed mitigated his level of *phlegm* to mostly bearable levels. My brother may have said a few comments that came across with a bit too much macho swagger, which no doubt registered on sensitive ears, but overall, he was not terribly offensive. I decided that if this was the direction the entire holiday event was to take, I could live with it.

Finally, it was time for the long-awaited Thanksgiving dinner. Although more of a secular family, we nevertheless felt obligated to keep up appearances in front of our gathered guests and say grace this one time a year. I forgot all about my own agnostic leanings and began to pray fervently that all would continue to go well. Then we looked up, and it was time to begin the meal in earnest.

For the next ten to fifteen minutes, the food kept everybody too busy to talk. An occasional, polite "Oh! This is delicious!" between bites was the extent of the conversation, and I thanked God for that blessed time. Sadly, as our hunger lessened, people started to shift their attentions from the food in front of them to their companions. *Oh Lord, save us!* I again prayed internally. *Let this, the talk of thy charges, stay light and innocuous!* Then, as the conversation developed, I couldn't help but notice that for the last few minutes, my brother had been smiling broadly. I could only hope that it was the thought of the delicious dessert to come, but really, I knew better.

"So, speaking of Hitler . . . " Lucas began as he looked, still smiling, at the guests at the table.

"What! No one's been speaking about Hitler!" I wanted to scream as I nearly gave myself whiplash twisting my head up in shock. But I didn't. I didn't do anything but stare like a deer caught in headlights. My eyes darted over to my guests, whose mouths now were hanging open mid-chew, while my brother continued in what he no doubt thought was nothing short of charming and hilarious.

"Yes, apparently some recent evidence has surfaced supporting the idea that our esteemed Governor, Arnold Schwarzenegger, was actually the product of one of Hitler's last genetic experiments for producing the Aryan Superman. And that his recent rise to power here in America, is not only no accident, but also is just the beginning stages. There's been a lot of talk about changing the Constitution to allow those born outside of the U.S. to have the chance to run for the highest office in the land. All of this," my brother then paused conspiratorially, " is in strict accordance to the master plan."

The only response at the dinner table was a profound and horrified silence, followed by my mom's nervous muttering, "More peas anyone?"

I quickly excused myself, not having the heart to open the can of worms that would be an honest discussion of all the things that were wrong with what we had just heard, instead flying to the room a few doors down which contained my stand-up piano, which my own tiny apartment was too small to contain. I began to play moody music like any tortured madman or phantom of the opera might. I could only assume that my German friends, whom I had abandoned to their fate, would quickly follow suit upon which I would start apologizing to them profusely. Oddly, however, they stayed put at the table for a while even though they must have been quite done with their meals. *Could it have been manners?*

Finally, Sabine came in to join me, and equally unable to broach a discussion of the horrors we had just witnessed, she immediately began to talk in depth about music. So I continued to play dumb and not talk about the obvious discomfort we were all feeling.

Meanwhile, back at the table, as I later learned, my father and Wolfgang had entered into a spirited discussion about global warming. Some background is needed to be able to understand just how wretched this conversation could get. For one, the film *An Inconvenient Truth* had yet to bring to the public the visual displays of charts and graphs and live footage of the melting poles that would win over popular opinion far more powerfully than the best unread reports had done, and furthermore, the topic was still marginally under debate in some circles. But Wolfgang was a scientist with his PhD in physics from Oxford University, whose life's work happened to be the study of the complex effects of global warming on ocean currents, so you could say he was somewhat ahead of the curve in his certainty that mankind's overall behavior has indeed had an effect on climate change.

The other major element in the equation was my father's contrary nature and his proven track record for arguing with people, just to be difficult, on subjects that they clearly have more knowledge of than he ever possibly could. My father would argue with a judge about the law, a plumber about the best way to fix a pipe, a doctor on what was *really* the best remedy for this or that condition, and even as late as the early nineties, he was still trying to argue with me that there was in fact no real evidence that cigarette smoking had any clearly established links to the impairment of people's health—all in the name of a desire to show off his own, broad, if often thin, knowledge base.

"I'm no slouch as a scientist either, you know!" he apparently argued to Wolfie, "And there are many studies out there that contradict everything you've just said about global warming!"

Poor confused Wolfie, didn't know what else to do but to stay at the table and continue to try to lead my father to the truth about global warming, the impossibility of which, soon led him to higher and higher levels of frustrated rage. When the rest of the dinner party finally broke up, my father was as cheery as could be, thinking he had just been engaging in a spirited but friendly bout of scientific discussion. But when Wolfgang rose from the table, he did so to find Sabine and to demand that they flee this house of . . . I believe the quote was . . . "total assholes."

Everything I feared had come true. In fact, it was even worse than I had imagined. I spent the next several minutes trying to console Wolfie, only to find that he was, inconsolable. In part, Wolfgang had become furious because his father and mine had very similar personalities, and he tended to get into the same types of arguments with his own progenitor to the point that they had completely soured their own relationship, more or less irreparably. So, that Thanksgiving dinner was like a re-visitation of all the worst moments from his youth. Although I was both sympathetic and apologetic, I also found a little fault with Wolfgang. I couldn't help but wonder how such a smart guy couldn't see the value in doing what I had done, namely, run away.

Of course, no one should be subjected to this sort of social inanity in the first place, and that's why I initially had tried my hardest *not* to invite Sabine and Wolfgang over for Thanksgiving dinner. If only they would have bothered to notice. But even still, if you find yourself in a weird situation, *why sit through the whole show?* I felt that his decision to stay and argue only confirmed a trait that I had already suspected in my friend, which was an anger at the world's lack of logic, which after a while, becomes itself, completely illogical. On the other hand, perhaps I just felt that way, because while it's one thing to call your own family a bunch of assholes, it's quite another to hear a friend say it repeatedly.

The next day, my brother and father, the two members of my family that are the most alike, each came up to me to apologize. Not for their own behavior of course, but for each other's.

"Boy! Dad just wouldn't stop harassing your friend after you left the table. It was ridiculous! At least, I think I was able to keep the conversation lighthearted and fun before that!"

That's right I thought, *Germans just love Hitler jokes! Nothing warms up a couple from Munich that you just met like jokes about Der Fuhrer.*

Later, my Dad cornered me to say, "Well, I thought Lucas' behavior was totally unacceptable yesterday, telling a wretched and offensive joke like that! Fortunately though, I steered the conversation after that into some very fruitful scientific discussion. "In fact," he continued with particular warmth and pride, "I think I helped your friend to see that there are always two sides to any issue, and that the truth often lies somewhere in the middle."

Sure it does, I thought, *tell it to the dying polar bears.* Within a year or so of this holiday disaster, I finally met Wolfgang's own father at Wolfgang and Sabine's wedding. It was then that I had a chance to listen to some Teutonic bluster, which I believe was even stronger and more relentless than my father's English variety. But I noticed that since all the guests at the reception merely nodded their heads to any of Wolfgang's father's potentially provocative statements, he quickly sought out his son for a truly lively discussion.

It seemed like another festive event was going to be ruined when Sabine quickly directed the DJ to start playing an old school Michael Jackson record to which, to my great surprise, Wolfgang and one of his childhood friends visiting from Germany immediately responded. They both abandoned any discussion they were engaged in and hit the dance floor, breaking out in incredibly authentic imitations of all of Michael's 1984 era dance moves, which as kids, they had apparently practiced obsessively whenever their family lives became too much to bear.

Perhaps I had been too hasty in my judgment of Wolfgang and what I thought was his lack of coping mechanisms. Meanwhile, Wolfgang's father, bereft again of his favorite sounding post, looked around the room until he saw me standing by the bar and started to walk towards me.

I thought about quickly ducking outside, but instead, I said to myself, *Fuck it! Tell it to the dying polar bears.* I put down my drink, hit the dance floor, and tried to pull off my own miserable version of the moonwalk, all the while thinking about picking up a copy of *Thriller* to have handy for the next time I have guests over to my family's house for a major holiday.

Children of the Night

by Larry Zeiger

One hot, muggy August evening in 1961, thunder rumbled through my family's old turn-of-the-century house. Lightning streaked the sky. I had just turned thirteen, and my parents considered me old enough to baby-sit for my six-year-old brother, Dickie, while they went to a movie at the Cedar and Lee Theater, which was everybody's favorite hangout on bad weather days in Ohio. My father couldn't wait to see the latest Shirley MacLaine and Dean Martin movie, *All in a Night's Work,* but my mother was concerned about the impending storm that promised at least two inches of rain.

"I don't know if we should go, Mickey. The weather forecast is really horrible! What if the streets flood? Maybe we should stay home tonight."

"This is Cleveland, Sylvia. The weather is always like this," my father responded astutely as if he were a master meteorologist. "The theater is only a few blocks away, and a little rain never hurt anyone. Now are we going or not?"

My mother agreed to take the *harrowing* five-block journey to the theater. Overly concerned about leaving me in charge, she asked, "Are you sure you and Dickie will be okay?"

I assured her that I was a mature, sophisticated kid who was fully capable of making adult decisions, which included taking care of my rambunctious little brother.

"I left some pot roast in the fridge if you get hungry," my mother said. That was no surprise to me. Ever since I was born, there was always pot roast in the refrigerator.

My parents left for their night out at the movies in their '56 Chevy Sedan, which the entire neighborhood could hear as it roared down our driveway amidst the torrential rainfall.

I suddenly felt so independent as if I were the *Man of the House.* I turned on our modern new 18 inch RCA Victor TV, waited a few minutes for the picture to appear, and then flipped through the dial seeing what was on the three stations. Instantly, Dickie interrupted my program search.

"Play with me! Play with me NOW!" my brother demanded.

"Not now, Dickie! Let's watch *Leave it to Beaver* and after that, my favorite movie, *Dracula* with Bela Lugosi.

"Dracula? Who's he?"

"Dracula's a vampire, and he will scare the shit out of you!"

He began to whimper. "You said a bad word!"

"No I didn't," I replied, and then became suddenly philosophical. "There are no such things as 'good words' and 'bad words.' There are *good* people and *bad* people, but words are just words!" I felt so mature with my astute observations.

"I don't get it."

"Dickie, why don't you play with your model cars?" I quickly suggested.

"No!"

"Your model train?"

"I don't want to play with my model anything! I want to go upstairs! We never go up there, and I'm afraid to go by myself. Take me. Please! Please! Please! *Larry, Please!*" he pleaded with that annoying six-year-old whiny voice.

At that moment, thunder rippled through our house. Dickie ran over to me and held on to my leg. "That thunder is so loud. It scares me!"

"Then why do you want to go upstairs? There's nothing to do up there. Mom and Dad just use it to store things like old books and magazines and winter clothing. If you're afraid of a little thunder, why would you want to go upstairs into the spooky, creepy, cobweb-infested attic? Come on, the *Beaver* is just about to start! Let's go watch."

"No! I want to go upstairs! You never give me anything I really want. You're my brother. I thought you loved me. I need to grow up. I need to *experience the world.* Now take me upstairs! I want to see if there are ghosts up there!"

Suddenly, a branch of the tree hit the roof of our house followed by more lightning and another crash of thunder, and then . . . a creaking sound from the other side of the house.

"Come on," he insisted. "I want to see why no one ever goes upstairs." My brother always liked to explore the unknown, and he was a true master of manipulation.

"All right, let's go." I answered, figuring one good scare, and that would be it for him. We climbed the dark staircase, reached the top landing, and entered the bedroom that no one ever used. The walls were filled with my father's college collection of Vargas sketches of nude women. Before my father met my mother, he had the rather bizarre hobby of catching Monarch butterflies and strategically placing the colorful insects over the breasts and pelvic regions of the women in the pictures. My dad was proud of his "artistic" creation while my mother never allowed anyone to go upstairs to the attic bedroom to view the "exhibit."

"Those are so funny," Dickie observed, "but why did Dad put butterflies all over the naked girls?"

"It's a blending of art and nature, Dickie."

"I don't get it."

"After you are *Bar Mitzvahed*, you will!"

The wind began to howl like a banshee. As we walked closer toward the door of the walk-in closest that led to the attic, my brother became more assertive.

"I want to see what's behind that door."

Suddenly, the crackling sounds of thunder shook the room. Dickie grabbed my hand tightly. With a little tremor in his voice, he bravely proclaimed, "Open the closet door. I'm not afraid!"

But I was. "Dickie, let's go downstairs. It's almost your bedtime," I said in my most authoritarian voice.

But my younger brother became even more persistent. "Open the door! I want to see what's behind it."

He looked up at me with those enormous eyes filled with wonder, and I was forced to give in. We opened the door slowly. The large attic closet was warm, dark and musty. It was where my mother would hang our winter clothing sealed in plastic for the summer months. The howling wind from outside must have seeped in through one of the windows causing the large plastic bags to move . . . as if there were something living inside of them! I jumped back, but my brother continued to explore.

"Dickie, let's go! I've seen enough!"

"What are you scared or something? It's only plastic blowing in the wind."

That moment, the lights began to flicker, and in seconds, we found ourselves in complete darkness. I could feel a soft breeze on my neck that gave me chills – and then, more thunder followed by brief flashes of lightning. A few seconds later, the light came back on, but my brother had disappeared. I turned immediately for the door.

"Dickie, where are you? Dickie? Quit playing around!" There was dead silence. "Dickie? Answer me now! This is *not* funny! Mom and Dad'll kill you!"

Then I heard a rustling of plastic and noticed my brother was hiding behind one of my mother's fake fur coats. I decided to go along with his playful little game. "Oh Dickie. What will I do without you? You must have been *vaporized* or swept away by nighttime spirits." I could hear more rustling of plastic. "Goodbye brother. I'm leaving. Too bad it has to end this way."

Suddenly, with tears in his eyes, my brother ran into my arms. "That was mean!" he proclaimed. "You were playing with my emotions," an unusual assessment for a six-year-old (but not when you consider that nineteen years later he would become a lawyer).

We went downstairs, and after telling my brother that it was time for him to go to bed, he began screaming and throwing tantrums. To quiet his petulant, piercing *baby-babble*, I immediately made a bargain with him. "If I give you a scoop of vanilla ice cream, will you shut up?"

"I want chocolate syrup and whipped cream too. Please! Please! *Please!*"

After the third scoop of ice cream, my brother took off to play with his toy cars, his teddy bear, and his beloved Dumbo. Soon after, he went to sleep as torrential rains fell and gusts of wind rattled the windows.

Finally, I had a little peace in my life. I turned on the television and plopped myself down on the old green velvet sofa. Todd Browning's classic of *Dracula* was just starting. The storm outside intensified, and the occasional gusts of wind seeping through the windows adjacent to the couch sent chills down my spine but created the mood I wanted.

I turned out all the lights and became completely immersed, almost hypnotized by the legend of the enigmatic Prince of Darkness. The fact that the Count in his stylish black cape could instantly transform himself into a bat was utterly cool to me. On the other hand, I didn't quite understand why the two sexy women in the castle, Mina and Lucy, could fall under the Count's spell and let him suck the blood from their necks without ever putting up a fight. I found it hard to believe that anyone could be hypnotized merely by looking in the eyes of someone else, even if that someone were a vampire.

During the commercial break I began to reconsider the subject of hypnosis from a more rational perspective. After all, wasn't it Annette Funicello, that sexy Mouseketeer, who made me "get out the broom and sweep the place clean" as a child? Then there was Connie Stevens, that fantastic star of the classics, *Parrish* and *Susan Slade*. She was my dream girl to whom I would have given the world, just to be standing next to her! And was there any guy at the age of thirteen who didn't go nuts when he saw Sandra Dee running on the beach in *A Summer Place?*

After the commercial break, things began to become even more terrifying and provocative. Dracula flew through Lucy Weston's window and kneeled beside her bed. With a perverse smile of sensuous delight on his pancake-white face, he sank his fangs into her neck.

"*Ewwww!* How gross is that!" I said out loud. And yet, there was something about Dracula and Lucy that made me pose the question to myself: *Would I have to wear a cape and lots of eye make-up in order to have a seductive effect on women like Annette, Connie, Sandra . . . or Lucy?*

My mind began to wander as I thought about Jenny Felcher, the first girl I had dated, and how we snuck into the Cain Park Theater to watch the summer outdoor musical, *Oklahoma*, from the hillside. Just before the play began, we heard barking dogs in the darkness of the night.

"The barking of those dogs is so awful!" Jenny exclaimed. "They sound like wolves."

I responded in a lush romantic Transylvanian accent, "Listen to them. They are the 'children of the night.' What music they make," at which point, she declared, "You're weird. Take me home." I felt like a balloon in deflation mode, and it was my last date with Jenny Felcher.

My thoughts then returned to the movie, *Dracula*. It was the climactic moment when Van Helsing was about to battle with the Count. Another commercial for Ajax, "the foaming cleanser." The wind intensified, and I could hear creaking sounds from the attic, *or was it just my imagination?* I closed my eyes and imagined Dracula's intense eyes and sardonic smile. The Count reminded me of my father who was born in Budapest, the same region of the world as Dracula. On the other hand, my father spoke perfect English and, thankfully, never wore capes or sucked blood from lovely women . . . although as a physician he did take blood from them. *Could there be a connection?*

The booming sounds of thunder and the bright flashes of lightning became a dissonant symphony with no end in sight. *Was that the storm outside . . . or the one in the movie?* I pulled a blanket over my head.

Dracula was about to assault another victim in the attic of his castle. He walked into a long closet where several large plastic bags appeared to be filled with . . . *Wait a minute! Was that attic in the castle? Or was it in my house?* And then I saw the bodies of several naked women sealed in plastic! When the Count unzipped the bags, the women, one by one, came to life and smiled deadly smiles while Monarch butterflies flapped their wings against their bodies. In a chorus of hideous voices, vampire women beckoned, "Larry, come with us, and enjoy eternal life!"

There was a constant knocking in my head. I looked away, and to my horror saw Lucy Weston, dressed in a translucent nightgown, blood dripping from her ruby red lips, sitting in the chair by the fireplace where my mother would do her daily knitting. "Everything is fine, Larry." said the hideous apparition. "Become part of our dark world! Join us, Larry. Be immortal and . . . live forever!"

Suddenly, the Prince of Darkness, making wolf-like howls, appeared from behind the piano. He began to circle my body with his grotesque cape that was covered with spatters of fresh human blood. I tried desperately to wake myself from this nightmare.

"It's no use, Larry. You're one of us." Lucy proclaimed, her fangs dripping blood onto the carpet.

"I am *not* one of you! Now get back into the TV!" I declared.

"You are one of us!" Dracula shouted.

"One of us, Larry . . . one of us . . . one of us . . ." Lucy's voice echoed throughout the house.

Suddenly, Dracula disappeared and moments later, reappeared outside the house on the front porch staring back at me through the living room window with a look so intense, so evil, that I could not move.

Out of nowhere, Lucy appeared by his side. "Larry, open the door!"

The knocking sound in my head grew louder and louder. "Open the door!" Dracula screamed.

Mesmerized by the sight of a vampire and a near-naked lady on our front porch, I began to wonder, *What could the neighbors be thinking? Would my friends ostracize me forever? What would the Rabbi say to me Saturday at the synagogue?* The knocking continued. I suddenly realized that I was no longer in control of my existence. I moved away from the window.

"Open the door! What's wrong with you?" the Prince of Darkness bellowed.

In a trancelike state, I turned away from this evil force and slowly walked to the back of the house. Instantly, Dracula appeared, his face smashed against a window, screaming "Larry, Open the door! Have you lost your mind?"

I stared into the face of Dracula, which suddenly *morphed* into the face . . . of my father! It was an incredible effect better than any Ray Harryhausen movie I had ever seen. I was aghast! Mortified! Transfixed! *Was it really my father or a clever disguise by the Prince of Darkness?*

"Your mother and I are pleading with you, Larry. Open the door! We forgot our keys!"

Caught between two worlds, I immediately turned from the man at the back door and ran to the front of the house. And then looking through the window, I saw my mother with a shattered look on her face, screaming, "Let us in, Larry! Please! Why are you doing this to us?"

For some strange reason, I was not able to react. I looked at her but couldn't speak. *Was this a trick? Maybe the woman at the door was Lucy . . . and not my mother!*

Suddenly, my little brother appeared on the staircase, shouting, "What's all the racket? I can't sleep!"

I avoided Dickie and returned to the back of the house and saw my ice skates on the floor by the door. Wanting to escape this nightmarish world of which I had no control, I slipped on the skates while my parents watched in horror through the kitchen window outside our house. I then opened the door, and on a rain-drenched night in late summer, I descended the steps of our porch ready to skate on an imaginary frozen lake but, instead, fell into my father's arms. He grabbed my shoulders and shook me, and yelled, "What's wrong with you! Wake up! Have you lost your mind?"

My mother ran up the driveway, just as my father was shaking the daylights out of me. Tears streaming down her face, she cried out, "Larry, please don't do this to us! Tell us you're just . . . just acting!"

My brother screamed at the top of his lungs, "Larry's scaring me! He's crazy-nuts like a cuckoo!" By this time, half the neighbors were racing over to our house to see what had happened.

I suddenly snapped out of whatever dark dream had possessed me. I had no idea why I was wearing my ice skates in August. I didn't dare tell my parents about seeing the Prince of Darkness in our living room, nor did I say a word about the near-naked Lucy sitting in my mother's favorite knitting chair.

My mother and father embraced me and insisted that I must have been sleepwalking. But at the age of thirteen, I had never heard of anyone sleepwalking except for victims of vampires in 1930's gothic horror movies. After I removed my ice skates, my parents continued hugging me and made me assure them that I was not insane. My mother, not quite convinced that I had made a complete return to reality, suggested that I tell her exactly what happened that night to cause me to act so strangely.

Not wanting to discuss my visions of naked women and Monarch butterflies with my mother, I instead found the courage to confess my Freudian nightmare to my father. "Dad, I was so frightened. I hope I never sleepwalk again or have this horrible nightmare. It was so real. I swear I saw Dracula in our living room, and you won't believe this, but he was . . . he was . . . surrounded by naked ladies with butterflies all over their bodies!"

With the wisdom of a philosopher, my father responded with great simplicity. "Butterflies are beautiful insects, Larry."

"It's not the butterflies, Dad. It's . . . well . . . you know . . . "

With great compassion, my father interrupted me and said, "As you grow older my son, these dreams may reoccur. Life becomes stranger and more beautiful, and then one day, Larry, it all becomes . . . so real."

I wasn't quite sure what my father was talking about, but I thanked him and pretended to understand. When the storm subsided, I said 'goodnight' to my parents and my brother and went to my bedroom. Even though I wanted to act like an adult, I still left the door to the hallway open just enough to let a stream of light into my room. I then made sure the windows were locked and the curtains closed. I sank into my bed, covered myself with blankets, and for the moment, felt safe and secure.

I closed my eyes and thought about my girlfriend, Jenny, in her cute little bikini running on the sands at Mentor Headlands Beach. The vision was suddenly interrupted when I heard the flapping of butterfly wings in my room. I jumped out of my bed, checked the closets, looked behind the curtains, and searched the hallway but found nothing. *Must be my overactive imagination,* I thought.

I returned to my bed, and drifted into the darkness of night where even more colorful butterflies and beautiful women danced in my dreams and later . . . into my life.

FOURTEEN

THE JOURNEY WITHIN

Larry and Jack meet at The Fairouz Café, a wonderful Middle Eastern restaurant and art gallery, to discuss major turning points in their lives, events that truly have shaped their characters.

Jack tells a story about the ups and downs of a childhood experience that has a major impact on his adult life. Larry counters with his tale about a trip to the Emergency Room where he finds himself retreating from the world of reality into a world inside himself that is both wildly unpredictable and incredibly revealing.

For his wine and story pairing, Jack selects *Elevation Peaks and Valleys Sauvignon Blanc* from the South Coast Winery. The clear, clean, crisp taste of the wine reminds him of a time when life appears so uncomplicated, but change is just around the corner.

Larry's medical story is so abstract and fanciful that the owner of the restaurant, Al Nashashibi, who is also a gifted artist, insists that Larry selects the complex and lively 2006 *Artezin Zinfandel* from Mendocino County. The richness of the fantastic *Artezin,* not only represents Larry's total being, but the wine is also filled with the necessary amounts of Resveratrol to make Larry's medical story both revelatory and heartfelt.

The Poseidon Syndrome Vs. The Big Wheel Effect

BY JACK BEDDOWS

Statistically speaking, older siblings are far more likely to go on to achieve greater success in the world than their younger family members. At first, this seems like a broad and unfounded generalization, and for the younger brothers and sisters out there, one that tends to evoke feelings of resentment and skepticism. However, this is just because it is often too painful to probe the obvious rationale for what at first appears to be an arbitrary statement. The painful truth is that just as a racehorse can be trained to win or lose depending on the succession of opponents its trainer runs against it, so too do older siblings learn to dominate their younger brothers and sisters, often leaving them just a little bit behind the curve.

One time in junior high, my friend, Cameron, confessed to me in an offhand manner when we were hanging out one afternoon during our senior year in college, "I tied my little brother to a deck chair and pushed him into our pool."

"Boy, Cam, that must have sucked for him," I replied. Being a younger brother myself, I could honestly relate to the situation.

He continued calmly, "Yeah, especially because I didn't realize how hard it was going to be to drag him out of the deep end before he drowned. I barely got him out of there, and it was just in the nick of time!"

Although very familiar with tales such as these, both from my own life, and from the lives of friends that I grew up with in the Boston area, there was still something particularly poignant about not only the content of the story, but also the off-handed manner of Cameron's telling of it. It was then that I first postulated my explanation of the dynamics of older and younger siblings.

You are much more likely to go through life with a sense of calm assurance if, as a child playing the game, *The Great God Poseidon Requires Sacrifice*, you are the one pushing the lawn chair off the diving board into the deep end and not the one who is tied to it while sinking to the bottom of the pool. So what of younger siblings? Are we all doomed to become angst-ridden writers and artists, social workers and psychology majors in an attempt to come to grips with the fickleness of a fate that placed us into slot B instead of slot A, seemingly against the dictates of karma? And what of those who whisper to themselves, "One day!" while burning in their belly for more?

One day, I was riding around in front of our house in upstate New York, on my favorite toy. Part dune buggy, part excess-sugar-burning-machine, and part trusty steed all rolled into one, I wouldn't have traded my Big Wheel for anything in the world. Except, of course, I'd often think, for a real light saber like Luke Skywalker's, if somehow technology were to make that next important leap towards developing laser swords. But then, that goes without saying.

To the left of me was the steep decline that we always just called "The Hill," and to the right, the road that continued long and flat until it reached the busier cross street where I was not allowed to play. But I was happy in the confines of my allotted zone, occasionally jetting into high speed and then slowly circling back, over and over again. I was just enjoying the exercise while pretending I was anything from a jet fighter to an underwater explorer with a propulsion pack like in the James Bond film, *Thunderball*. Suddenly, my older brother Lucas appeared with one of his neighborhood friends in tow. "Hey! I bet you can't ride your Big Wheel all the way up the hill!" he shouted at me out of nowhere.

"I bet I can!" I replied.

"Oh yeah? I'll tell you what . . . if you can ride your Big Wheel up this hill, I'll give you a whole dollar!"

"*Really?*" I asked in disbelief.

"Mmmm, of course! If you can't make it, I get your next three weeks of allowances."

"My allowance?"

"Aw, forget about the bet!" my brother's friend chimed in, "He can't make it anyway!"

"I can too!" I shouted back, before turning to my brother to accept the challenge.

"It's a deal!" I exclaimed, just happy to be the center of attention, when normally I was left to play by myself.

So off I went down the hill on my trusty steed and lone companion. But I had never ridden my Big Wheel all the way up the hill before. In fact, I'd never even tried. As I assessed the challenge from a strip of road about fifteen feet away from the start of the incline, I imagined myself as a miniature Evel Knievel with a giant crowd of spectators that had come to see me brave the impossible. Their screams of encouragement roared around me as I pedaled off the line, pumping as hard as I could to build up speed. When I hit the hill, I started flying up it like a bat out of hell. "This is going to be easy!" I shouted out loud.

Exactly two seconds later, it felt like a barrel of rubber cement had been poured on top of me, and the hill was suddenly forcing me to pedal backwards. My legs were burning as I struggled to make it up the hill, but it was no use. The hill was just too steep for me.

I would have acquiesced to defeat right then, if the plastic handlebars attached to the front wheel hadn't suddenly wrenched to the left, guiding me up the hill at a diagonal. Not having much physics under my belt, I attributed this to my Big Wheel looking out for me as I gratefully found that cutting up at a diagonal was far easier than the straight ascent. It wasn't the mad dash to glory that I hoped for, but at least, I was still in the running. But even then, it wasn't going to be easy.

Instead of Evel Knievel, I was now a mountain climber whose hired guides had abandoned him in the pass, leaving him with only a single tank of oxygen, maybe not enough to get to the top. The next four or five minutes were agonizing. Each thrust of my legs took more and more life out of me. All the while, my brother and his friend stood at the top of the hill with their arms folded on their chests, staring at me with cold, blank stares. As I entered the top third of the climb, I was starting to lose faith.

But just when I was about to give up, Lucas and his buddy suddenly shouted, "Come on! You can do it!" in strangely enthusiastic tones. It was odd how suddenly they were all smiles and cheers, but this sudden change in attitude was certainly a welcomed one for me. Innocently, I imagined that my brother didn't mind losing the bet if it meant he could see me conquer the impossible. So I labored on, my sails filled with fresh winds of encouragement.

I felt like I was going to have a heart attack, but in the last few strokes, I knew for sure that I was going to make it. I stood up triumphantly and ground down in slow motion, finally nosing my Big Wheel over the edge of the top of the hill.

"I . . . did . . . it!" I could barely wheeze out as I stood up on my wobbly legs.

"You sure did!" my brother answered cheerily.

"I can't believe I did it! Can I have my dollar now?" I asked with a delirious mix of pride and exhaustion.

It was then that my brother and his friend burst into guffaws until my brother barked out, "I'm not giving you squat! I just wanted to see you go up that hill!" Then as quickly as they came, the two boys turned around and walked away, laughing to themselves all the while. The whole incident took less than seven minutes.

After shouting a loud but ineffectual "Hey!" I again found myself alone, exhausted, bitter, and confused. Confused about *so many things*. I spent several moments with my head down, wallowing in painfully mixed emotions. Then I felt something nudge my palm. I turned and looked down to see the certainty of that red and yellow body with the dependable oversized black plastic wheels and the glorious handlebar streamers of the Big Wheel.

As I relive these childhood events, I realize that although I still have to acknowledge the power of the Poseidon Syndrome, the considerations of its impact have to be taken in tandem with what I now call the Big Wheel Effect. Yes, because of the seemingly random machinations of older brothers and sisters, younger siblings may go on to doubt even the desirability of pursuing worldly goals. And what's the point if you can't even trust how the game is played? But on the other hand, there's no doubt that younger siblings are challenged and tested in ways that even the Navy Seals might find a tad harsh, and thus they develop a most enviable strength of character assuming of course, that the strain doesn't lead them straight to a mental hospital.

So while older siblings seem to have the brash, untested confidence of the hare, the younger siblings may possibly gain the determination and steady plodding of the tortoise, which in the long run can prove to be even more useful. Because of the Big Wheel Effect, younger siblings often go through life fueled by the power of what I often refer to as *introspective resolve*. While this may or may not bring the most impressive results in the world at large, it can lead to significant and worthwhile personal developments, undervalued as they may be by the typical tenets of society.

This is certainly a nice, consoling theory to meditate on while sinking to the bottom of the pool on a piece of cheap aluminum lawn furniture that you've recently been tied to in order to appease . . . *the hunger of the gods.*

Microscopic Me

BY LARRY ZEIGER

My fingers tap away on the keyboard producing words with empty meanings and contrived thoughts. Still, I don't want to stop, not even to take an Ibuprofen. The pain is now confined to my right side. Last week it was my left. *Why can't I focus?* For weeks I've had writer's block, and my story about a guy who is plagued with indecision and his inability to commit to anything in life is completely lacking in conflict and resolution. My characters are shallow. The plot is meaningless and dull. I stare at the computer screen for several minutes . . . waiting . . . waiting for that brilliant idea and that superbly original plot device. But this layering of conundrums gives me a massive headache.

I'm getting off track. I feel my pulse race. Worse, I have this throbbing sensation on my right side, and that damn mosquito keeps buzzing in my ear and sucking the blood out of the veins. *Could the venom from the mosquito be spreading throughout my entire body?*

I immediately get on the phone and call my doctor. "This is Larry Zeiger. I need to speak to Dr. Payne. I need to see him immediately! I have this bite on my arm. It's . . . it's about the size of a baseball!"

I'm becoming neurotic.

"Oh, I can get you in, uh . . . next Thursday at 3 p.m.," the receptionist says calmly.

"Next Thursday!" I scream. "You don't understand! I'M IN PAIN! I need to see the doctor now!"

"I can hear you Mr. Zeiger. You don't have to yell. Calm down! The best I can do is uh . . . next Tuesday at 8 a.m."

"I could be dead by next Tuesday! The bite is growing bigger and bigger by the second! Haven't you ever seen *Invasion of the Body Snatchers*? The poison is traveling through my system like . . . like a tornado, and you're telling me, I have to wait five days for what is undoubtedly a life or death situation! Isn't there someone I can see *now?*"

"Are you able to drive, Mr. Zeiger?"

"Yes! Yes! I absolutely can drive."

"Then come to the Emergency Room. It's open twenty-four hours everyday, and someone will be able to take care of you without an appointment. That's the best I can do. Sorry." She says the word, "sorry" with an annoying musical element in her voice.

I immediately get in my car and drive to the hospital. I park my car, race through the double doors, and approach the receptionist. I show her the lump on my arm, which is now the size of Australia. She, on the other hand, dismisses it as simply "a small bite."

"I need to see a doctor as fast as I can! Honestly, I've never had anything like this before. I don't know what it is. Something is *definitely* wrong!"

The unsympathetic receptionist looks at me as if I am a hypochondriac. "Just sit down," she says calmly, "and the doctor will be with you shortly."

"How *shortly*?" I ask, "like in five minutes *shortly*?"

"Just sit," she replies as if I am her dog. "Would you like a glass of water? There's a cooler behind you."

I'm panic-stricken. "I don't want water. *I want to see a doctor!*"

"You will have to wait your turn, Mr. Zeiger. There are others ahead of you."

I look around and notice that nearly every seat is taken. Crestfallen, I realize I may not be seen for hours . . . or perhaps days.

A well-dressed woman, resembling a young version of Michele Bachmann, enters the Urgent Care facility. With a cheerful disposition and a forced smile, she introduces herself to the nurse practitioner. "Hi! My name is Barbara

Boxforth. I'm the rep from Dose-More Pharmaceuticals. At Dose-More, we have a whole new line of sedatives, and they work really well on people. Better than anything on the market!" She reaches into her purse, and several samples emerge. "Try these on your patients, and they'll love 'em! And if you or your doctors place an order today, we at Dose-More will provide you with a free wine tasting and/or ice cream social for everyone in E.R."

The wide-eyed nurse smiles back, and Barbara gives her a box of Godiva Chocolates and in a soft voice replies, "And this is nothing. The wine tasting is *the best!* Wait until you taste the McManis Family Vineyards Cabernet Sauvignon! It will just open up all your arteries! So remember to talk it up! Dose-More stands by its products, because our pills in correct doses just make people feel better. Here's my card. Call me, and have a happy healthy day . . . and night! *Dose-More – it's the only way to go!*"

The Boxworth freak walks towards me, smiles at my pale, sickly face and hands me, along with every other ailing patient, a Dose-More pen before she departs from the Urgent Care facility.

After standing for several minutes, I finally find a vacant chair and sit down next to a young couple. The girl clutches her boyfriend who looks as if he will keel over any minute. He begins to sneeze incessantly on my left leg. I feel the moisture from his sneeze penetrating my pants. The girl turns to me and says, "I'm so sorry. He can't help himself. He caught some weird bug and has been throwing up all day." The young man begins to cough . . . a heaving, choking, bacteria-spreading cough. I get up from the chair and try to move away from him, but there is no other place to sit. At that moment, the nurse calls out a name.

"Arnold Petrie." *No response.* She says the name louder. "Arnold Petrie?" Suddenly, a very ill man gets up, takes two steps towards the nurse and collapses on the floor. No one moves. The nurse lifts him off the ground as he mumbles, "So long, I've been here *soooo* long . . ." and then collapses into her arms as she carries him into the examining room.

How long? I wonder. *How long will I have to wait? Ten minutes? Twenty minutes? An hour? A day? Couldn't these fakers sitting around me realize there is someone sitting in this Emergency Care facility with REAL problems?*

I become more feverish, and my right side feels swollen. Could it be . . . the West Nile Virus or the even more dreadful Congolese Gangreen I read about in the *National Enquirer*? I am certain this insidious bug will consume every organ of my body and spread from my arm to my neck to my head and then . . . and then . . . *to my brain*! I break into a cold sweat.

Thirty minutes pass. I look around the room. The same people are seated around me . . . coughing, sneezing, wheezing, choking, and moaning. A man in a wheelchair suddenly leaps in the air, at which point, a woman sitting near me tosses her crutches across the room nearly hitting one of the nurses at the drinking fountain. Without any assistance, the man and women embrace in wild abandon and perform a *pas de deux* to the Irving Berlin tune, *Cheek to Cheek,* which is being played over the intercom. I can't believe I am seeing this, or . . . *am I hallucinating?* The music abruptly changes, and the couple breaks into a wildly elaborate disco routine to the music of the Bee Gees. Just as the final refrain of *Staying Alive! Staying Alive* echoes in my head, the couple asks me to dance with them.

"I'm sorry, I just . . . I just don't do Disco when I'm . . . feeling like this."

The man and woman look at me with blank stares, and then like magic, they disappear into thin air. Suddenly, Marla Medina, a nurse at the facility, attempts to shake me back into reality, but my mind is still fuzzy and filled with oddball *Dancing with the Stars* apparitions.

"Mr. Zeiger, please come with me. The doctor is ready for you," she declares with a morose tone to her voice.

In the bleak, gloomy examining room, Dr. Hildegard looks at me with concern. "Let's see what's going on today," he says. "Uh huh. Mmmmm yes . . . uh . . . looks like you have some sort of bite . . . and some swelling."

I am amazed at how bright he is.

"Yes, and in the last two hours, I've felt a little tenderness on my right side. Doctor, is this some sort of flesh-eating bacteria? Once it starts eating away at me, will it ever stop? Will it eat my skin? My organs? And my brain? Is that what I have, doctor? Answer me! ANSWER ME NOW!"

Clearly seeing that I am losing control of all rational thought, Dr. Hildegard quickly interrupts me. "I'm going to put you on an IV and do some blood work. Would you like something to help you relax?"

Help me relax? If they want me to take meds to relax, then that means I'm going to be here for a long time . . . maybe forever! I feel tense, and my blood pressure rises to unbelievable heights.

"Here, I'll turn the TV on for you. It should take a little while to get your blood work back. You'll be fine . . . just fine." the doctor says with grandfatherly wisdom.

Just before he departs with my blood, I hear a rumble of thunder outside and a flash of lightning fills the room.

I think to myself, *Is he a real doctor or an emissary from the afterlife?*

Alone in the room, I watch Al Pacino in *Scarface* on American Movie Classics. I'm just in time to witness Tony Montana being ambushed from every conceivable angle. Just after this horrific scene, a nurse enters the room, walks to my side, and gives me a sedative to take with a glass of water. In a soothing voice that reminds me of the Wicked Witch of the West, she says, "Here, drink this. Drink it all down and . . . *sleep . . . sleep a while . . . just sleep . . . sleeeeeep . . .*"

I drink the potion, and moments later, I suddenly feel myself drifting into another world. I begin to wonder, *Is this all part of a scheme to get me out of the way? To destroy me, because I'm a failure at everything I do?*

I hear whispers in the hallway.

"Too many patients! Too many patients!"

"What does it matter if we lose just one more?"

"Does the world really need one more frustrated writer? They're a dime a dozen."

I am losing all sense of reality. I have to stay awake. No drug can put me . . . to sleep . . . to sleep . . . to sleep . . . Stay awake you imbecile! Stay awake . . . awake . . . awake . . . falling . . . falling . . . falling asleep . . . sleep . . . sleep . . . sleep . . .

And I am out like a light . . . *or am I?* I look around the hospital room, and suddenly, there I am! A microscopic version of me, no larger than an inch, appears at the end of my bed. Speaking in a tiny voice, *Microscopic Me* asks, "How did I get so small?"

I answer back. "What are you doing? How could you . . . I mean . . . How could I be in two places at once?"

Microscopic Me looks at *Life-Size Me* in the hospital bed and replies, "Something is wrong with this picture!"

"You're telling me," I respond. "This is incredible! There can't be two of me. It's impossible! It's gotta be the crazy drugs the doc gave me!"

"It's very weird, I agree," says *Microscopic Me.* "But sometimes it takes an unexpected plot device, like this one, to knock you back into reality to resolve the physical, emotional, and intellectual dimensions of your conflicting heart and soul. Now, honestly, this is a story you could get published!"

I am mortified and speechless. Before I can give any type of rational response, the tiny version of *Me* climbs onto my hospital bed, jumps on my arm, then swings from the line, and plunges himself into the IV bag. In the biggest voice he can conjure up, he shouts, "I will get to the bottom of what's ailing you in your incoherent internal world. I will check out your Endogenous Infradian Biorhythms which are obviously out of whack!"

And then I see the most incredible sight; *Microscopic Me* is sucked into my vein, and in a flash of a millisecond, he disappears, completely absorbed inside of me. I suddenly feel woozy. I close my eyes for a moment, and when I open them, to my surprise and horror, I have become . . . *Microscopic Me!* Even more shocking, I am being transported through my own body on a fully rigged . . . blood vessel!

"What's happening to me?" I cry out, at which point the vessel stops in front of a tiny establishment, which has a sign posted out front which reads: WELCOME TO THE I -V LEAGUE.

Two odd blobs step forward and introduce themselves as Macrophage and Microgilia and invite me on a tour of my body and soul to discover why my rational and emotional lives are on a major collision course. *How can I refuse such an offer!* Before I can say a word, the blood vessel, with me in it, takes off speeding through my veins and arteries in what will certainly be a unique journey of a lifetime. First we travel in my esophagus, through my pharynx and then into my stomach. Along the way Macrophage points out a dark ominous hole. "This is just the beginning of an ulcer caused by self-induced stress."

"Hey, wait a minute! It doesn't have to be an ulcer. I can control it. I'll do yoga and meditation and . . .and . . . pilates! I'll even do deep breathing exercises before I go to bed!"

"You say you'll do these things, but you know you never will. You're doomed, man! A big frickin' loser!" Moments later, he looks outside the vessel and shouts, "Just as I thought! Look at that! Now, do you see what I mean?" He points to a smoldering soupy substance coming towards us. "It's acid, dude, drilling a hole in the lining of your stomach . . . maybe your esophagus too! You're a mess!"

Microgilia adds, "You have too much going on in your life. Your right brain is fighting with your left brain, and your heart is rebelling. In fact, I think we should visit your brain right now so you can witness this insidious spectacle!"

Macrophage jabs the blood vessel, and in an instant, we land on the border between my left brain and right brain. "Here we are at the Corpus Collosum. Bet you thought you'd never see this in your lifetime!"

I can't believe what I'm seeing. My brain is a giant factory with a sharp divide in the center. The left brain, my rational side, is filled with miniature men and women in suits, pushing buttons on a massive computer screen while simultaneously studying maps of my life. The workers fire off synapses in my brain and write down every reaction. The creative elements of my right brain are in full view . . . artists, writers, philosophers, and musicians exchanging ideas but never certain what to do with them. One brain cell keeps repeating the same words over and over again: "I don't know how to end the story! I don't know how to end the story! I don't know how to end . . ."

Another brain cell responds, "What are the character's motives? There's no evidence that he can resolve any issues!"

And a third brain cell adds, "Where is the turning point? I don't think he has a hook. His life has no arc, no heart, no purpose, and there is absolutely no denouement in sight!"

I can't stand watching this scene for another second. The tension is killing me.

To calm me down, Macrophage suggests that we travel southward to witness the interaction of organs in my Hip Joint. "The Hip Joint is where all your body parts gather to unwind, and anyone who is anyone will be there. You will be amazed at what your organs do when you're anesthetized. It's really *very hip* and insanely trendy!"

"But remember," Microgilia adds, "you can only be an observer in the hip joint, *not* a participant. So watch and learn, but don't say a word!"

And so once again, we board my blood vessel and travel southward through my esophagus, past my heart, into my stomach, and intestines.

Arriving at the Hip Joint is quite an experience. Cellular representatives of my essential organs sit at high top bar tables sipping martinis, discussing body politics, and enjoying the stylistic vocals of Hypothalamus, Olfactory Bulb, and Gluteus Maximus who perform Cole Porter's *I've Got You Under My Skin.* Following this act, a strange looking organ who calls himself Testiclees, who is dressed in a sequined jumpsuit, nearly steals the show with his Hip Hop rendition of *Ain't No Mountain High* while in the background, multiple video screens show Fellini's *La Dolce Vita.* The Joint is overflowing with lively organs having the time of their lives!

Suddenly, Cingulate Gyrus, the processor of rational thoughts, enters The Joint and approaches Aorta, an artery youthful in spirit and a conveyer of life to all parts of my body. The two immediately break into a scuffle.

"You son-of-a bitch, Gyrus! You've ruined everything for this guy! You and your rational brain cells! You have no emotions! No depth of character! What's wrong with you?" screams Aorta.

"What's wrong with me, Aorta? It's you who are the problem! You with your . . . *feelings . . . nothing more than feelings!*"

"I'm sick of that old song, Gyrus. I am the heart and soul of this guy and *the life force!* You, on the other hand, are nothing more than a dullard! This poor guy we inhabit is being consumed by trying to rationalize every moment of his existence. Thanks to you, there is no freedom in his life to explore and contemplate the real world. He needs to create and take time to expand his life space!"

"Oh sure," Gyrus responds sarcastically, "he needs to increase his life space but not the way you want him to. He'll go broke as a writer. He has no future. Your heartfelt ideas will kill him! Instead, he should work a good nine-to-five job, invest wisely, and organize his life minute by minute with analytical, rational standards. He must take a more learned approach like René Descartes who said you must 'systematically deduce life from direct observation.' *He thinks, therefore he is!*"

"La de dah de dah . . . blah blah blah! You're positively wrong! This guy should be an artist and a free thinker. Let him experiment and expand his life – not build a wall around it! Check out Aristotle, and you'll see that you're not allowing him to feel, to see beauty, to experiment, and to develop his emotional intelligence. Let him write a book. Let him create a song. Let him paint a picture. Look at him! He's nothing more than an empty canvas without a single drop of color. But you, Cingulate Gyrus, *Mr. Brain-iac*, have made him into a boring heartless, emotionless blob of negative space!"

Just as I am about to have an emotional collapse, my appendix enters The Hip Joint and jumps into the argument. "The problem with both of you is you never understand the meaning of the word, *compromise.* Haven't you heard of *Laissez-Faire* economics? Just leave him alone! Let him make his own decisions!"

"What do you know? You're nothing more than an appendix!"

Gyrus screams. "You don't have a single fuckin' brain cell! Why are you even contributing to this dialogue?"

Olfactory Bulb continues the attack. "At least I have the ability to smell. But Appendix, you . . . you are nothing but a useless organ!"

As Testiclees sips on his extra dry martini with two olives, he offers his philosophical commentary, "Look at me, Appendix. I have a purpose. My job is hard, but I stimulate this guy with all the right sensations. But you, on the other hand, are nothin' but a pain in his right side!"

As the organs in The Hip Joint begin to jeer the alienated entity, Appendix becomes choked up with tears and sadly responds, "I'm so hurt by all of you. You make me feel ashamed to be part of this man's body."

At this point, I appear to be the only one who feels sorry for my poor, rejected appendix. Suddenly, there is thunderous knocking in the passageway to my hip. To my astonishment, in walks FOX commentator, celebrated author, and rock star politician, Sarah Palin, carrying her Savage Model 110 hunting rifle.

Testiclees is the first to respond. "An alien in our midst! You don't belong here!"

"Oh, come on . . . I'm just your everyday hockey mom with a gun. And a future! I'm also the new Oprah, and I'll betcha I can solve any issue on any dining room table in the world as we know it!"

Testiclees looks at Sarah with dismay and asks, "How in the world did you get inside *our* body?"

"That's top secret classical info, you *fuddy duddy*! I'll never tell! You really are strange lookin'. Are you some sort of illegal alien from . . . you know, that place . . . Mars? "

"This is insane!" exclaims Gyrus. "Is there no logic left in our world? She doesn't belong here!"

Sarah stares at all the organs in the joint. "Oh are you saying this is some sort of private club of . . . of Socialists? Ya' know, I feel like I'm in Moscow. I'll bet I can see Putin just around the corner."

Testiclees responds, "No! You're in The Hip Joint . . . in this man's body!"

"Ewwww! That's sick! And you, Testiclees are the ugliest thing I've ever seen! Don't you ever rear your ugly head in my airspace!"

There is a sudden commotion in the passageway leading to The Hip Joint, and I am shocked to see . . . *no it can't be* . . . Samuel Wurzelbacher, a.k.a. Joe the Plumber!

"Now who the blazes are you?" exclaims Testiclees pointing to the new alien.

"Hey you funky mass, I'm Joe the Plumber. I'm the world famous *common man!* I'm covering the war in that place . . . whatdaya call it? Uh . . . it's Baza or Gaza or somethin' like that. You know, that's in the Middle East somewhere, and I'm getting paid handsomely, like maybe a million bucks for my unbiased, no nonsense reporting. And then I have deals with Piers Morgan *and* Sean Hannity and an upcoming book deal and maybe a *Playgirl* centerfold too like that Levi guy . . . and then I'll run for senator of some state. The sky's the limit, so watch out, 'cause I'm the American common man with a dream on the horizon!"

Sarah taps Joe on the shoulder. "I don't mean to interrupt your speech, Joe, but my projected income for the upcoming year is over ten million with my book sales, the FOX gig, and now the Discovery Channel ALASKA Reality TV series, so that makes me at least nine million dollars more important than you! And my book is loaded with hockey metaphors. Can ya dig it?"

"Cool! I wanna be just like you, Sarah . . . minus the baggage!"

Just as Joe makes this comment, the appendix, who has now positioned himself next to the plumber, begins moaning and making belching sounds. Joe turns to the organ and asks, "Hey Blobo, do you have any spigots, valves, or drains that need fixin'?"

"My name is Appendix – *not Blobo*! And you two are nothing but sicko aliens. You guys need to be deported!"

"Hey Appendix, you butt ugly mudda! You and these humanoids are ruining the total ambience of our existence! Now get outta here!" exclaims Gluteus Maximus.

This is nothing more than a bad dream, I think to myself. *Hideous hallucinations brought on by FDA approved pharmaceutical drugs!* I make a major decision. I have to escape this horrible nightmare. I don't belong in this world. I open my mouth and scream, "I can't take this anymore! I've got to take control of my screwed-up life!"

Suddenly, everyone stares at *Me* as if I am a freak of nature.

"Where did you come from?" Sarah Palin asks. " You just can't invade this guy's space like we did. I mean like Joe and me are politician and lamestream media stars. We have the right to be here!"

"You know what? I'm sick of being trapped inside myself. I have the right to speak out and be heard!" I declare with newfound courage.

"There ya go again speakin' about *your* rights. Ya know Free Will no longer exists in a world run by them Socialist dictators who dominate the world with insecurity and fear and other stuff," declares Sarah.

"Spoken like a true hockey mom!" exclaims Joe.

"Not a hockey mom any more! I'm a *mama grizzly*, and ya know what that means!"

"Hey, that's pretty funny!" chime in Tongue and Cheek.

And then with confidence that has always been lacking in my life, I proclaim: "You're wrong! None of this is very funny!" Everyone takes a step back from me as I move through the crowd of confused organs and celebrated politicos. They know I mean business. And with newfound confidence and determination, I declare: "I'm calling the shots from now on! I have the power to make my own decisions – to think through life logically and creatively. I am gettin' out of this joint!"

"I'll help you!" screams my appendix. I don't belong here either."

"Useless organ! Useless organ!" Testiclees, Gyrus, the Olfactory Bulb, Sarah and Joe scream in unison as chaos ensues.

"*Death Panels! Death Panels!* Where are they when we need them?" screams Sarah, as if she is the newly elected Warrior Princess of All Eternity.

And then a chain reaction so unpredictable, so terrifying, and so utterly bizarre occurs. Joe the Plumber drops a wrench on Sarah Palin's left foot. Sarah loses her balance, trips over Testiclees, and falls on her hunting rifle, which causes the safety to be dislodged. The gun fires and shoots . . . *my appendix*!

The organs in The Hip Joint gasp as the wounded appendix staggers towards me.

"You hate me! You all hate me!" shouts the wounded appendix. "Why do you make fun of me? Why do you call me a *useless* organ? I just want *to exist*, and be an integral part of *this universe*!"

Sirens go off in my body. Chaos reigns. Gyrus shouts, "All organs, back to your original body positions! The party's over!"

The appendix looks me straight in the eye as he completely collapses and suddenly disappears into thin air. I turn around and see a fog bank moving over me, and then I am in total darkness.

Seconds later, I open my eyes . . . and find myself in a hospital bed at Paradise Point Clinic in La Jolla, California.

"Mr. Zeiger? Mr. Zeiger? It's all over," says the nurse.

"What . . . what do you mean, 'It's all over'?" I ask in a semi-comatose state.

"Your appendix . . . we took it out," the nurse says calmly. "But you know, you didn't need it anyway. It's a useless organ."

"And the huge welt on my arm?"

"Oh, just a mosquito bite. Nothing to worry about. A little Calamine lotion, and it'll be gone in a few days."

The nurse exits the room, and I suddenly feel wide-awake, exhilarated.

I leave the hospital three days later, and when I arrive home, I think about my hallucinations, and suddenly, an idea explodes in my brain! I'll write a story about a guy like me who takes a journey inside himself. I visualize the incredible settings of the brain, heart, hip joint, blood vessels and antibodies; the dynamic interaction of all elements of a human body that make up this character's life. The search for understanding in the external and internal worlds will be the key ingredients of this short story . . . no, wait . . . maybe there's too much material for a short story . . . perhaps this unique vision should be a novel . . . yes, a novel rivaling the best of Dean Koontz, Robin Cook, and . . . and Dostoevsky! And I will call this sensational work: *Microscopic Me – A Medical Allegory,* an epic work about the battles that rage within me.

I sit down in my most comfortable chair and stare at the blank screen on my laptop and think about the unlimited possibilities of plot devices, allegories, illusions, and a stunning climax to which all people will relate. And when they read the poetic last sentence of my masterwork, they will say, *What a fabulous writer this guy is! His story changed my life!* And just think, now it will be my turn to be offered a multi-million dollar book deal, just like Sarah Palin but I . . . I will *embrace* the media and never call them *lame.* Instead, I will tell then how much I appreciate their wisdom and power to select me as a candidate . . . *for the Pulitzer!*

Synapses fire across my brain in perfect harmony with my heart and soul as I create my inspired literary work of art.

FIFTEEN

SWAN SONGS

Advanced Placement Exams, final exams, California State Standardized Exams, Senior Awards Night, Undergraduate Awards Night, Grad Night, Senior Prom, undergraduate student scheduling, final grades, unruly students, unruly administrators, endless staff meetings – the chaos of the end of the school year activities motivate Jack and Larry to meet at 98 Bottles, a wine and beer bar in the art district of San Diego.

In an attempt to reduce their anxiety and blood pressure, and hopefully experience a momentary catharsis, Larry and Jack order glasses of *3 Ring Shiraz*. The bottle of wine, highly recommended by restaurant entrepreneur, Steve Anthony, and the bartender, Danny, reminds Larry and Jack of the circus-like atmosphere that has recently consumed their professional careers as educators.

Candid stories begin to unfold at such a rapid rate that they decide to order additional glasses of the *Uncensored Red Blend* by Geyser Peak. The wine is a perfect compliment for the late afternoon as Larry and Jack continue to discuss their education-disaster stories with absolutely nothing held back.

As the soft, supple, rich flavors sweep through their palettes and stimulate their imaginations with depth and complexity, Jack and Larry experience an ultimate catharsis as they exchange stories of their lives.

How Gwyneth Paltrow Ruined My Teaching Career

BY JACK BEDDOWS

I walk down the hall to my class and reach for the doorknob. Meanwhile, inside . . .

"Well, it's not like the Chinese don't deserve it."

"What do you mean, James?"

"I mean, David, that this whole situation is the inevitable result of our decades-long trend of outsourcing manufacturing to foreign businesses to the point that we as a nation no longer produce anything. The Chinese are merely stepping up to fill the void as the true economic powerhouse that we used to be."

"Yes, I suppose you're right. And looking at it that way, just think of all the years of quiet determination and persistency the Chinese have shown! Why just the other day I saw a box of Jackie Chan Instant Green Tea in a discount bin at the grocery store. Imagine the frustrated executives behind that failed attempt at reaching the American market! *Everyone love Jackie Chan! Everyone love green tea! So what not to love? This be selling like hotcakes!*"

"Ha! That's very funny, David! And your Mandarin accent is excellent! But really, we shouldn't be engaging in humor that perpetuates stereotypes. Oh! Wait! Here comes the teacher . . . "

I open the door.

"Hey guys, what's going on? How was Social Studies?"

"Oh man! Billy farted! It was so loud!"

"Okay guys, let's settle down."

It was a testing week, when the students were exhorted to do their best on long, standardized exams that have no bearing on their grades or admission to college, and teachers were again reminded that they should have been teaching with these tests in mind all along, according to mandates from the district, the state, the federal government, the President of the United States and God, in that order. This was a newer test with which I was personally unfamiliar, and since back-to-back class periods were assigned for its administration, I had assumed it would be quite lengthy. After the first day of the three-day testing schedule, my students all came in grumbling.

"So how was it so far?" I asked.

"Boring!" shouted Brian, one of the class clowns.

He was a nice enough kid who goofed around a lot to get attention, but generally in a good-hearted way. He looked like Prince, if Prince had early on become addicted to Jack-in-the-Box and Wienerschnitzel. And like most of the boys in class, he had been rendered more or less retarded by the onslaught of puberty.

"Boring! Boring!" he shouted again to no one in particular.

"The test was actually really short," said Genessa, one of my favorite students. The girls in the class were typically more mature than the boys and had their behavior more or less under control. In any event, they could usually finish sentences without screaming out loud like Rap star, Flava Flav, for no discernable reason.

"The test was over in about twenty minutes," Genessa continued, "so we mostly just watched a movie."

"YEAH, BOOOY!"

"Yes David. Thank you for that witty social commentary. Why don't you take a seat? So, what film did you guys end up watching?" I then asked, wondering what to do with the kids if the English section turned out to be just as short. Trying to teach a regular lesson on a testing day was hardly an option as the students would all be far too squirrelly.

"The movie was gross!" another student, Kevin, shouted out in response. "It had all these people from the Holocaust walking around like skeletons. It was crazy!"

"Wow! A Holocaust documentary after taking a standardized exam . . . that sounds . . . uh . . . *interesting*. So, let's . . . uh . . . try something different! Clear your desks and get out a no. 2 pencil with an eraser!"

"*AAAWWWWWW!!*"

It turned out that the English section wasn't any longer than the social studies portion of the test so I did have to find something to occupy a large chunk of the students' time once they finished the exam. It was my fourth year teaching, but my first year at this high school, and I didn't have much extracurricular material stored away in the room. But as I looked around at the few things I did have handy, I was delighted to find a VHS tape of the Oscar winning film, *Shakespeare in Love* stuffed into a bottom drawer. In my last school, the film was shown regularly to ninth graders as an introduction to Shakespeare, so I didn't think it would be necessary for my tenth grade honors students to go through all of the hullabaloo of having signed parent permission slips simply because this prize- winning film had a brief flash of nudity in it.

If I did go through that whole process of distributing and collecting parent permission slips, it would take up one of the three testing days, and the students wouldn't be able to see the entire film. Not only that, I would also be back to not knowing what the hell to do with my students for that gaping hour that would be left over once even the slow pokes in class finished the first day's testing material. As a result, I made the educated decision to show this brilliant film after the students had completed each day's standardized test without distributing permission slips.

As I popped the tape into the VCR, I dismissed my momentary qualms easily enough as all of the movie's literary qualities were weighing so heavily in my mind. And anyway, I thought dismissively, if the students can watch documentaries showing real-life torture victims, piles of human remains and the other horrors of the Nazi death camps, I'd say they're mature enough to be allowed to see a human nipple or two. But I hadn't counted on the fact that these *particular* nipples belonged to Gwyneth Paltrow . . . *Gwyneth Paltrow and those perfect breasts.* Little did I know, the real drama was just beginning.

Since the start of the school year, I had developed an uneasy alliance with a slightly snotty, overachieving student named Sarah Rodenhausen. Unlike the rest of the class, Sarah always did her work and tried to show that she knew what she was talking about. I couldn't help but feel somewhat grateful towards her. She also took my side when other students acted up, rolling her eyes at the brain-damaged behavior I typically had to suffer through. But could her acts of commiseration have been related to grade-grubbing? Of course, they could have. But frankly, I was often so stressed out that I still appreciated her sympathetic nature, despite her possible motivation.

On the other hand, while Sarah was a model student, she couldn't seem to help but lord it over her classmates who weren't as organized, or in some ways, as smart as she felt she was. Even more off-putting, every now and then she revealed little personal details about her life that illustrated just how unnaturally sheltered she really was. I think it was the convoluted description of the necessities of her being constantly chaperoned outside of school and closely watched at home that really put me on my guard.

"Wow Sarah! Your uncle *really* sounds like a character! He told you he was going to pick you up at 3:30 but really he was there at 3:00, just keeping an eye on you the whole time?"

But I didn't realize how tenuous our alliance really was until Gwyneth Paltrow's breasts wedged between us and shattered it to pieces. Perhaps if they had been ordinary breasts, Sarah Rodenhausen could have maintained perspective on the naturalness of the human form and its acceptable inclusion into meaningful works of art, such as *Shakespeare in Love*. But when Sarah was confronted with the sight of Gwyneth Paltrow's breasts for those two and half, hell-fire filled seconds, it stirred up so many feelings of repression and envy inside of her that she instantly went from teacher's pet to turncoat, and I quickly found myself in the center of a tremendous shit-storm.

And so I was snitched out by young Sarah, and the next week was hell on earth for me, filled with endless explanations repeated over and over in meetings with the principal, the vice principal, and Sarah's parents. Two things were now under question about my teaching: one was my lack of protocol in skipping the permission slips which I felt was unnecessary due to quality of the film; the other, more pressing question was whether or not I was showing something lewd and inappropriate to the students. As my accusers sat across from me, their blank stares passed through me like X-rays, leaving behind only the cancerous feel of their obvious lack of faith in even my basic humanity.

One of the problems I was facing was the fact that the administrators, who had already given me several hints that they may be culturally illiterate, knew nothing about this highly praised film. In fact, the principal didn't even believe in showing films as an aid to teaching at all. Another problem, at this school in particular, was that anything that could potentially lead to parent outrage immediately shocked my superiors out of the ability to use their rational minds. However, when they started their inquiries, I was determined to justify myself and to educate them about the film at the same time.

"You see," I began to explain, "The movie in question won seven Academy Awards, including one for best picture and one for the screenplay, which was written by Marc Norman and Tom Stoppard, the author of the highly celebrated play, *Rosencrantz & Guildenstern are Dead*."

In response, the administrators merely continued with their blank stares that, only to the most untrained eye, could pass for listening.

"You know, *Rosencrantz & Guildenstern Are Dead?*" I continued, "It's studied in pretty much every high school in the nation."

"Oh yes. That's right. Rose Crans and Gilda Stern and uh . . . Tom Stephard. Mmmmm, yes," the vice principal mumbled.

"That's right, Tom *Stoppard*." I said with a sigh. "Then, of course, there's William Shakespeare, the man generally considered to be the most important writer in the history of the English language. Showing *Shakespeare in Love* is a great way to give context to the world that this celebrated author lived in. And as I'm sure you're aware, increasing a student's comfort level by providing context for literary works greatly increases the chances that the student will be successful in tackling the language of those works."

"Mmmmm, comfort level." The principal replied succinctly, in tones as equally closed off as those of her administrative compatriot. "But the thing is," she continued, "I think the students should be *reading* in an English class, not watching movies."

"Well, of course," I answered, "But I showed the film during downtime in a testing schedule, and it was not meant as a substitute for *reading* a Shakespearean play! And as they have Shakespeare coming up again next semester, I thought it would be a good way to help get them motivated. In fact, this movie was intended by the producers of the film to be shown in high schools. They actually created an accompanying work called "Shakespeare in the Classroom," which is made up of monologues by all of the famous actors from the picture with highly informational commentaries on Elizabethan life and concluding hopes that *Shakespeare in Love* will help high school students to deepen their appreciation for Shakespeare's writing."

At this juncture, I was fairly sure I had conveyed the point that this was, in fact, not a piece of pornography that I had shown the students, but a piece of art. But no, it was as if the people listening to me were under a spell that made them impervious to rational thought.

"There was nudity in the picture though? Naked breasts?" they asked with a mixture of longing and horror.

"For a second or two, yes. But I don't see why that's so terrible, I mean the students were just coming from a social studies class where they viewed a documentary showing real-life torture victims, and no one's complaining about . . ."

"The breasts, Jack! The breasts! You can't show breasts without a permission slip!"

It was clear that the only way to keep the peace was to admit that I had screwed up. So I did. In the months after Gwyneth Paltrow's breasts almost got me fired, I always tried to be pleasant. After all, I had just left my old school district for what I had initially thought would be a better situation, and this meant I had no tenure and could be let go of at anytime. Under the circumstances, I strived for extreme politeness. But besides the administrators, who ran the school like the French monarchy in the last days before the revolution, the guidance counselors could also be problematic.

At Halcyon Daze High, many of the counselors and administrators made no attempt to hold students accountable for their behavior. Instead, they chose to live in a state of perpetual fear of the monster that they and their kind had delivered to us like the tainted seeds of Beowulf. Increased litigiousness had blasted the educational landscape like a nuclear bomb, and administrators and counselors seemed to live in fear of kids or their parents saying 'Boo!' One day, despite my desire not to make waves, I found I absolutely *had* to talk to one of the vice principals about some outrageous behavior I experienced when covering a computer science class for one of my peers. But when I voiced my concerns, ever so politely, the administrator only responded with phony disbelief.

"Why, I've always been told how well behaved our student body is! I have to tell you, complaints like these aren't usual at all!" The whole time he spoke, he bobbed his head back and forth like Howdy Doody.

"Really?" I replied. "Despite the forty-two uses of the f-word in the first five minutes of class that I mentioned? The open bottle of coke that was thrown against one student's back, the entire contents of which then proceeded to immediately soak into the carpet near all of the lab's power strips? The constant eating of powdered donuts, which no doubt brought the rat that then came scurrying across the floor to the accompaniment of yet another flood of profanity from the students? And what about the playing of rap music and video games for the entire length of the period, and the lap dance in the lab room? *Really?* Well-behaved?

"What grade was that again?" he asked curtly.

"Ninth grade."

"Hmm. I heard the new ninth graders were a little rough."

Though typically not quite as out of hand as that, some of my own classes were exhausting as well. Many of the students in my regular English classes had the winning combination of cavernous holes in their basic educational backgrounds and extreme apathy. In response to this situation, I worked very hard to impart what I considered to be the most important principles of language arts: thinking clearly, communicating well with others, and having a sense of social and historical perspective. Call me crazy, but I believed these skills could help the kids to improve their lot in life, and so I tried my best to get them onboard some kind of self-improvement kick. And as the months passed, and I seemed to be reaching at least some of the students, I realized that I would have liked it if *that* were the criterion by which I would be evaluated for rehiring. For a little while, I experienced a brief flowering of hope that this might even be the case.

The principal had visited me in the classroom several times that year, and luckily enough, had always caught me at some of my finer moments. She always walked away with a notebook full of positive comments as I typically thought to myself, *Oh thank God, she didn't come in yesterday and see what the kids were up to then!*

On the afternoon of my last observation of the year, she welcomed me into her office, and after a few pleasantries, invited me to come around her desk to look over all of the good teaching qualities she had observed and recorded for my review. But as I leaned over in front of her desk lamp, with my hand in the pocket of my blazer, a shadow fell on the record of my good deeds, and it formed the exact outline of a pair of shapely breasts! My eyes lit up as I noticed that the edge of one of my buttons was forming a shadowy nipple lightly protruding from the round shapes cast by my billowing coat. I quickly moved my hand to change the shadow's shape, but it was too late!

"Cursèd Lilith! First among the damned!" The principal swore between her teeth. She then shook her head rapidly from side to side and said, "Oh excuse me, where were we?"

I quickly tried to segue way back to the positive conversation we had been having just a few moments before, but it was no use. Within the next minute, the principal was wrapping up our meeting and showing me the door in a most distracted manner.

During my year at Halcyon Daze, I became good friends with one of the only voices of sanity in the entire school, Larry Zeiger, long time English and film teacher. When I told him what had transpired, he responded, "*Shakespeare in Love* is an Oscar winning film which makes Shakespeare come to life for kids! I took my students to see the film in the theater when it first came out and never had a single complaint about it. In fact, students and parents thanked me for the wonderful field trip to the movies!"

Just my luck, I thought.

Besides teaching a full load of classes, Larry also ran a program where students produced, directed, wrote, choreographed and promoted an original musical theater production. By the time I met Larry, this had become a three-decade tradition that was hugely popular in the community. These musicals were always humorous and topical, often satirizing current events. They also had live music, and that's how I got involved. I played piano for that year's spring show. I also sang, acted in one scene, and ran rehearsals when Larry needed to recover at the local coffee shop. After a few months of preparation, the show opened and was a huge success.

The original musical production pulled together in the mysterious way that shows often do, right after dress rehearsals that leave you utterly terrified of the whole thing falling apart. The students and the parents had a wonderful time during the three-week run. We all did.

But during breaks at all the performances, I was shocked as a near-endless stream of parents approached me to say, "So! I hear you're taking over for Larry since he's retiring this year. I think that's wonderful! We've heard so many good things about you!" Larry, apparently, had been talking me up to people. Also, most of the cast had, without my knowledge, petitioned the administration to hire me for the next year. They all wanted to keep their musical program going, and they saw me as the natural choice for replacing Larry. Surely this, along with my solid teaching reviews would get me asked back for the next school year, *right?*

However, the parents that liked me, the students petitioning for me, and Larry, who was so certain the administrators would take his advice and hire me back for the next school year, had no effect on those doing the hiring. As the school year drew to a close, my inquiries about future employment were continually put off, until at last, any open positions that I would have been suited for were filled by teachers whose main qualifications seemed to be that they would never show the movie, *Shakespeare in Love.* With hiring freezes and a collapsing economy looming over the landscape of the foreseeable future in public education, it seemed that Gwyneth Paltrow and her flawless bosom had done me in for good.

When Larry found out that I wasn't being rehired, he said, "I can't believe it! You're one of the best teachers in the school! I guess they're just going to let my program simply evaporate, despite all the money I've raised with it over the years and all the benefits that students have derived. So much for the arts! This is getting me down, Jack." Then his eyes lit up with a brilliant idea. "You know what? We need to go get a drink! We should try the new wine bar they opened up in Ocean Beach, it's called *The Third Corner*, and I hear the wine, the food, and the staff are terrific!"

And so, a few hours and a few glasses of wine later, I was sitting embroiled in feelings of rejection, bitterness, and anxiety about the future, when suddenly I realized something wonderful. *I was free!* I didn't have a job, it was true, but I was free from all the nonsense I had been laboring under at this crazy school all year long.

"Truth be told, Larry," I said in this flash of inspiration, "Do I really want to be hired where the general values are so off-base as to make it unbearable anyway?"

"That's true, I suppose." Larry commented. "I must admit, I'm certainly ready to be getting out of teaching after the way things have been going in recent years. I'm so passionate about the arts and what do the school do? They keep cutting these programs, which I know have such benefit for all students. But still, it's just so weird after thirty-three years of teaching to think of a life when I'm not teaching!"

And you know, I owe this all to Gwyneth Paltrow and her big scene in *Shakespeare in Love.* Maybe all things do happen for the best, Larry. What do you think?

"I think we should make a toast to our futures. May they be filled with many more artistic endeavors and great conversations like this one! And who knows, maybe we'll write a book together swapping stories about the crazy things that have happened in our lives!

"And lets drink to Shakespeare and Gwyneth Paltrow who have really changed my life for the better!" I proudly declared, as we toasted with glasses of the rich, full-bodied *3 Ring Shiraz*, a wine with a rich bouquet and a fine finish.

I Want My $55.00 Back!

by Larry Zeiger

Wake-up Call

March 8, 2007 - my 5, 544th day of teaching. I roll over in bed, shut off the alarm, and stare at the ceiling. At this point in my life, I have taught 6,679 students, corrected 132,718 essays, taken attendance 29,719 times, and directed 3,123 students in high school musicals. *Where has all the time gone?* I get out of bed and look in the mirror. The image that stares back is that of a slightly disheveled, morose individual who is about to self-destruct and dissolve into a million pieces. Trying to refocus, I blink several times, but sadly, the image remains the same.

I enter the kitchen and drink a cup of very strong Sumatra. The barking of the two dogs on the balcony next door is driving me crazy. If I only I had the nerve to lace those doggy bowls with some Melatonin, just enough to knock the pooches out, maybe, just maybe, I could have had a good night's sleep.

I read the headlines of the *L.A. Times* – more bombings in Iraq, more people killed, but the "surge is working." Too much to handle while eating a bowl of organic oatmeal, so I jump to the next page where a Bloomingdale's ad for Calvin Klein's men's underwear is next to an article about the millions of dollars spent on High Stakes Testing Exams, part of the No Child Left Behind disaster. *Oh please!* Just another attempt to raise a nation of bubbleheads who sit at backbreaking wooden desks and regurgitate information taught by robotically programmed teachers who fear if they stray from the state-sponsored curriculum, they will be tossed into the streets to become 7-11 clerks. If the government were smart, they'd appoint me Secretary of Education. *I'd fix everything!*

I toss the newspaper in the recycle can and put my cereal bowl and coffee cup in the sink with the three-day-old dirty dishes. I notice a piece of unopened mail on the kitchen sink from the district office on teacher credentialing. I open the letter to discover that after thirty-three years of teaching in California and in possession of a Lifetime Credential, I am no longer qualified to teach! I continue to read the ominous letter and discover that I lack something called a Cross-cultural, Academic, and Language Development Credential. Having one English as a Second Language Learner in my class means that I have to enroll in additional classes and take more exams to test my worthiness as a California educator . . . or risk losing my job!

How can they do this to me? Doesn't it matter that I have devoted myself to teaching for more than half my life and have worked countless hours directing theater productions, running film programs, raising money for scholarships, and even sponsoring the Jewish Culture and Wit Club which is made up of all Latino non-Jewish, English as a Second Language students! The current president's name is Jesus and the vice-president is Christian! *How much more "cross-cultural" can you get?*

Suddenly, I begin to perspire. My heart rate is up. I take deep breaths and immediately try twenty seconds of meditation. I then make the mistake of reading the last part of the letter. In order to continue teaching, I will have to pay $55.00 for an Emergency Credential, and in addition, enroll in the Teacher Certification Program and have an "expert" from the Department of Education observe my teaching techniques to see if I comply with the "rigorous educational standards" of the State of California. *Does this mean that with the California state budget in complete disarray, the taxpayers are going to pay for this brilliant government expert's transportation, hotel lodging, and food while this "genius" on educational practices evaluates me?*

I immediately write out a check for $55.00, slap a stamp on the envelope, run to the corner at the end of my street and deposit my check to the ailing state budget in the mailbox. I look at my watch. It is 6:28 a.m. Better hurry . . .

I run back to my condo, jump in the tub and turn the shower massager to full blast. The pulsating hot water hits me in the head and back, jarring my brains and pounding my arthritic neck. I feel a momentary catharsis. I never want to leave the secure confinements of my bathtub, but my Sharper Image clock on the wall reveals that I now have only nineteen minutes to get dressed and drive the 1.6 miles to work, race up the twenty-seven steps to my windowless classroom to greet the forty-two eager minds waiting for me at the door before the shrieking bell rings at 7:30 a.m.

At 7:27 a.m. I pull into my parking space at the school and do a quick sprint across campus. Like clockwork, I stick the key in the door of my classroom with eight seconds to spare. Heart pounding, a rivulet of sweat streaming down my face, I am ready to teach – to make life and learning relevant for every student in my class.

The Beginning of the End – Period 1

In my first period class, the assignment for the day, a favorite of students, is to create a short story, poetic work, or descriptive piece that reflects the mood and emotional context of an orchestrated musical composition.

Gustavo De Leon, who recently moved to San Diego from Mazatlan, has selected *Rhapsody in Blue* for the inspiration of his original narrative. As Gershwin's music fills the classroom, Gustavo reads his original story of what he imagines to be a trip to New York City, filled with "the excitement, the lights, and the crowds of people" which he metaphorically refers to as "a living city symphony of sound." This is the most creative project Gustavo had ever done in my class, and the students are completely immersed in his imaginative presentation and the symphonic Gershwin music.

About halfway through Gustavo's presentation, Paula Banger, the English Language and Arts Administrator, a *fashionista wannabe,* enters my classroom to do her monthly observation of my teaching methods. Banger, whose only teaching experience has been three years in an elementary school, and who makes about $25,000.00 more than I do, sits down in the one vacant desk in the front of the classroom. Utilizing her sixty-five words per minute typing skills, she begins clicking away on her Apple MacBook Pro A1297 laptop in wild abandonment. Most of the students turn disapprovingly towards her, appalled that she is destroying the mood of the assignment and the class.

At the end of the period, Banger approaches me and in a raspy monotone utters, "I find the presentations *kinda* good but don't understand how this mood stuff fits into the curriculum and uh . . . what English has got to do with uh . . . with uh . . . uh . . . that Tchaikovsky music.

"It's Gershwin. George Gershwin."

"*Whatever.* I'll leave my evaluation of your teaching techniques in your mailbox. I'm not sure how your . . . um . . . your lessons or methodology meet the California State Standards of Excellence, but it was . . . uh . . . *entertaining,* but we're actually *not* in the entertainment business, if you know what I mean. I wish I could talk more and show you how to meet those state guidelines but instead, I'll leave a copy of those standards in your mailbox. It's real interesting reading," she mutters, shoving her laptop into her designer leather case. "It was . . . *real nice* . . . and you have *nice* kids too, but they want you to teach them the . . . uh . . . important things, like uh, you know what I mean. Oh, but I have to run to my next class for another observation. Bye now!" she says cheerfully, "and have a good day!"

And so *Miss Cultural-Lack-of-Awareness* leaves my classroom on her daily agenda of terror, fully prepared to intimidate the next staff member she will evaluate.

"She has no idea what she's talking about!" exclaims, Todd, one of my more astute students. "Do they pay her?"

"More than I make . . . "

"I know I wasn't supposed to be listening, but she has no idea that *mood* is a critical element of literature – and life! She just doesn't get it. And this assignment is *so creative,* Zeiger! All the kids love it. It's not right what she said to you."

I don't respond, and Todd leaves my classroom. The thought about that $55.00 check I had mailed to the State of California hits me in the head with hurricane force. *What if I had refused to pay? Would the school district cancel my teaching contract? Arrest me? What would I do with the rest of my life? Become an author? Write a book? What if I can't find a publisher?*

I suddenly envision my condo filled from floor to ceiling with thousands of unsold self-published books. The nightmare is just beginning.

The Sky is Falling – Period 4

Later that morning, I meet with the school police to fill out forms and answer questions regarding the eleven-year-old boy who fell through the roof of the school's theater. How could this possibly have happened? The story goes like this . . .

There I am, donating my Saturday to helping my students construct sets for the upcoming production, *Too Hot to Handle,* when suddenly the tortured screams of Marvin Grunger permeate the theater as he drops through the roof, smashing a light fixture in the ceiling, lands on a table top, and then falls to the floor. To the horror of everyone watching, he miraculously gets up with blood gushing from his left hand, and staggers towards me pleading, "I don't want to die! I don't want to die! Save me! Please save me!"

My heart is pounding. I immediately dial 911 on my cell phone while Casey, one of my most dedicated students, tries to calm down the hysterical child by administering pressure on the wound to stop the bleeding. But Marvin continues to scream.

"I'm innocent! I'm innocent! I was up on the roof to get my handball! You see, my buddies and I were tossing it around outside the theater and . . . and . . . I just tossed it *too high* . . . and it landed on top of this . . . this building. I climbed the ladder to the roof to get my ball and . . . and as you can see, I'm innocent! I'm innocent! I'm innocent! I'm *not* dying, am I? PLEASE DON'T LET ME DIE!"

The ambulance, police, and security arrive about the same time and take the screaming, helpless child to the hospital where he has surgery to save two of his nearly completely severed fingers. It is a horrible afternoon I will never forget.

That night, I have trouble sleeping thinking about the fate of the child. *But how much worse can things get?*

The next morning I sit in the administrator's conference room as the police and vice principal, Teddy Faukus, inform me that Marvin Grunger was *not* trying to retrieve his handball from the roof of the theater. He was, in fact, part of a gang of four eleven-year-old local boys who were attempting to rob the theater box office! I then learn from the police that prior to Marvin falling through the roof of the theater, the motley crew had robbed the junior high school down the street. Because of the success of that venture (they had stolen three boxes of pencils, a teacher's grade book and $17.33 from the cash box in the drama teacher's office), they had decided to hit the high school.

Marvin, being the smallest kid in the gang, volunteered to climb through a vent in the roof of the high school theater, not realizing that this was low-budget school construction, that the ceiling would collapse from his weight, and that there were forty-seven high school students and me in the theater down below.

The police inform me that I will have to appear in court the week before the opening of *Too Hot to Handle* to testify against Marvin while Vice Principal Faukus chastises me because the lead actor in the current musical, Casey, who is also an Eagle Scout, has been giving "blood trail tours" of the theater and charging a fee to students. According to Faukus, this is entirely *my* fault due to the fact that I have "no control over my students." I don't say a word, and minutes later, I leave school for my lunch break and go to the nearest Starbucks to have a cup of tea to quiet my nerves.

I really need more than just antioxidants though.

Deep Breathing

I enter Starbucks, order a tall *Chai Latte*, and wait for my name to be called just as a disheveled, tattoo-covered man enters the store and pushes his way to the front of the line, screaming, "I need six shots of espresso in your largest cup! I need it now! Six *grande* shots in that big fuckin' cup!"

The clerk smiles that Starbucks corporation grin and asks, "So you'd like a *Venti?*"

The man angrily responds, "You heard me! I want the biggest cup you have! If it's *Venti,* then give me *Venti!*" Everyone becomes quiet as the smiling clerk pours the six shots of espresso into a *Venti* cup. When she gives him the cup, he shouts, "This is *not* your biggest cup! I want *your biggest fuckin' cup!*"

"It is, sir. It's a *Venti!* It *is* our biggest cup!"

"I don't care what you call it! But I know there's a bigger one! I want the thirty-two ouncer! And I want it now! Do you hear me?"

Almost all the Starbucks patrons slowly ease themselves out of their chairs and move toward the exit door.

Just as things are about to really get out of control, the manager rescues the clerk and diffuses the situation by telling the guy, "Sir, I'm so sorry, but we ran out of those . . . uh . . . *giant cups* yesterday, so what I'll do is give you two of the *Venti* cups and six extra shots for a grand total of twelve shots of espresso . . . all on the house!

The man does not respond and seconds later, downs the two *Venti* cups of twelve shots of espresso and oddly enough, calms down. I, on the other hand, am so tense that I never even went to the counter to get my tall *Chai Latte.* Instead, I drive back to school, acid reflux in full gear, to teach my afternoon classes.

Village of the Damned – Period 5

As I walk to my fifth period class, Solange Pottier, a new counselor at the school, notifies me that she has "no other option" but to put two ninth grade boys in my seniors-only musical theater class.

"Sorry," she says plaintively as she sits back in her office sipping a cup of soothing Chamomile tea. "No place else to put them. They don't want to sing . . . they don't want to dance, but I figure you can come up with some kind of . . . uh . . . uh . . . *alternative* curriculum for them. You see, you have two spaces left on your roster, and so I, uh, have to put them *somewhere* . . . so . . . well . . . you got 'em! There's nothing else I can do. You're an arts teacher. You can live with it. I just know you can." She gives a fake smile followed by a faintly audible chuckle, and I leave for my next class.

Frankie Dunsworth and Dickie Head are no ordinary ninth grade boys. Not only do they *not* want to be in my musical theater class, but they immediately develop devious plans to show me how much they detest the class by creating distractions whenever they can. Worse, Frankie and Dickie are just overcoming drug and discipline problems and have done time in Juvenile Hall. As a result, the school district has hired David Klinker, a college student/part-time security guard, to be with them at all times and watch every move they make. But nothing seems to help the impending chaos.

When we are in the theater rehearsing, the two boys chase each other up and down the aisles and then run into the classrooms behind the stage screaming nonsensical expressions and code words like "Pat Swigler!" "Nu Nu Nutbrain!" " Comos destroyer!" "Electrocute the dog!" and "Swigglers forever!" Every student in my class wants to strangle them, and I consider the possibilities.

After twenty minutes of chasing Frankie and Dickie around the theater, David Klinker boldly announces to me, "I rather be unemployed than do this shit!" He walks out of my class, and I never see him again.

As Klinker departs, Frankie and Dickie scream at the top of their lungs, "Loopydoopy on Klinker!" and then run circles around the theater, psychologically terrorizing my students and me for the remaining seven minutes of the class.

I feel nauseous and there are still two periods left in the day.

The Hitchcock Technique – Period 6

A few days ago, Marla Potso, a new student at the school, tells me she is severely far-sighted and needs to sit in the back of the classroom so she takes a seat next to high school basketball star, Arturo Gomez. I notice, however, that whenever I show a film and turn out the lights, Marla puts her right hand on Arturo's left leg, and he, in turn, places his left hand on her right thigh. They then move closer to each other, and while pretending to watch the movie, they explore each other's body parts in the darkness of my classroom. *They are doing the same routine today.*

According to the nurse and the head counselor, I am to always keep an eye on Marla, not because she is prone to lascivious behavior, but because she *may*, or *may not,* have a heart condition. Just after the period begins, I receive a note from Marla's counselor telling me that until Marla's doctor completes more tests on her, other reactions I may observe in class could include "seizures, allergic reactions, and/or sudden emotional outbursts."

The note from the counselor also tells me that until the family receives the definitive report from the doctor, I must never turn the lights out in class while showing a film in my Cinema Arts class, because a sign of a seizure could be as simple as Marla closing her eyes or putting her head down on the desk – or in this case, Arturo's shoulder. She is also not allowed to do any oral projects for fear she might get nervous in front of the class and simply collapse.

An additional note from the nurse instructs me to assign two students (without telling Marla) as "Marla watchdogs." In the event Marla closes her eyes or puts her head down on the desk (signs of a "possible" seizure), I am immediately to send the "watchdogs" to the office – one to contact the nurse (who is rarely at school due to budget cutbacks) and the other to get the defibrillator. In the meantime, I am instructed to immediately rip Marla's blouse off, and when the defibrillator arrives, I am to attach the electrodes to her chest.

Hey, wait a minute! I am not a doctor! What if she's just napping and *not* having a seizure, and I pull her blouse off in front of the forty other students in my over-crowded class and then shock her with those electrodes? *Will I be sued? Will I wind up being victimized by Nancy Grace? Will I have to sneak away to France like Roman Polanski? Or will Arturo clobber me over the head for planting electrodes on his girl's chest?*

I can't do this! I have nearly 190 students to teach each day. Imagine a lawyer with 190 clients in a single day? Or a parent with 190 kids? Has government turned public education into a massive dysfunctional system run by bureaucrats and politicians who have never ever been in front of five overcrowded classrooms each day assuming the role of instructor, parent, director, therapist, actor, magician – and doctor?

Is there any way I can climb into the mailbox on the corner of my street and get my $55.00 check back?

For the rest of the period, I keep my eyes on Marla and Arturo who are caught in a passionate embrace while the rest of the class watches the last part of Alfred Hitchcock's *Rear Window* in semi-darkness.

The Volcano Erupts – Period 7

In the middle of the final period of the day, the pristine, under worked Lily White, head counselor and aspiring administrator, enters my classroom with an aggressive gate and a massive twitch in her left eye. "I need to talk to you . . . *now!*" she utters in a raspy voice.

"But I'm teaching my class," I respond. *I can tell this is a conversation I want to avoid at all costs.*

"Would you please . . . step in the hall?"

"And leave my students unattended?"

"*In the hall!*" she demands in expert commander-in-chief form.

My students sense something is wrong and become unusually quiet, striving to overhear every syllable, every word, every sentence from the hallway conversation between Lily and me.

"Is there a problem?" I ask naively.

She turns a crimson color. "What's wrong with you?"

"What do you mean – 'what's wrong with me'?"

"Today, no less than six students wanted to transfer out of your theater class! Six! Do you know how much work that causes me?" Lily's voice intensifies, "*Do you?*"

"That's because the students in question never requested my theater class in the first place. They don't want to perform. What they want is to take P.E.! *Not* my musical theatre class, and in the case of Marla Potso . . . she's *not even allowed* to perform! These students never wanted to take my class! It's as simple as that."

"Well, I'm not taking them out!"

"And what about the ten students who were added to my class this week? They *want* to take my class, but there aren't enough seats! The kids are sitting on tables! Have you *even* noticed?"

"Sitting on tables? Big deal! What's that got to do with anything anyway?" Lily White proclaims with that eye twitch doing double time.

"Look, I have some of the biggest classes in the school. I'm here till 9 p.m. rehearsing every night. That's a thirteen-hour day! Check out your best friend who teaches across the hall – your coffee buddy, Victoria Saddleback. She has sixty fewer students than I do, and she has a student teacher and a teaching assistant! Do you call that fair?"

"Victoria is an *excellent* teacher, and she has *demanding* classes."

"And she leaves like a bat out of hell at 2:15 p.m. every day!"

Sensing she is losing the battle, Lily instantly changes the subject. "You just don't understand. Just imagine what it's like from my point of view when your kids want schedule changes *all the time*. This adds to my workload!"

I can't handle this conversation another second and simply explode. Raising my voice in the pitch and timber of George C. Scott in *Patton*, I let Lily have it. "You will never ever interrupt my class again with this utter nonsense! Now just go away! Get out of my life! I have students to teach! Goodbye Lily White!"

The *miscreant of educational standards* looks at me perversely while grinding her teeth. "You just don't get it, do you? You don't understand rules! You don't understand standards! And you've never *ever* followed a procedure!"

I close the door in Lily White's face and enter my classroom. To my surprise, all the students, experts in voyeurism and overhearing conversations they are not supposed to hear, are absolutely silent.

I am in no mood to continue teaching. Fortunately, only four minutes remain in the last period of the day. A brief moment of serious contemplation consumes me. All I can think about is standardized testing, overcrowded classrooms, endless hours of work, teacher complaints, counselor complaints, administrator complaints, parent complaints, student complaints, and the defibrillator hanging on the wall in the nurse's office.

I speak quietly and deliberately to my students. "Class, the bell will ring in three minutes and forty-four seconds. I want you to line up at the door *now,* because when that bell rings, you will have no more than five seconds to exit this classroom and then . . . and then . . . *I am gone* . . . like a candle burning out with no wick left to light!"

My students stare at me with *Oh-my-God-he's-gone crazy* looks on their faces.

Sensing that I might at any moment implode into a million atomic sized particles, they immediately line up at the door, and when the bell rings, they quickly depart.

But I am ahead of them.

The Escape Artist

I race down the stairs of the school into the parking lot and soon find myself on 5 South heading toward the Mexican border with no idea what my final destination will be. All I can think about is – *I want my $55.00 back!*

I take a detour and drive straight to the Board of Education, enter the business office and desperately proclaim, "I am a teacher! I've taught for thirty-three years and no longer want to be a part of this bureaucratic disaster. I want those retirement forms . . . *now!* Give them to me *now!*"

The woman looks at me with a petrified expression. If there were a button beneath the counter that she could have pressed in an emergency condition to alert security to a mentally confused crackpot about to go over the top, she would have pressed that button several times. She tries to calm me down.

"We have a packet of information for you to read." She hands me about fifty pages stapled together. "And if you choose to retire this year, you still have almost two months to return these forms to us. Take them home, look them over, and, like I said, you have plenty of time to get them back to us."

But I am way ahead of her. While she is saying those fifty-one words to me, I have already located the *important* documents, and in an instant, my signature is on every one of them.

"You know you don't have to do this right now. You might even change your mind. It uh, happens, you know . . . "

I pay no attention to her. In a matter of seconds, I sign the last page in the packet.

"Wow, that was the fastest I've ever seen anyone retire since I've worked here! You must really want *out!*"

I leave the Board of Education and walk to my car, and then begin to wonder, *Am I doing the right thing?*

As soon as I arrive home, I sit at my computer and write a letter to Governor Schwarzenegger. It is a brilliant three page, single-spaced tome detailing my education, credentials, committees I have led, awards received, extracurricular activities, and my passion for education. I conclude the letter by asking for my $55.00 back in light of the fact, that I am no longer going to be teaching and will, therefore, not need the stupid certificate the state of California is going to send me.

Several weeks pass by, and in May, I finally receive a letter from the California Commission on Teacher Credentialing written by the Interim Executive Director of the California Commission. I think to myself – *Interim Executive Director? Interim? Does that mean he's leaving tomorrow? Maybe the Interim Executive Director does not have the proper credentials to write this letter.* Sadly, this interim guy responds to my letter as if he knows absolutely nothing about me. I am merely another cog in the broken wheel of our society's obsession with *standardized everything.* When I reach the second paragraph, I break out in a cold sweat.

"Unfortunately, the Commission on Teacher Credentialing is unable to refund your credential fees of $55.00. As acknowledged in Title 5, Section 80487, application fees are considered earned upon receipt and are not refundable."

What the heck is Title 5, Section 80487? Am I supposed to know this like the Bill of Rights? The letter is filled with acronyms like the CDE and the ELUM along with CLAD. I have no idea what any of these letters mean . . . nor do I care.

I sip a little Grey Goose mixed with Limoncello and go to bed and stare at the ceiling for most of the night while meaningless letters and numbers burn in my brain.

8048780487Title5-80387CDE-ELUM-CLAD-CDE-ELUM-CLAD-Title5-80487 80487804878048780487ELUMCLADCDEELUM NOT REFUNDABLE

The Perfect Test

After a sleepless night, I arrive at school, blood pressure returning to a normal 110 over 70. I climb the stairs to my classroom and have one of the best days of my teaching career. In my American literature class, my students are enraptured by the discussions of F. Scott Fitzgerald's *The Great Gatsby*. In my film appreciation class, the brilliant Giuseppe Tornatore's film, *Cinema Paradiso* brings tears to the eyes of my students as they view the poignant final scene showing the character of the film director, Salvatore, watching a reel of love scenes left to him by a man who has had a huge impact on the artist's creative and personal life.

And finally, in the last period of the day, my musical theater class, I announce that their original production of *Too Hot Too Handle* will be the final performance of my high school career. My students are very surprised and some are deeply saddened, but after thirty-three years of teaching, I find myself in a state of total exhilaration. I am finally going to *graduate* from high school. I no longer even care about the $55.00 I have "donated" to the State of California. I just hope the Department of Education plants a tree in my honor with the money I reluctantly have sent to them.

Five weeks later on the last day of my teaching career, after all my students have departed, I stare into my empty classroom, and am flooded with images of the people I have taught for more than half my life. Faces magically appear and disappear. I think about what my students have accomplished in the years since they have left my class.

Jon ('78), the dedicated fire captain; Steve ('78) and Bryan ('79), brilliant concert pianists; Gabriel ('94), director of video production company; Dan ('83), mathematics professional development specialist; Paul ('82), telecommunications technician and musician; Tom ('84), Joe ('84), and Emily ('90), dedicated physicians; Halle ('87), creator of Emmy Award nominated children's television series; Chris ('84), Oscar winning film editor; Jeffrey ('76), scientist and author; William ('88), real estate agent and author; Grant ('88), interactive media producer; Glen ('82), bass player, recording artist and teacher; Christopher ('88), film producer and director; Melinda ('84), political activist/ art curator; Scarlet ('84), professor, pianist, recording artist; Mara ('86), singer and Yoga instructor; Carey ('80) and Anthony ('83), business entrepreneurs; David ('94), film actor and author; Dusty ('02), musician and graphic designer; Michael ('91), technical animator, digital artist, and author; Seth ('85), financial broker; Sergio ('83), CEO of educational web publishing company; Chris ('88), veterinarian and musical comedy actor; Ramsey ('97), chief officer of the Recovery School District of New Orleans; David ('87), Hollywood entertainment lawyer; Michael ('01), playwright and director; Aaron ('80), film composer; Kelly ('86), physical therapist; Lynn ('78) superb opera singer; Colin ('05), caterer and social media marketing director; David ('82), sound engineer; Matt ('97), theatrical lighting director; Kit ('77), professional juggler, magician, and author; Steve ('88), CEO of a graphic design company; Devon ('99), political activist and filmmaker; Chris ('78) Ted ('83), Pete ('86), Michael ('94), Albert ('94), Matt ('95), restaurant entrepreneurs; Paul ('85), psychologist; Mark ('81), guitarist, songwriter, and recording artist; Ana ('93), marketing director; Spencer ('95) and Matt ('99), stage actors; Jayne ('81), university professor; Diana ('86), theater manager; Ben ('89),director/artist; Jason ('89), school administrator and educator; Rogelia ('93), health services case manager; Trish ('88), executive assistant for global management firm; Carlos ('98), technology consultant; Noah ('86), creator and star of television series; Judd ('87), television producer; Brian ('97), cinematographer; Brigitte ('81), Koryn ('04), and Stasia ('05), songwriters/recording artists; Richard ('77), actor/entertainment director; Michael ('97), financial advisor; Jeremy ('89), attorney and guitarist; Raul ('93) stage actor, director; Kabir ('93), engineer; Carlos ('91), TV news reporter/marketing director; Dylan ('05)and Eric ('06), jazz drummers/

percussionists; Sally ('84) and Nick ('77), architects; Breehn ('93), graphic artist, animator, and author; Jose ('89), parole agent; Rick ('89), entertainment director of Sea World; Tonya ('91), singer and actress; Edgar ('97), manager of Hugo Boss Store; Maureen ('80), jazz vocalist, recoding artist; Curtis ('76), front line manager for the FAA; Joel ('00), filmmaker; Tyler ('04), senior associate at hospital review agency; Courtney ('05), claims recovery analyst; Mark (80), director of information technology; Frankie ('86), singer, songwriter, and guitarist; Heather ('00), author of children's books; Ben ('87), California State Assemblyman; Randy ('88) and Lance ('89), visual effects/digital artists; Kyle ('88), software company director in Australia; Jason ('80), lead singer and guitarist in the band, *Chicago;* Eddie ('77), guitarist and songwriter; Jon ('84), award-winning metal sculpture artist; Steve ('87), health care insurance agent, guitarist, and singer; Muffin ('77), professional dancer; Cindy ('81), composer, singer, songwriter, author; Julie ('98), professional photographer and recording artist; Eduardo ('97), director of Center for Chicano Arts and Culture; Kelly ('82), gemologist; Chris ('86) and Eric ('86), recording artists and composers; Todd ('05), political activist and educator; Tom ('82), artist/educator in Afghanistan; Brian ('00), philanthropist and educator; Colin ('85), educator in Shizuoka, Japan; Amy ('92), motivational speaker on cosmetic surgery; Nicole ('98), Emmy Award nominated documentary filmmaker; Jesse ('04), cinematographer; Tyler ('06), director/writer, talent agent; Cindy ('82) and Honora ('05), broadcast journalists; Ed ('78), owner of construction/design company; Dwight ('84), feature film editor; Chris ('83), Oscar winning film editor; Rachel ('04), filmmaker; Jesse ('91), my tax attorney; David ('84), my insurance agent; Joe ('84), my doctor; Julien ('86), Loren ('87) Oscar ('99), imaginative artists whose spectacular paintings hang in my home. And then there are the memories of Karen ('77) Chip ('81), Burke ('81), Heather ('88), Dustin ('93), Jeremy ('96) and Gia ('97) that will never leave me.

These are my students, my friends, and my family. Thousands of faces and musical images appear in my mind. I smile and turn out the lights in my classroom. This *is* my life.

THE CELEBRATION BEGINS!

On December 15, 2012 Larry and Jack complete the final draft of *NICE LEGS! – A PAIRING OF WINE AND WORDS*, and to commemorate this momentous occasion, they stop at Barons Market in Point Loma, California to select a bottle of sparkling wine. Sensing that Jack and Larry are in a buoyant mood – Joe, Paul, Art, Oscar, Greg, Riley, Sara, Frank, Wendy, Danny, Rachel, Dana, George, Josh, Brian, Margaret, Jeff, Bijan, Casey, Mike, Kyrie, and Debi, who work at the store, are unanimous in their decision that for this momentous occasion, a bottle of *Veuve Clicquot Champagne* is the perfect choice.

Outside the store, Larry and Jack pop the cork and sample the crisp, delightful taste of this wonderful champagne as they celebrate the characters and stories in their book, the ultimate pairing of wine and words, which have consumed their lives and imaginations for over a year. To the authors' surprise, the entire staff of Barons joins them to share in the excitement of two of their favorite patrons.

It is a day that Larry and Jack will savor forever.